THE WORKS OF CHARLES DICKENS

XIV

BLEAK HOUSE

VOL. II

THE
LONDON
EDITION

LADY DEADLOCK IN THE WOOD.

Bleak House

VOL. II

By CHARLES DICKENS

LINCOLN'S INN

WITH ILLUSTRATIONS BY HABLOT K. BROWNE ("PHIZ")

LONDON
THE CAXTON PUBLISHING COMPANY
CLUN HOUSE, SURREY STREET, W.C.

CONTENTS OF VOL. II

LIST OF ILLUSTRATIONS

VOL. II

COLOURED PLATES

BLEAK HOUSE

CHAPTER XXXIV

A TURN OF THE SCREW

"NOW, what," says Mr. George, "may this be? Is it blank cartridge, or ball? A flash in the pan, or a shot?"

An open letter is the subject of the trooper's speculations, and it seems to perplex him mightily. He looks at it at arm's length, brings it close to him, holds it in his right hand, holds it in his left hand, reads it with his head on this side, with his head on that side, contracts his eyebrows, elevates them; still, cannot satisfy himself. He smooths it out upon the table with his heavy palm, and thoughtfully walking up and down the gallery, makes a halt before it every now and then, to come upon it with a fresh eye. Even that won't do. "Is it," Mr. George muses, "blank cartridge or ball?"

Phil Squod, with the aid of a brush and paint-pot, is employed in the distance whitening the targets; softly whistling, in quick-march time, and in drum-and-fife manner, that he must and he will go back again to the girl he left behind him.

"Phil!" The trooper beckons as he calls him.

Phil approaches in his usual way; sidling off at first as if he were going anywhere else, and then bearing down upon his commander like a bayonet-charge. Certain splashes of white show in high relief upon his dirty face, and he scrapes his one eye-brow with the handle of his brush.

"Attention, Phil! Listen to this."

"Steady, commander, steady."

"'Sir. Allow me to remind you (though there is no legal necessity for my doing so, as you are aware) that the bill at two months' date, drawn on yourself by Mr. Matthew Bagnet, and by you accepted, for the sum of ninety-seven pounds four shillings and ninepence, will become due to-morrow, when you will please be prepared to take up the same on presentation. Yours, JOSHUA SMALLWEED.'—What do you make of that, Phil?"

"Mischief, guv'ner."

"Why?"

"I think," replies Phil, after pensively tracing out a cross-wrinkle in his forehead with the brush-handle, "that mischeevious consequences is always meant when money's asked for."

"Lookye, Phil," says the trooper, sitting on the table. "First and last, I have paid, I may say, half as much again as this principal, in interest and one thing and another."

Phil intimates, by sidling back a pace or two, with a very unaccountable wrench of his wry face, that he does not regard the transaction as being made more promising by this incident.

"And lookye further, Phil," says the trooper, staying his premature conclusions with a wave of his hand. "There has always been an understanding that this bill was to be what they call Renewed. And it has been renewed, no end of times. What do you say now?"

"I say that I think the time has come to a end at last."

"You do? Humph! I am much of the same mind myself."

"Joshua Smallweed is him that was brought here in a chair?"

"The same."

"Guv'ner," says Phil, with exceeding gravity, "he's a leech in his dispositions, he's a screw and a wice in his actions, a snake in his twistings, and a lobster in his claws."

Having thus expressly uttered his sentiments, Mr. Squod, after waiting a little to ascertain if any further remark be expected of him, gets back, by his usual series of movements, to the target he has in hand; and vigorously signifies, through his former musical medium, that he must and he will return to that ideal young lady. George having folded the letter, walks in that direction.

"There *is* a way, commander," says Phil, looking cunningly at him, "of settling this."

"Paying the money, I suppose? I wish I could."

Phil shakes his head. "No, guv'ner, no; not so bad as that. There *is* a way," says Phil, with a highly artistic turn of his brush—" what I'm a-doing at present."

" Whitewashing."

Phil nods.

" A pretty way that would be ! Do you know what would become of the Bagnets in that case ? Do you know they would be ruined to pay off my old scores ? *You're* a moral character," says the trooper, eyeing him in his large way with no small indignation, " upon my life you are, Phil ! "

Phil, on one knee at the target, is in course of protesting earnestly, though not without many allegorical scoops of his brush, and smoothings of the white surface round the rim with his thumb, that he had forgotten the Bagnet responsibility, and would not so much as injure a hair of the head of any member of that worthy family, when steps are audible in the long passage without, and a cheerful voice is heard to wonder whether George is at home. Phil, with a look at his master, hobbles up, saying, "Here's the guv'ner, Mrs. Bagnet ! Here he is ! " and the old girl herself, accompanied by Mr. Bagnet, appears.

The old girl never appears in walking trim, in any season of the year, without a grey cloth cloak, coarse and much worn but very clean, which is, undoubtedly, the identical garment rendered so interesting to Mr. Bagnet by having made its way home to Europe from another quarter of the globe, in company with Mrs. Bagnet and an umbrella. The latter faithful appendage is also invariably a part of the old girl's presence out of doors. It is of no colour known in this life, and has a corrugated wooden crook for a handle, with a metallic object let into its prow or beak, resembling a little model of a fanlight over a street door, or one of the oval glasses out of a pair of spectacles : which ornamental object has not that tenacious capacity of sticking to its post that might be desired in an article long associated with the British army. The old girl's umbrella is of a flabby habit of waist, and seems to be in need of stays—an appearance that is possibly referable to its having served, through a series of years, at home as a cupboard, and on journeys as a carpet bag. She never puts it up, having the greatest reliance on her well-proved cloak with its capacious hood ; but generally uses the instrument as a wand with which to point out joints of meat or bunches of greens in marketing, or to arrest the attention of tradesmen by a friendly poke. Without her market-basket, which is a sort of wicker well with two flapping lids, she never stirs abroad. Attended by these her trusty companions, therefore, her honest sunburnt face looking cheerily out of a rough straw bonnet, Mrs. Bagnet now arrives, fresh-coloured and bright, in George's Shooting Gallery.

" Well, George, old fellow," says she, " and how do *you* do, this sun-shiny morning ? "

Giving him a friendly shake of the hand, Mrs. Bagnet draws a long breath after her walk, and sits down to enjoy a rest. Having a faculty, matured on the tops of baggage-waggons, and in other such positions, of resting easily anywhere, she perches on a rough bench, unties her bonnet-strings, pushes back her bonnet, crosses her arms, and looks perfectly comfortable.

Mr. Bagnet, in the meantime, has shaken hands with his old comrade, and with Phil: on whom Mrs. Bagnet likewise bestows a good-humoured nod and smile.

"Now, George," said Mrs. Bagnet briskly, "here we are, Lignum and myself;" she often speaks of her husband by this appellation, on account, as it is supposed, of Lignum Vitæ having been his old regimental nickname when they first became acquainted, in compliment to the extreme hardness and toughness of his physiognomy; "just looked in, we have, to make it all correct as usual about that security. Give him the new bill to sign, George, and he'll sign it like a man."

"I was coming to you this morning," observes the trooper reluctantly.

"Yes, we thought you'd come to us this morning, but we turned out early, and left Woolwich, the best of boys, to mind his sisters, and came to you instead—as you see! For Lignum, he's tied so close now, and gets so little exercise, that a walk does him good. But what's the matter, George?" asks Mrs. Bagnet, stopping in her cheerful talk. "You don't look yourself."

"I am not quite myself," returns the trooper; "I have been a little put out, Mrs. Bagnet."

Her bright quick eye catches the truth directly. "George!" holding up her forefinger. "Don't tell me there's anything wrong about that security of Lignum's. Don't do it, George, on account of the children!"

The trooper looks at her with a troubled visage.

"George," says Mrs. Bagnet, using both her arms for emphasis, and occasionally bringing down her open hands upon her knees. "If you have allowed anything wrong to come to that security of Lignum's, and if you have let him in for it, and if you have put us in danger of being sold up—and I see sold up in your face, George, as plain as print—you have done a shameful action, and have deceived us cruelly. I tell you, cruelly, George. There!"

Mr. Bagnet, otherwise as immovable as a pump or a lamp-post, puts his large white hand on the top of his bald head, as if to defend it from a shower-bath, and looks with great uneasiness at Mrs. Bagnet.

"George!" says that old girl, "I wonder at you! George, I am ashamed of you! George, I couldn't have believed you would have done it! I always knew you to be a rolling stone that gathered no moss; but I never thought you would have taken away what little moss there was for Bagnet and the children to lie upon. You know what a hard-working, steady-going chap he is. You know what Quebec and Malta and Woolwich are—and I never did think you would, or could, have had the heart to serve us so. O George!" Mrs. Bagnet gathers up her cloak to wipe her eyes on, in a very genuine manner, "How could you do it?"

Mrs. Bagnet ceasing, Mr. Bagnet removes his hand from his head, as if the shower-bath were over, and looks disconsolately at Mr. George; who has turned quite white, and looks distressfully at the grey cloak and straw bonnet.

"Mat," says the trooper, in a subdued voice, addressing him, but still looking at his wife; "I am sorry you take it so much to heart, because I do hope it's not so bad as that comes to. I certainly have, this morning, received this letter;" which he reads aloud; "but I hope it may be set right yet. As to a rolling stone, why, what you say is true. I *am* a rolling stone; and I never rolled in anybody's way, I fully believe, that I rolled the least good to. But it's impossible for an old vagabond comrade to like your wife and family better than *I* like 'em, Mat, and I trust you'll look upon me as forgivingly as you can. Don't think I've kept anything from you. I haven't had the letter more than a quarter of an hour."

"Old girl!" murmurs Mr. Bagnet, after a short silence, "will you tell him my opinion?"

"Oh! Why didn't he marry," Mrs. Bagnet answers, half laughing and half crying, "Joe Pouch's widder in North America? Then he wouldn't have got himself into these troubles."

"The old girl," says Mr. Bagnet, "puts it correct—why didn't you?"

"Well, she has a better husband by this time, I hope," returns the trooper. "Anyhow, here I stand, this present day, *not* married to Joe Pouch's widder. What shall I do? You see all I have got about me. It's not mine; it's yours. Give the word, and I'll sell off every morsel. If I could have hoped it would have brought in nearly the sum wanted, I'd have sold all long ago. Don't believe that I'll leave you or yours in the lurch, Mat. I'd sell myself first. I only wish," says the trooper, giving himself a disparaging blow in the chest, "that I knew of any one who'd buy such a second-hand piece of old stores."

"Old girl," murmurs Mr. Bagnet, "give him another bit of my mind."

"George," says the old girl, "you are not so much to be blamed, on full consideration, except for ever taking this business without the means."

"And that was like me!" observes the penitent trooper, shaking his head. "Like me, I know."

"Silence! The old girl," says Mr. Bagnet, "is correct—in her way of giving my opinions—hear me out!"

"That was when you never ought to have asked for the security, George, and when you never ought to have got it, all things considered. But what's done can't be undone. You are always an honourable and straightforward fellow, as far as lays in your power, though a little flighty. On the other hand, you can't admit but what it's natural in us to be anxious, with such a thing hanging over our heads. So forget and forgive all round, George. Come! Forget and forgive all round!"

Mrs. Bagnet, giving him one of her honest hands, and giving her husband the other, Mr. George gives each of them one of his, and holds them while he speaks.

"I do assure you both, there's nothing I wouldn't do to discharge this obligation. But whatever I have been able to scrape together, has gone every two months in keeping it up. We have lived plainly enough here, Phil and I. But the Gallery don't quite do what was expected of it, and it's not—in short, it's not the Mint. It was wrong in me to take it? Well, so it was. But I was in a manner drawn into that step, and I thought it might steady me, and set me up, and you'll try to overlook my having such expectations, and upon my soul, I am very much obliged to you, and very much ashamed of myself." With these concluding words, Mr. George gives a shake to each of the hands he holds, and, relinquishing them, backs a pace or two, in a broad-chested upright attitude, as if he had made a final confession, and were immediately going to be shot with all military honours.

"George, hear me out!" says Mr. Bagnet, glancing at his wife. "Old girl, go on!"

Mr. Bagnet, being in this singular manner heard out, has merely to observe that the letter must be attended to without any delay; that it is advisable that George and he should immediately wait on Mr. Smallweed in person; and that the primary object is to save and hold harmless Mr. Bagnet, who had none of the money. Mr. George entirely assenting, puts on his hat, and prepares to march with Mr. Bagnet to the enemy's camp.

"Don't you mind a woman's hasty word, George," says Mrs. Bagnet, patting him on the shoulder. "I trust my old Lignum to you, and I am sure you'll bring him through it."

The trooper returns, that this is kindly said, and that he *will* bring Lignum through it somehow. Upon which Mrs. Bagnet, with her cloak, basket, and umbrella, goes home, bright-eyed again, to the rest of her family; and the comrades sally forth on the hopeful errand of mollifying Mr. Smallweed.

Whether there are two people in England less likely to come satisfactorily out of any negotiation with Mr. Smallweed than Mr. George and Mr. Matthew Bagnet, may be very reasonably questioned. Also, notwithstanding their martial appearance, broad square shoulders, and heavy tread, whether there are, within the same limits, two more simple and unaccustomed children, in all the Smallweedy affairs of life. As they proceed with great gravity through the streets towards the region of Mount Pleasant, Mr. Bagnet, observing his companion to be thoughtful, considers it a friendly part to refer to Mrs. Bagnet's late sally.

"George, you know the old girl—she's as sweet and as mild as milk. But touch her on the children—or myself—and she's off like gunpowder."

"It does her credit, Mat!"

"George," says Mr. Bagnet, looking straight before him, "the old girl —can't do anything—that don't do her credit. More or less. I never say so. Discipline must be maintained."

"She's worth her weight in gold," returns the trooper.

"In gold?" says Mr. Bagnet. "I'll tell you what. The old girl's weight—is twelve stone six. Would I take that weight—in any metal—

for the old girl? No. Why not? Because the old girl's metal is far more precious—than the preciousest metal. And she's *all* metal!"

"You are right, Mat!"

"When she took me—and accepted of the ring—she 'listed under me and the children—heart and head; for life. She's that earnest," says Mr. Bagnet, "and true to her colours—that, touch us with a finger—and she turns out—and stands to her arms. If the old girl fires wide —once in a way—at the call of duty—look over it, George. For she's loyal!"

"Why, bless her, Mat!" returns the trooper, "I think the higher of her for it!"

"You are right!" says Mr. Bagnet with the warmest enthusiasm, though without relaxing the rigidity of a single muscle. "Think as high of the old girl—as the rock of Gibraltar—and still you'll be thinking low —of such merits. But I never own to it before her. Discipline must be maintained."

These encomiums bring them to Mount Pleasant, and to Grandfather Smallweed's house. The door is opened by the perennial Judy, who, having surveyed them from top to toe, with no particular favour, but indeed with a malignant sneer, leaves them standing there, while she consults the oracle as to their admission. The oracle may be inferred to give consent, from the circumstance of her returning with the words on her honey lips "that they can come in if they want to it." Thus privileged they come in, and find Mr. Smallweed with his feet in the drawer of his chair as if it were a paper foot-bath, and Mrs. Smallweed obscured with the cushion like a bird that is not to sing.

"My dear friend," says Grandfather Smallweed, with those two lean affectionate arms of his stretched forth. "How de do? How de do? Who is our friend, my dear friend?"

"Why this," returns George, not able to be very conciliatory at first, "is Matthew Bagnet, who has obliged me in that matter of ours, you know."

"Oh! Mr. Bagnet? Surely!" The old man looks at him under his hand. "Hope you're well, Mr. Bagnet? Fine man, Mr. George! Military air, sir!"

No chairs being offered, Mr. George brings one forward for Bagnet, and one for himself. They sit down; Mr. Bagnet as if he had no power of bending himself, except at the hips, for that purpose.

"Judy," says Mr. Smallweed, "bring the pipe."

"Why, I don't know," Mr. George interposes, "that the young woman need give herself that trouble, for to tell you the truth, I am not inclined to smoke it to-day."

"Ain't you?" returns the old man. "Judy, bring the pipe."

"The fact is, Mr. Smallweed," proceeds George, "that I find myself in rather an unpleasant state of mind. It appears to me, sir, that your friend in the city has been playing tricks."

"Oh dear no!" says Grandfather Smallweed. "He never does that!"

"Don't he? Well, I am glad to hear it, because I thought it might be *his* doing. This, you know, I am speaking of. This letter."

Grandfather Smallweed smiles in a very ugly way, in recognition of the letter.

"What does it mean?" asks Mr. George.

"Judy," says the old man, "have you got the pipe? Give it to me. Did you say what does it mean, my good friend?"

"Ay! Now, come, come, you know, Mr. Smallweed," urges the trooper, constraining himself to speak as smoothly and confidentially as he can, holding the open letter in one hand, and resting the broad knuckles of the other on his thigh; "a good lot of money has passed between us, and we are face to face at the present moment, and are both well aware of the understanding there has always been. 1 am prepared to do the usual thing which I have done regularly, and to keep this matter going. I never got a letter like this from you before, and I have been a little put about by it this morning; because here's my friend Matthew Bagnet, who, you know, had none of the money——"

"I *don't* know it, you know," says the old man, quietly.

"Why, con-found you—it, I mean—I tell you so; don't I?"

"Oh, yes, you tell me so," returns Grandfather Smallweed. "But I don't know it."

"Well!" says the trooper, swallowing his fire. "*I* know it."

Mr. Smallweed replies with excellent temper, "Ah! that's quite another thing!" And adds, "but it don't matter. Mr. Bagnet's situation is all one, whether or no."

The unfortunate George makes a great effort to arrange the affair comfortably, and to propitiate Mr. Smallweed by taking him upon his own terms.

"That's just what I mean. As you say, Mr. Smallweed, here's Matthew Bagnet liable to be fixed whether or no. Now, you see, that makes his good lady very uneasy in her mind, and me too; for, whereas I'm a harum-scarum sort of a good-for-nought, that more kicks than half-pence come natural to, why he's a steady family man, don't you see? Now, Mr. Smallweed," says the trooper, gaining confidence as he proceeds in this soldierly mode of doing business; "although you and I are good friends enough in a certain sort of way, I am well aware that I can't ask you to let my friend Bagnet off entirely."

"Oh dear, you are too modest. You can *ask* me anything, Mr. George." (There is an Ogreish kind of jocularity in Grandfather Smallweed to-day.)

"And you can refuse, you mean, eh? Or not you so much, perhaps, as your friend in the city? Ha ha ha!"

"Ha ha ha!" echoes Grandfather Smallweed. In such a very hard manner, and with eyes so particularly green, that Mr. Bagnet's natural gravity is much deepened by the contemplation of that venerable man.

"Come!" says the sanguine George, "I am glad to find we can be pleasant, because I want to arrange this pleasantly. Here's my friend

Bagnet, and here am I. We'll settle the matter on the spot, if you please, Mr. Smallweed, in the usual way. And you'll ease my friend Bagnet's mind, and his family's mind, a good deal, if you'll just mention to him what our understanding is."

Here some shrill spectre cries out in a mocking manner, "Oh good gracious! Oh!"—unless, indeed, it be the sportive Judy, who is found to be silent when the startled visitors look round, but whose chin has received a recent toss, expressive of derision and contempt. Mr. Bagnet's gravity becomes yet more profound.

"But I think you asked me, Mr. George;" old Smallweed, who all this time has had the pipe in his hand, is the speaker now; "I think you asked me, what did the letter mean?"

"Why, yes, I did," returns the trooper, in his off-hand way: "but I don't care to know particularly, if it's all correct and pleasant."

Mr. Smallweed, purposely balking himself in an aim at the trooper's head, throws the pipe on the ground and breaks it to pieces.

"That's what it means, my dear friend. I'll smash you. I'll crumble you. I'll powder you. Go to the devil!"

The two friends rise and look at one another. Mr. Bagnet's gravity has now attained its profoundest point.

"Go to the devil!" repeats the old man. "I'll have no more of your pipe-smokings and swaggerings. What? You're an independent dragoon, too! Go to my lawyer (you remember where; you have been there before), and show your independence now, will you? Come, my dear friend, there's a chance for you. Open the street door, Judy; put these blusterers out! Call in help if they don't go. Put 'em out!"

He vociferates this so loudly, that Mr. Bagnet, laying his hands on the shoulders of his comrade, before the latter can recover from his amazement, gets him on the outside of the street door; which is instantly slammed by the triumphant Judy. Utterly confounded, Mr. George awhile stands looking at the knocker. Mr. Bagnet, in a perfect abyss of gravity, walks up and down before the little parlour window, like a sentry, and looks in every time he passes; apparently revolving something in his mind.

"Come, Mat!" says Mr. George, when he has recovered himself, "we must try the lawyer. Now, what do you think of this rascal?"

Mr. Bagnet, stopping to take a farewell look into the parlour, replies, with one shake of his head directed at the interior, "If my old girl had been here—I'd have told him!" Having so discharged himself of the subject of his cogitations, he falls into step, and marches off with the trooper, shoulder to shoulder.

When they present themselves in Lincoln's Inn Fields, Mr. Tulkinghorn is engaged, and not to be seen. He is not at all willing to see them; for when they have waited a full hour, and the clerk, on his bell being rung, takes the opportunity of mentioning as much, he brings forth no more encouraging message than that Mr. Tulkinghorn has nothing to say to them, and they had better not wait. They do wait, however, with the perseverance of military tactics; and at last the bell rings again, and the client in possession comes out of Mr. Tulkinghorn's room.

The client is a handsome old lady; no other than Mrs. Rouncewell, housekeeper at Chesney Wold. She comes out of the sanctuary with a fair old-fashioned curtsey, and softly shuts the door. She is treated with some distinction there; for the clerk steps out of his pew to show her through the outer office, and to let her out. The old lady is thanking him for his attention, when she observes the comrades in waiting.

"I beg your pardon, sir, but I think those gentlemen are military?"

The clerk referring the question to them with his eye, and Mr. George not turning round from the almanack over the fire-place, Mr. Bagnet takes upon himself to reply, "Yes, ma'am. Formerly."

"I thought so. I was sure of it. My heart warms, gentlemen, at the sight of you. It always does at the sight of such. God bless you, gentlemen! You'll excuse an old woman; but I had a son once who went for a soldier. A fine handsome youth he was, and good in his bold way, though some people did disparage him to his poor mother. I ask your pardon for troubling you, sir. God bless you, gentlemen!"

"Same to you, ma'am!" returns Mr. Bagnet, with right good will.

There is something very touching in the earnestness of the old lady's voice, and in the tremble that goes through her quaint old figure. But Mr. George is so occupied with the almanack over the fire-place (calculating the coming months by it, perhaps), that he does not look round until she has gone away, and the door is closed upon her.

"George," Mr. Bagnet gruffly whispers, when he does turn from the almanack at last. "Don't be cast down! 'Why, soldiers, why—should we be melancholy, boys?' Cheer up, my hearty!"

The clerk having now again gone in to say that they are still there, and Mr. Tulkinghorn being heard to return with some irascibility, "Let 'em come in then!" they pass into the great room with the painted ceiling, and find him standing before the fire.

"Now, you men, what do you want? Serjeant, I told you the last time I saw you that I don't desire your company here."

Serjeant replies—dashed within the last few minutes as to his usual manner of speech, and even as to his usual carriage—that he has received this letter, has been to Mr. Smallweed about it, and has been referred there.

"I have nothing to say to you," rejoins Mr. Tulkinghorn. "If you get into debt, you must pay your debts, or take the consequences. You have no occasion to come here to learn that, I suppose?"

Serjeant is sorry to say that he is not prepared with the money.

"Very well! Then the other man—this man, if this is he—must pay it for you."

Serjeant is sorry to add that the other man is not prepared with the money either.

"Very well! Then you must pay it between you, or you must both

MR. SMALLWEED BREAKS THE PIPE OF PEACE.

So Mr. Tulkinghorn, putting on his spectacles, sits down and writes the undertaking; which he slowly reads and explains to Bagnet, who has all this time been staring at the ceiling, and who puts his hand on his bald head again, under this new verbal shower-bath, and seems exceedingly in need of the old girl through whom to express his sentiments. The trooper then takes from his breast-pocket a folded paper, which he lays with an unwilling hand at the lawyer's elbow. "'Tis only a letter of instructions, sir. The last I ever had from him."

Look at a millstone, Mr. George, for some change in its expression, and you will find it quite as soon as in the face of Mr. Tulkinghorn when he opens and reads the letter! He refolds it, and lays it in his desk, with a countenance as imperturbable as Death.

Nor has he anything more to say or do, but to nod once in the same frigid and discourteous manner, and to say briefly, "You can go. Show these men out, there!" Being shown out, they repair to Mr. Bagnet's residence to dine.

Boiled beef and greens constitute the day's variety on the former repast of boiled pork and greens; and Mrs. Bagnet serves out the meal in the same way, and seasons it with the best of temper: being that rare sort of old girl that she receives Good to her arms without a hint that it might be Better; and catches light from any little spot of darkness near her. The spot on this occasion is the darkened brow of Mr. George; he is unusually thoughtful and depressed. At first Mrs. Bagnet trusts to the combined endearments of Quebec and Malta to restore him; but finding those young ladies sensible that their existing Bluffy is not the Bluffy of their usual frolicsome acquaintance, she winks off the light infantry, and leaves him to deploy at leisure on the open ground of the domestic hearth.

But he does not. He remains in close order, clouded and depressed. During the lengthy cleaning up and pattening process, when he and Mr. Bagnet are supplied with their pipes, he is no better than he was at dinner. He forgets to smoke, looks at the fire and ponders, lets his pipe out, fills the breast of Mr. Bagnet with perturbation and dismay, by showing that he has no enjoyment of tobacco.

Therefore when Mrs. Bagnet at last appears, rosy from the invigorating pail, and sits down to her work, Mr. Bagnet growls, "Old girl!" and winks monitions to her to find out what's the matter.

"Why, George!" says Mrs. Bagnet, quietly threading her needle. "How low you are!"

"Am I? Not good company? Well, I am afraid I am not."

"He ain't at all like Bluffy, mother!" cries little Malta.

"Because he ain't well, I think, mother," adds Quebec.

"Sure that's a bad sign not to be like Bluffy, too!" returns the trooper, kissing the young damsels. "But it's true," with a sigh— "true, I am afraid. These little ones are always right!"

"George," says Mrs. Bagnet, working busily, "if I thought you cross enough to think of anything that a shrill old soldier's wife—who could

be sued for it, and both suffer. You have had the mon
refund it. You are not to pocket other people's pounds,
pence, and escape scot free."

The lawyer sits down in his easy-chair and stirs the fire.
hopes he will have the goodness to——

"I tell you, serjeant, I have nothing to say to you. I don'
associates, and don't want you here. This matter is not at
course of practice, and is not in my office. Mr. Smallweed is go
to offer these affairs to me, but they are not in my way. You
to Melchisedech's in Clifford's Inn."

"I must make an apology to you, sir," says Mr. George, "for
myself upon you with so little encouragement—which is almost
pleasant to me as it can be to you; but would you let me say a
word to you?"

Mr. Tulkinghorn rises with his hands in his pockets, and walk
one of the window recesses. "Now! I have no time to waste."
midst of his perfect assumption of indifference, he directs a sharp lo
the trooper; taking care to stand with his own back to the light, an
have the other with his face towards it.

"Well, sir," says Mr. George, "this man with me is the other pa
implicated in this unfortunate affair—nominally, only nominally—a
my sole object is to prevent his getting into trouble on my account.
is a most respectable man with a wife and family; formerly in the Roy
Artillery——"

"My friend, I don't care a pinch of snuff for the whole Royal Artillery
establishment—officers, men, tumbrils, waggons, horses, guns, and am-
munition."

"'Tis likely, sir. But I care a good deal for Bagnet and his wife and
family being injured on my account. And if I could bring them through
this matter, I should have no help for it but to give up without any other
consideration, what you wanted of me the other day."

"Have you got it here?"

"I have got it here, sir."

"Serjeant," the lawyer proceeds in his dry passionless manner, far
more hopeless in the dealing with, than any amount of vehemence, "make
up your mind while I speak to you, for this is final. After I have
finished speaking I have closed the subject, and I won't re-open it.
Understand that. You can leave here, for a few days, what you say you
have brought here, if you choose; you can take it away at once, if you
choose. In case you choose to leave it here, I can do this for you—I can
replace this matter on its old footing, and I can go so far besides as to
give you a written undertaking that this man Bagnet shall never be
troubled in any way until you have been proceeded against to the utmost
—that your means shall be exhausted before the creditor looks to his.
This is in fact all but freeing him. Have you decided?"

The trooper puts his hand into his breast, and answers with a long
breath, "I must do it, sir."

have bitten her tongue off afterwards, and ought to have done it almost —said this morning, I don't know what I shouldn't say to you now."

"My kind soul of a darling," returns the trooper. "Not a morsel of it."

"Because really and truly, George, what I said and meant to say, was that I trusted Lignum to you, and was sure you'd bring him through it. And you *have* brought him through it, noble !"

"Thank'ee, my dear !" says George. "I am glad of your good opinion."

In giving Mrs. Bagnet's hand, with her work in it, a friendly shake— for she took her seat beside him—the trooper's attention is attracted to her face. After looking at it for a little while as she plies her needle, he looks to young Woolwich, sitting on his stool in the corner, and beckons that fifer to him.

"See there, my boy," says George, very gently smoothing the mother's hair with his hand, "there's a good loving forehead for you! All bright with love of you, my boy. A little touched by the sun and the weather through following your father about and taking care of you, but as fresh and wholesome as a ripe apple on a tree."

Mr. Bagnet's face expresses, so far as in its wooden material lies, the highest approbation and acquiescence.

"The time will come, my boy," pursues the trooper, "when this hair of your mother's will be grey, and this forehead all crossed and re-crossed with wrinkles—and a fine old lady she'll be then. Take care, while you are young, that you can think in those days, '*I* never whitened a hair of her dear head—*I* never marked a sorrowful line in her face !' For of all the many things that you can think of when you are a man, you had better have *that* by you, Woolwich !"

Mr. George concludes by rising from his chair, seating the boy beside his mother in it, and saying, with something of a hurry about him, that he'll smoke his pipe in the street a bit.

CHAPTER XXXV

ESTHER'S NARRATIVE

I LAY ill through several weeks, and the usual tenor of my life became like an old remembrance. But, this was not the effect of time, so much as of the change in all my habits, made by the helplessness and inaction of a sick room. Before I had been confined to it many days, everything else seemed to have retired into a remote distance, where there was little or no separation between the various stages of my life which had been really divided by years. In falling ill, I seemed to have crossed a dark lake, and to have left all my experiences, mingled together by the great distance, on the healthy shore.

My housekeeping duties, though at first it caused me great anxiety to think that they were unperformed, were soon as far off as the oldest of the old duties at Greenleaf, or the summer afternoons when I went home from school with my portfolio under my arm, and my childish shadow at my side, to my godmother's house. I had never known before how short life really was, and into how small a space the mind could put it.

While I was very ill, the way in which these divisions of time became confused with one another, distressed my mind exceedingly. At once a child, an elder girl, and the little woman I had been so happy as, I was not only oppressed by cares and difficulties adapted to each station, but by the great perplexity of endlessly trying to reconcile them. I suppose that few who have not been in such a condition can quite understand what I mean, or what painful unrest arose from this source.

For the same reason I am almost afraid to hint at that time in my disorder—it seemed one long night, but I believe there were both nights and days in it—when I laboured up colossal staircases, ever striving to reach the top, and ever turned, as I have seen a worm in a garden path, by some obstruction, and labouring again. I knew perfectly at intervals, and I think vaguely at most times, that I was in my bed; and I talked with Charley, and felt her touch, and knew her very well; yet I would find myself complaining, "Oh more of these never-ending stairs, Charley—more and more—piled up to the sky, I think!" and labouring on again.

Dare I hint at that worst time when, strung together somewhere in great black space, there was a flaming necklace, or ring, or starry circle of some kind, of which *I* was one of the beads! And when my only prayer was to be taken off from the rest, and when it was such inexplicable agony and misery to be a part of the dreadful thing?

Perhaps the less I say of these sick experiences, the less tedious and the more intelligible I shall be. I do not recall them to make others unhappy, or because I am now the least unhappy in remembering them. It may be that if we knew more of such strange afflictions, we might be better able to alleviate their intensity.

The repose that succeeded, the long delicious sleep, the blissful rest, when in my weakness I was too calm to have any care for myself, and could have heard (or so I think now) that I was dying; with no other emotion than with a pitying love for those I left behind—this state can be perhaps more widely understood. I was in this state when I first shrunk from the light as it twinkled on me once more, and knew with a boundless joy for which no words are rapturous enough, that I should see again.

I had heard my Ada crying at the door, day and night; I had heard her calling to me that I was cruel and did not love her; I had heard her praying and imploring to be let in to nurse and comfort me, and to leave my bedside no more; but I had only said, when I could speak, "Never, my sweet girl, never!" and I had over and over again, reminded Charley that she was to keep my darling from the room, whether I lived or died.

Charley had been true to me in that time of need, and with her little hand and her great heart had kept the door fast.

But now, my sight strengthening, and the glorious light coming every day more fully and brightly on me, I could read the letters that my dear wrote to me every morning and evening, and could put them to my lips and lay my cheek upon them with no fear of hurting her. I could see my little maid, so tender and so careful, going about the two rooms setting everything in order, and speaking cheerfully to Ada from the open window again. I could understand the stillness in the house, and the thoughtfulness it expressed on the part of all those who had always been so good to me. I could weep in the exquisite felicity of my heart, and be as happy in my weakness as ever I had been in my strength.

By-and-by, my strength began to be restored. Instead of lying, with so strange a calmness, watching what was done for me, as if it were done for some one else whom I was quietly sorry for, I helped it a little, and so on to a little more, and much more, until I became useful to myself, and interested, and attached to life again.

How well I remember the pleasant afternoon when I was raised in bed with pillows for the first time, to enjoy a great tea-drinking with Charley! The little creature—sent into the world, surely, to minister to the weak and sick—was so happy, and so busy, and stopped so often in her preparations to lay her head upon my bosom, and fondle me, and cry with joyful tears she was so glad, she was so glad! that I was obliged to say, "Charley, if you go on in this way, I must lie down again, my darling, for I am weaker than I thought I was!" So Charley became as quiet as a mouse, and took her bright face here and there, across and across the two rooms, out of the shade into the divine sunshine, and out of the sunshine into the shade, while I watched her peacefully. When all her preparations were concluded and the pretty tea-table with its little delicacies to tempt me, and its white cloth, and its flowers, and everything so lovingly and beautifully arranged for me by Ada downstairs, was ready at the bedside, I felt sure I was steady enough to say something to Charley that was not new to my thoughts.

First, I complimented Charley on the room ; and indeed, it was so fresh and airy, so spotless and neat, that I could scarce believe I had been lying there so long. This delighted Charley, and her face was brighter than before.

"Yet, Charley," said I, looking round, "I miss something, surely, that I am accustomed to?"

Poor little Charley looked round too, and pretended to shake her head, as if there were nothing absent.

"Are the pictures all as they used to be?" I asked her.

"Every one of them, miss," said Charley.

"And the furniture, Charley?"

"Except where I have moved it about, to make more room, miss."

"And yet," said I, "I miss some familiar object. Ah, I know what it is, Charley! It's the looking-glass."

Charley got up from the table, making as if she had forgotten something, and went into the next room; and I heard her sob there.

I had thought of this very often. I was now certain of it. I could thank God that it was not a shock to me now. I called Charley back; and when she came—at first pretending to smile, but as she drew nearer to me, looking grieved—I took her in my arms, and said, "It matters very little, Charley. I hope I can do without my old face very well."

I was presently so far advanced as to be able to sit up in a great chair, and even giddily to walk into the adjoining room, leaning on Charley. The mirror was gone from its usual place in that room too; but what I had to bear, was none the harder to bear for that.

My guardian had throughout been earnest to visit me, and there was now no good reason why I should deny myself that happiness. He came one morning; and when he first came in, could only hold me in his embrace, and say, "My dear, dear girl!" I had long known—who could know better?—what a deep fountain of affection and generosity his heart was; and was it not worth my trivial suffering and change to fill such a place in it? "Oh yes!" I thought. "He has seen me, and he loves me better than he did; he has seen me, and is even fonder of me than he was before; and what have I to mourn for!"

He sat down by me on the sofa, supporting me with his arm. For a little while he sat with his hand over his face, but when he removed it, fell into his usual manner. There never can have been, there never can be, a pleasanter manner.

"My little woman," said he, "what a sad time this has been. Such an inflexible little woman, too, through all!"

"Only for the best, Guardian," said I.

"For the best?" he repeated tenderly. "Of course, for the best. But here have Ada and I been perfectly forlorn and miserable; here has your friend Caddy been coming and going late and early; here has every one about the house been utterly lost and dejected; here has even poor Rick been writing—to *me* too—in his anxiety for you!"

I had read of Caddy in Ada's letters, but not of Richard. I told him so.

"Why, no, my dear," he replied. "I have thought it better not to mention it to her."

"And you speak of his writing to *you*," said I, repeating his emphasis. "As if it were not natural for him to do so, Guardian; as if he could write to a better friend!"

"He thinks he could, my love," returned my guardian, "and to many a better. The truth is, he wrote to me under a sort of protest, while unable to write to you with any hope of an answer—wrote coldly, haughtily, distantly, resentfully. Well, dearest little woman, we must look forbearingly on it. He is not to blame. Jarndyce and Jarndyce has warped him out of himself, and perverted me in his eyes. I have known it do as bad deeds, and worse, many a time. If two angels could be concerned in it, I believe it would change their nature."

"It has not changed yours, Guardian."

"Oh yes, it has, my dear," he said laughingly. "It has made the south wind easterly, I don't know how often. Rick mistrusts and suspects me—goes to lawyers, and is taught to mistrust and suspect me. Hears I have conflicting interests ; claims clashing against his, and what not. Whereas, Heaven knows, that if I could get out of the mountains of Wiglomeration on which my unfortunate name has been so long bestowed (which I can't), or could level them by the extinction of my own original right (which I can't either, and no human power ever can, anyhow, I believe, to such a pass have we got), I would do it this hour. I would rather restore to poor Rick his proper nature, than be endowed with all the money that dead suitors, broken, heart and soul, upon the wheel of Chancery, have left unclaimed with the Accountant-General—and that's money enough, my dear, to be cast into a pyramid, in memory of Chancery's transcendent wickedness."

"Is it possible, Guardian," I asked, amazed, "that Richard can be suspicious of you ?"

"Ah, my love, my love," he said, "it is in the subtle poison of such abuses to breed such diseases. His blood is infected, and objects lose their natural aspects in his sight. It is not *his* fault."

"But it is a terrible misfortune, Guardian."

"It is a terrible misfortune, little woman, to be ever drawn within the influences of Jarndyce and Jarndyce. I know none greater. By little and little he has been induced to trust in that rotten reed, and it communicates some portion of its rottenness to everything around him. But again, I say, with all my soul, we must be patient with poor Rick, and not blame him. What a troop of fine fresh hearts, like his, have I seen in my time turned by the same means !"

I could not help expressing something of my wonder and regret that his benevolent disinterested intentions had prospered so little.

"We must not say so, Dame Durden," he cheerfully replied ; "Ada is the happier, I hope ; and that is much. I did think that I and both these young creatures might be friends, instead of distrustful foes, and that we might so far counteract the suit, and prove too strong for it. But it was too much to expect. Jarndyce and Jarndyce was the curtain of Rick's cradle."

"But, Guardian, may we not hope that a little experience will teach him what a false and wretched thing it is ?"

"We *will* hope so, my Esther," said Mr. Jarndyce, "and that it may not teach him so too late. In any case we must not be hard on him. There are not many grown and matured men living while we speak, good men too, who, if they were thrown into this same court as suitors, would not be vitally changed and depreciated within three years—within two—within one. How can we stand amazed at poor Rick ? A young man so unfortunate," here he fell into a lower tone, as if he were thinking aloud, "cannot at first believe (who could ?) that Chancery is what it is. He looks to it, flushed and fitfully, to do something with his interests, and bring them to some settlement. It procrastinates, disappoints, tries, tortures him; wears out his sanguine hopes and patience, thread by thread; but he still looks to it, and hankers after it, and finds his whole world treacherous and hollow. Well, well, well! Enough of this, my dear!"

He had supported me, as at first, all this time; and his tenderness was so precious to me, that I leaned my head upon his shoulder and loved him as if he had been my father. I resolved in my own mind in this little pause, by some means, to see Richard when I grew strong, and try to set him right.

"There are better subjects than these," said my guardian, "for such a joyful time as the time of our dear girl's recovery. And I had a commission to broach one of them, as soon as I should begin to talk. When shall Ada come to see you, my love?"

I had been thinking of that too. A little in connection with the absent mirrors, but not much; for I knew my loving girl would be changed by no change in my looks.

"Dear guardian," said I, "as I have shut her out so long—though indeed, indeed, she is like the light to me——"

"I know it well, Dame Durden, well."

He was so good, his touch expressed such endearing compassion and affection, and the tone of his voice carried such comfort into my heart, that I stopped for a little while, quite unable to go on. "Yes, yes, you are tired," said he. "Rest a little."

"As I have kept Ada out so long," I began afresh after a short while, "I think I should like to have my own way a little longer, Guardian. It would be best to be away from here before I see her. If Charley and I were to go to some country lodging as soon as I can move, and if I had a week there, in which to grow stronger and to be revived by the sweet air, and to look forward to the happiness of having Ada with me again, I think it would be better for us."

I hope it was not a poor thing in me to wish to be a little more used to my altered self, before I met the eyes of the dear girl I longed so ardently to see; but it is the truth. I did. He understood me, I was sure; but I was not afraid of that. If it were a poor thing, I knew he would pass it over.

"Our spoilt little woman," said my guardian, "shall have her own way even in her inflexibility, though at the price, I know, of tears downstairs. And see here! Here is Boythorn, heart of chivalry, breathing such ferocious vows as never were breathed on paper before, that if you don't go and occupy his whole house, he having already turned out of it expressly for that purpose, by Heaven and by earth he'll pull it down, and not leave one brick standing on another!"

And my guardian put a letter in my hand; without any ordinary beginning such as "My dear Jarndyce," but rushing at once into the words, "I swear if Miss Summerson do not come down and take possession of my house, which I vacate for her this day at one o'clock, P.M.," and then with the utmost seriousness, and in the most emphatic terms, going on to make the extraordinary declaration he had quoted. We did not appreciate the writer the less for laughing heartily over it ; and we settled that I should send him a letter of thanks on the morrow, and accept his offer. It was a most agreeable one to me ; for all the places I could have thought of, I should have liked to go to none so well as Chesney Wold.

"Now, little housewife," said my guardian, looking at his watch, "I was strictly timed before I came upstairs, for you must not be tired too soon ; and my time has waned away to the last minute. I have one other petition. Little Miss Flite, hearing a rumour that you were ill, made nothing of walking down here—twenty miles, poor soul, in a pair of dancing shoes—to inquire. It was Heaven's mercy we were at home, or she would have walked back again."

The old conspiracy to make me happy ! Everybody seemed to be in it !

"Now, pet," said my guardian, "if it would not be irksome to you to admit the harmless little creature one- afternoon, before you save Boythorn's otherwise devoted house from demolition, I believe you would make her prouder and better pleased with herself than I—though my eminent name *is* Jarndyce—could do in a lifetime."

I have no doubt he knew there would be something in the simple image of the poor afflicted creature, that would fall like a gentle lesson on my mind at that time. I felt it as he spoke to me. I could not tell him heartily enough how ready I was to receive her. I had always pitied her ; never so much as now. I had always been glad of my little power to soothe her under her calamity ; but never, never, half so glad before.

We arranged a time for Miss Flite to come out by the coach, and share my early dinner. When my guardian left me, I turned my face away upon my couch, and prayed to be forgiven if I, surrounded by such blessings, had magnified to myself the little trial that I had to undergo. The childish prayer of that old birthday, when I had aspired to be industrious, contented, and true-hearted, and to do some good to some one, and win some love to myself if I could, came back into my mind with a reproachful sense of all the happiness I had since enjoyed, and all the affectionate hearts that had been turned towards me. If I were weak now, what had I profited by those mercies ? I repeated the old childish prayer in its old childish words, and found that its old peace had not departed from it.

My guardian now came every day. In a week or so more, I could walk about our rooms, and hold long talks with Ada from behind the window-curtain. Yet I never saw her ; for I had not as yet the courage to look at the dear face, though I could have done so easily without her seeing me.

On the appointed day Miss Flite arrived. The poor little creature ran into my room quite forgetful of her usual dignity, and, crying from her very heart of hearts, "My dear Fitz-Jarndyce !" fell upon my neck and kissed me twenty times.

"Dear me!" said she, putting her hand into her reticule, "I have nothing here but documents, my dear Fitz-Jarndyce; I must borrow a pocket-handkerchief."

Charley gave her one, and the good creature certainly made use of it, for she held it to her eyes with both hands, and sat so, shedding tears for the next ten minutes.

"With pleasure, my dear Fitz-Jarndyce," she was careful to explain. "Not the least pain. Pleasure to see you well again. Pleasure at having the honour of being admitted to see you. I am so much fonder of you, my love, than of the Chancellor. Though I *do* attend court regularly. By-the-bye, my dear, mentioning pocket-handkerchiefs——"

Miss Flite here looked at Charley, who had been to meet her at the place where the coach stopped. Charley glanced at me, and looked unwilling to pursue the suggestion.

"Ve-ry right!" said Miss Flite, "ve-ry correct. Truly! Highly indiscreet of me to mention it; but my dear Miss Fitz-Jarndyce, I am afraid I am at times (between ourselves, you wouldn't think it) a little—rambling, you know," said Miss Flite, touching her forehead. "Nothing more."

"What were you going to tell me?" said I, smiling, for I saw she wanted to go on. "You have roused my curiosity, and now you must gratify it."

Miss Flite looked to Charley for advice in this important crisis, who said, "If you please, ma'am, you had better tell then," and therein gratified Miss Flite beyond measure.

"So sagacious, our young friend," said she to me, in her mysterious way. "Diminutive. But ve-ry sagacious! Well, my dear, it's a pretty anecdote. Nothing more. Still I think it charming. Who should follow us down the road from the coach, my dear, but a poor person in a very ungenteel bonnet——"

"Jenny, if you please, miss," said Charley.

"Just so!" Miss Flite acquiesced with the greatest suavity. "Jenny. Ye-es! And what does she tell our young friend, but that there has been a lady with a veil inquiring at her cottage after my dear Fitz-Jarndyce's health, and taking a handkerchief away with her as a little keepsake, merely because it was my amiable Fitz-Jarndyce's! Now, you know, so very prepossessing in the lady with the veil!"

"If you please, miss," said Charley, to whom I looked in some astonishment, "Jenny says that when her baby died, you left a handkerchief there, and that she put it away and kept it with the baby's little things. I think, if you please, partly because it was yours, miss, and partly because it had covered the baby."

"Diminutive," whispered Miss Flite, making a variety of motions about her own forehead to express intellect in Charley. "But ex-ceedingly sagacious! And so clear! My love, she's clearer than any Counsel I ever heard!"

"Yes, Charley," I returned. "I remember it. Well?"

"Well, miss," said Charley, "and that's the handkerchief the lady took. And Jenny wants you to know that she wouldn't have made away with it herself for a heap of money, but that the lady took it, and left some money instead. Jenny don't know her at all, if you please, miss."

"Why, who can she be?" said I.

"My love," Miss Flite suggested, advancing her lips to my ear, with her most mysterious look, "in *my* opinion—don't mention this to our diminutive friend—she's the Lord Chancellor's wife. He's married, you know. And I understand she leads him a terrible life. Throws his lordship's papers into the fire, my dear, if he won't pay the jeweller!"

I did not think very much about this lady then, for I had an impression that it might be Caddy. Besides, my attention was diverted by my visitor, who was cold after her ride, and looked hungry; and who, our dinner being brought in, required some little assistance in arraying herself with great satisfaction in a pitiable old scarf, and a much-worn and often-mended pair of gloves, which she had brought down in a paper parcel. I had to preside, too, over the entertainment, consisting of a dish of fish, a roast fowl, a sweetbread, vegetables, pudding, and Madeira; and it was so pleasant to see how she enjoyed it, and with what state and ceremony she did honour to it, that I was soon thinking of nothing else.

When we had finished, and had our little dessert before us, embellished by the hands of my dear, who would yield the superintendence of everything prepared for me to no one; Miss Flite was so very chatty and happy, that I thought I would lead her to her own history, as she was always pleased to talk about herself. I began by saying "You have attended on the Lord Chancellor many years, Miss Flite?"

"Oh many, many, many years, my dear. But I expect a Judgment. Shortly."

There was an anxiety even in her hopefulness, that made me doubtful if I had done right in approaching the subject. I thought I would say no more about it.

"My father expected a Judgment," said Miss Flite. "My brother. My sister. They all expected a Judgment. The same that I expect."

"They are all——"

"Ye-es. Dead of course, my dear," said she.

As I saw she would go on, I thought it best to try to be serviceable to her by meeting the theme, rather than avoiding it.

"Would it not be wiser," said I, "to expect this Judgment no more?"

"Why, my dear," she answered promptly, "of course it would!"

"And to attend the court no more?"

"Equally of course," said she. "Very wearing to be always in expectation of what never comes, my dear Fitz-Jarndyce! Wearing, I assure you, to the bone!"

She slightly showed me her arm, and it was fearfully thin indeed.

"But, my dear," she went on, in her mysterious way, "there's a dreadful attraction in the place. Hush! Don't mention it to our diminutive friend when she comes in. Or it may frighten her. With good reason. There's a cruel attraction in the place. You *can't* leave it. And you *must* expect."

I tried to assure her that this was not so. She heard me patiently and smilingly, but was ready with her own answer.

"Ay, ay, ay! You think so, because I am a little rambling. Ve-ry absurd, to be a little rambling, is it not? Ve-ry confusing, too. To the head. I find it so. But, my dear, I have been there many years, and I have noticed. It's the Mace and Seal upon the table."

What could they do, did she think? I mildly asked her.

"Draw," returned Miss Flite. "Draw people on, my dear. Draw peace out of them. Sense out of them. Good looks out of them. Good qualities out of them. I have felt them even drawing my rest away in the night. Cold and glittering devils!"

She tapped me several times upon the arm, and nodded good-humouredly, as if she were anxious I should understand that I had no cause to fear her, though she spoke so gloomily, and confided these awful secrets to me.

"Let me see," said she. "I'll tell you my own case. Before they ever drew me—before I had ever seen them—what was it I used to do? Tambourine playing? No, Tambour work. I and my sister worked at tambour work. Our father and our brother had a builder's business. We all lived together. Ve-ry respectably, my dear! First, our father was drawn—slowly. Home was drawn with him. In a few years, he was a fierce, sour, angry bankrupt, without a kind word or a kind look for any one. He had been so different, Fitz-Jarndyce. He was drawn to a debtors' prison. There he died. Then our brother was drawn—swiftly—to drunkenness. And rags. And death. Then my sister was drawn. Hush! Never ask to what! Then I was ill, and in misery; and heard, as I had often heard before, that this was all the work of Chancery. When I got better, I went to look at the Monster. And then I found out how it was, and I was drawn to stay there."

Having got over her own short narrative, in the delivery of which she had spoken in a low, strained voice, as if the shock were fresh upon her, she gradually resumed her usual air of amiable importance.

"You don't quite credit me, my dear! Well well! You will, some day. I am a little rambling. But I have noticed. I have seen many new faces come, unsuspicious, within the influence of the Mace and Seal, in these many years. As my father's came there. As my brother's. As my sister's. As my own. I hear Conversation Kenge, and the rest of them, say to the new faces, 'Here's little Miss Flite! Oh you are new here; and you must come and be presented to little Miss Flite!' Ve-ry good. Proud I am sure to have the honour! And we all laugh. But, Fitz-Jarndyce, I know what will happen. I know, far better than they do, when the attraction has begun. I know the signs, my dear. I saw them begin in Gridley. And I saw them end. Fitz-Jarndyce, my love," speaking low again, "I saw them beginning in our friend the Ward in Jarndyce. Let some one hold him back. Or he'll be drawn to ruin."

She looked at me in silence for some moments, with her face gradually softening into a smile. Seeming to fear that she had been too gloomy, and seeming also to lose the connection in her mind, she said, politely, as she sipped her glass of wine, "Yes, my dear, as I was saying, I expect a Judgment. Shortly. Then I shall release my birds, you know, and confer estates."

I was much impressed by her allusion to Richard, and by the sad meaning, so sadly illustrated in her poor pinched form, that made its way through all her incoherence. But happily for her, she was quite complacent again now, and beamed with nods and smiles.

"But, my dear," she said gaily, reaching another hand to put it upon mine. "You have not congratulated me on my physician. Positively not once, yet!"

I was obliged to confess that I did not quite know what she meant.

"My physician, Mr. Woodcourt, my dear, who was so exceedingly attentive to me. Though his services were rendered quite gratuitously. Until the Day of Judgment. I mean *the* judgment that will dissolve the spell upon me of the Mace and Seal."

"Mr. Woodcourt is so far away, now," said I, "that I thought the time for such congratulation was past, Miss Flite."

"But, my child," she returned, "is it possible that you don't know what has happened?"

"No," said I.

"Not what everybody has been talking of, my beloved Fitz-Jarndyce!"

"No," said I. "You forget how long I have been here."

"True! My dear, for the moment—true. I blame myself. But my memory has been drawn out of me, with everything else, by what I mentioned. Ve-ry strong influence, is it not? Well, my dear, there has been a terrible shipwreck over in those East-Indian seas."

"Mr. Woodcourt shipwrecked!"

"Don't be agitated, my dear. He is safe. An awful scene. Death in all shapes. Hundreds of dead and dying. Fire, storm, and darkness. Numbers of the drowning thrown upon a rock. There, and through it all, my dear physician was a hero. Calm and brave, through everything. Saved many lives, never complained in hunger and thirst, wrapto naked people in his spare clothes, took the lead, showed them ' *the* do, governed them, tended the sick, buried the dead, and. *features* poor survivors safely off at last! My dear, the poor e*hey got to* all but worshipped him. They fell down at his fe*it.* *You shall read* the land, and blessed him. The whole count*slowly and imper-* Where's my bag of documents? I have g*could not see the words,* it, you shall read it!"

And I *did* read all the noble hi*I felt so triumphant ever to* fectly then, for my eyes were *generous and gallant deeds; I* and I cried so much that account she had cut o have known the felt such glowing exultation in his renown ; I so admired and loved what he had done ; that I envied the storm-worn people who had fallen at his feet and blessed him as their preserver. I could myself have kneeled down then, so far away, and blessed him, in my rapture that he should be so truly good and brave. I felt that no one—mother, sister, wife—could honour him more than I. I did, indeed !

My poor little visitor made me a present of the account, and when, as the evening began to close in, she rose to take her leave, lest she should miss the coach by which she was to return, she was still full of the shipwreck, which I had not yet sufficiently composed myself to understand in all its details.

" My dear," said she, as she carefully folded up her scarf and gloves, " my brave physician ought to have a Title bestowed upon him. And no doubt he will. You are of that opinion ? "

That he well deserved one, yes. That he would ever have one, no.

" Why not, Fitz-Jarndyce ? " she asked rather sharply.

I said it was not the custom in England to confer titles on men distinguished by peaceful services, however good and great ; unless occasionally, when they consisted of the accumulation of some very large amount of money.

" Why, good gracious," said Miss Flite, " how can you say that ? Surely you know, my dear, that all the greatest ornaments of England in knowledge, imagination, active humanity, and improvement of every sort, are added to its nobility ! Look round you, my dear, and consider. *You* must be rambling a little now, I think, if you don't know that this is the great reason why titles will always last in the land ! "

I am afraid she believed what she said ; for there were moments when she was very mad indeed.

And now I must part with the little secret I have thus far tried to keep. I had thought, sometimes, that Mr. Woodcourt loved me ; and that if he had been richer, he would perhaps have told me that he loved me, before he went away. I had thought, sometimes, that if he had done so, I should have been glad of it. But, how much better it was w, that this had never happened ! What should I have suffered, if I as ad to write to him, and tell him that the poor face he had known bond was quite gone from me, and that I freely released him from his Oh, ne whom he had never seen !

spared he had so much better as it was ! With a great pang mercifully no chain for take back to my heart my childish prayer to be all my lowly way wn himself ; and there was nothing to be undone : upon its broader r for him to drag ; and I could go, please God, might aspire to me th of duty, and he could go his nobler way thought me when I ugh we were apart upon the journey, I ly, innocently, better far than he had in his eyes, at the journey's end.

CHAPTER XXXVI

CHESNEY WOLD

CHARLEY and I did not set off alone upon our expedition into Lincolnshire. My guardian had made up his mind not to lose sight of me until I was safe in Mr. Boythorn's house; so he accompanied us, and we were two days upon the road. I found every breath of air, and every scent, and every flower and leaf and blade of grass, and every passing cloud, and everything in nature, more beautiful and wonderful to me than I had ever found it yet. This was my first gain from my illness. How little I had lost, when the wide world was so full of delight for me.

My guardian intending to go back immediately, we appointed, on our way down, a day when my dear girl should come. I wrote her a letter, of which he took charge; and he left us within half-an-hour of our arrival at our destination, on a delightful evening in the early summer time.

If a good fairy had built the house for me with a wave of her wand, and I had been a princess and her favoured godchild, I could not have been more considered in it. So many preparations were made for me, and such an endearing remembrance was shown of all my little tastes and likings, that I could have sat down, overcome, a dozen times, before I had revisited half the rooms. I did better than that, however, by showing them all to Charley instead. Charley's delight calmed mine; and after we had had a walk in the garden, and Charley had exhausted her whole vocabulary of admiring expressions, I was as tranquilly happy as I ought to have been. It was a great comfort to be able to say to myself after tea, "Esther, my dear, I think you are quite sensible enough to sit down now, and write a note of thanks to your host." He had left a note of welcome for me, as sunny as his own face, and had confided his bird to my care, which I knew to be his highest mark of confidence. Accordingly I wrote a little note to him in London, telling him how all his favourite plants and trees were looking, and how the most astonishing of birds had chirped the honours of the house to me in the most hospitable manner, and how, after singing on my shoulder, to the inconceivable rapture of my little maid, he was then at roost in the usual corner of his cage, but whether dreaming or no I could not report. My note finished and sent off to the post, I made myself very busy in unpacking and arranging; and I sent Charley to bed in good time, and told her I should want her no more that night.

For I had not yet looked in the glass, and had never asked to have my own restored to me. I knew this to be a weakness which must be overcome; but I had always said to myself that I would begin afresh, when I got to where I now was. Therefore I had wanted to be alone, and therefore I said, now alone, in my own room, "Esther, if you are to be happy, if you are to have any right to pray to be true-hearted, you must keep your word, my dear." I was quite resolved to keep it; but I sat down for a little while first, to reflect upon all my blessings. And then I said my prayers, and thought a little more.

My hair had not been cut off, though it had been in danger more than once. It was long and thick. I let it down, and shook it out, and went up to the glass upon the dressing-table. There was a little muslin curtain drawn across it. I drew it back : and stood for a moment looking through such a veil of my own hair, that I could see nothing else. Then I put my hair aside, and looked at the reflection in the mirror; encouraged by seeing how placidly it looked at me. I was very much changed—Oh very, very much. At first, my face was so strange to me, that I think I should have put my hands before it and started back, but for the encouragement I have mentioned. Very soon it became more familiar, and then I knew the extent of the alteration in it better than I had done at first. It was not like what I had expected ; but I had expected nothing definite, and I dare say anything definite would have surprised me.

I had never been a beauty, and had never thought myself one ; but I had been very different from this. It was all gone now. Heaven was so good to me, that I could let it go with a few not bitter tears, and could stand there arranging my hair for the night quite thankfully.

One thing troubled me, and I considered it for a long time before I went to sleep. I had kept Mr. Woodcourt's flowers. When they were withered I had dried them, and put them in a book that I was fond of. Nobody knew this, not even Ada. I was doubtful whether I had a right to preserve what he had sent to one so different—whether it was generous towards him to do it. I wished to be generous to him, even in the secret depths of my heart, which he would never know, because I could have loved him—could have been devoted to him. At last I came to the conclusion that I might keep them ; if I treasured them only as a remembrance of what was irrevocably past and gone, never to be looked back on any more, in any other light. I hope this may not seem trivial. I was very much in earnest.

I took care to be up early in the morning, and to be before the glass when Charley came in on tiptoe.

"Dear, dear, miss ! " cried Charley, starting. " Is that you ? "

"Yes, Charley," said I, quietly putting up my hair. " And I am very well indeed, and very happy."

I saw it was a weight off Charley's mind, but it was a greater weight off mine. I knew the worst now, and was composed to it. I shall not conceal, as I go on, the weaknesses I could not quite conquer ; but they always passed from me soon, and the happier frame of mind stayed by me faithfully.

Wishing to be fully re-established in my strength and my good spirits before Ada came, I now laid down a little series of plans with Charley for being in the fresh air all day long. We were to be out before breakfast, and were to dine early, and were to be out again before and after dinner, and were to walk in the garden after tea, and were to go to rest betimes, and were to climb every hill and explore every road, lane, and field in the neighbourhood. As to restoratives and strengthening delicacies, Mr. Boythorn's good housekeeper was for ever trotting about with something to eat or drink in her hand; I could not even be heard of as resting in the park, but she would come trotting after me with a basket, her cheerful face shining with a lecture on the importance of frequent nourishment. Then there was a pony expressly for my riding, a chubby pony, with a short neck and a mane all over his eyes, who could canter —when he would—so easily and quietly, that he was a treasure. In a very few days, he would come to me in the paddock when I called him, and eat out of my hand, and follow me about. We arrived at such a capital understanding, that when he was jogging with me lazily, and rather obstinately, down some shady lane, if I patted his neck, and said, "Stubbs, I am surprised you don't canter when you know how much I like it; and I think you might oblige me, for you are only getting stupid and going to sleep," he would give his head a comical shake or two, and set off directly; while Charley would stand still and laugh with such enjoyment, that her laughter was like music. I don't know who had given Stubbs his name, but it seemed to belong to him as naturally as his rough coat. Once we put him in a little chaise, and drove him triumphantly through the green lanes for five miles; but all at once, as we were extolling him to the skies, he seemed to take it ill that he should have been accompanied so far by the circle of tantalising little gnats, that had been hovering round and round his ears the whole way without appearing to advance an inch; and stopped to think about it. I suppose he came to the decision that it was not to be borne; for he steadily refused to move, until I gave the reins to Charley and got out and walked; when he followed me with a sturdy sort of good humour, putting his head under my arm, and rubbing his ear against my sleeve. It was in vain for me to say, "Now, Stubbs, I feel quite sure from what I know of you, that you will go on if I ride a little while;" for the moment I left him, he stood stock still again. Consequently I was obliged to lead the way, as before; and in this order we returned home, to the great delight of the village.

Charley and I had reason to call it the most friendly of villages, I am sure; for in a week's time the people were so glad to see us go by, though ever so frequently in the course of a day, that there were faces of greeting in every cottage. I had known many of the grown people before, and almost all the children; but now the very steeple began to wear a familiar and affectionate look. Among my new friends was an old old woman who lived in such a little thatched and whitewashed dwelling, that when the outside shutter was turned up on its hinges, it shut up the whole house-front. This old lady had a grandson who was a sailor; and I wrote a letter to him for her, and drew at the top of it the chimney-corner in which she had brought him up, and where his old stool yet occupied its old place. This was considered by the whole village the most wonderful achievement in the world; but when an answer came back all the way from Plymouth, in which he mentioned that he was going to take the picture all the way to America, and from America would write again, I got all the credit that ought to have been given to the Post-office, and was invested with the merit of the whole system.

Thus, what with being so much in the air, playing with so many children, gossiping with so many people, sitting on invitation in so many cottages, going on with Charley's education, and writing long letters to Ada every day, I had scarcely any time to think about that little loss of mine, and was almost always cheerful. If I did think of it at odd moments now and then, I had only to be busy and forget it. I felt it more than I had hoped I should, once, when a child said, "Mother, why is the lady not a pretty lady now, like she used to be?" But when I found the child was not less fond of me, and drew its soft hand over my face with a kind of pitying protection in its touch, that soon set me up again. There were many little occurrences which suggested to me, with great consolation, how natural it is to gentle hearts to be considerate and delicate towards any inferiority. One of these particularly touched me. I happened to stroll into the little church when a marriage was just concluded, and the young couple had to sign the register.

The bridegroom, to whom the pen was handed first, made a rude cross for his mark; the bride, who came next, did the same. Now, I had known the bride when I was last there, not only as the prettiest girl in the place, but as having quite distinguished herself in the school; and I could not help looking at her with some surprise. She came aside and whispered to me, while tears of honest love and admiration stood in her bright eyes, "He's a dear good fellow, miss; but he can't write, yet— he's going to learn of me—and I wouldn't shame him for the world!" Why, what had I to fear, I thought, when there was this nobility in the soul of a labouring man's daughter!

The air blew as freshly and revivingly upon me as it had ever blown, and the healthy colour came into my new face as it had come into my old one. Charley was wonderful to see, she was so radiant and so rosy; and we both enjoyed the whole day, and slept soundly the whole night.

There was a favourite spot of mine in the park-woods of Chesney Wold, where a seat had been erected commanding a lovely view. The wood had been cleared and opened, to improve this point of sight; and the bright sunny landscape beyond was so beautiful that I rested there at least once every day. A picturesque part of the Hall, called the Ghost's Walk, was seen to advantage from this higher ground; and the startling name, and the old legend in the Dedlock family which I had heard from Mr. Boythorn, accounting for it, mingled with the view, and gave it something of a mysterious interest, in addition to its real charms. There was a bank here, too, which was a famous one for violets; and as it was a daily delight of Charley's to gather wild flowers, she took as much to the spot as I did.

It would be idle to inquire now why I never went close to the house, or never went inside it. The family were not there, I had heard on my arrival, and were not expected. I was far from being incurious or uninterested about the building; on the contrary, I often sat in this place, wondering how the rooms ranged, and whether any echo like a footstep really did resound at times, as the story said, upon the lonely Ghost's Walk. The indefinable feeling with which Lady Dedlock had impressed me, may have had some influence in keeping me from the house even when she was absent. I am not sure. Her face and figure were associated with it, naturally; but I cannot say that they repelled me from it, though something did. For whatever reason or no reason, I had never once gone near it, down to the day at which my story now arrives.

I was resting at my favourite point, after a long ramble, and Charley was gathering violets at a little distance from me. I had been looking at the Ghost's Walk lying in a deep shade of masonry afar off, and picturing to myself the female shape that was said to haunt it, when I became aware of a figure approaching through the wood. The perspective was so long, and so darkened by leaves, and the shadows of the branches on the ground made it so much more intricate to the eye, that at first I could not discern what figure it was. By little and little, it revealed itself to be a woman's—a lady's—Lady Dedlock's. She was alone, and coming to where I sat with a much quicker step, I observed to my surprise, than was usual with her.

I was fluttered by her being unexpectedly so near (she was almost within speaking distance before I knew her), and would have risen to continue my walk. But I could not. I was rendered motionless. Not so much by her hurried gesture of entreaty, not so much by her quick advance and outstretched hands, not so much by the great change in her manner, and the absence of her haughty self-restraint, as by a something in her face that I had pined for and dreamed of when I was a little child; something I had never seen in any face; something I had never seen in hers before.

A dread and faintness fell upon me, and I called to Charley. Lady Dedlock stopped, upon the instant, and changed back almost to what I had known her.

"Miss Summerson, I am afraid I have startled you," she said, now advancing slowly. "You can scarcely be strong yet. You have been very ill, I know. I have been much concerned to hear it."

I could no more have removed my eyes from her pale face, than I could have stirred from the bench on which I sat. She gave me her hand; and its deadly coldness, so at variance with the enforced composure of her features, deepened the fascination that overpowered me. I cannot say what was in my whirling thoughts.

"You are recovering again?" she asked kindly.

"I was quite well but a moment ago, Lady Dedlock."

"Is this your young attendant?"

"Yes."

"Will you send her on before, and walk towards your house with me?"

"Charley," said I, "take your flowers home, and I will follow you directly."

Charley, with her best curtsey, blushingly tied on her bonnet, and went her way. When she was gone, Lady Dedlock sat down on the seat beside me.

I cannot tell in any words what the state of my mind was, when I saw in her hand my handkerchief, with which I had covered the dead baby.

I looked at her; but I could not see her, I could not hear her, I could not draw my breath. The beating of my heart was so violent and wild, that I felt as if my life were breaking from me. But when she caught me to her breast, kissed me, wept over me, compassionated me, and called me back to myself; when she fell down on her knees and cried to me, "Oh my child, my child, I am your wicked and unhappy mother! Oh try to forgive me!"—when I saw her at my feet on the bare earth in her great agony of mind, I felt, through all my tumult of emotion, a burst of gratitude to the providence of God that I was so changed as that I never could disgrace her by any trace of likeness; as that nobody could ever now look at me, and look at her, and remotely think of any near tie between us.

I raised my mother up, praying and beseeching her not to stoop before me in such affliction and humiliation. I did so, in broken incoherent words; for, besides the trouble I was in, it frightened me to see her at *my* feet. I told her—or I tried to tell her—that if it were for me, her child, under any circumstances to take upon me to forgive her, I did it, and had done it, many, many years. I told her that my heart overflowed with love for her; that it was natural love, which nothing in the past had changed, or could change. That it was not for me, then resting for the first time on my mother's bosom, to take her to account for having given me life; but that my duty was to bless her and receive her, though the whole world turned from her, and that I only asked her leave to do it. I held my mother in my embrace, and she held me in hers; and among the still woods in the silence of the summer day, there seemed to be nothing but our two troubled minds that was not at peace.

"To bless and receive me," groaned my mother, "it is far too late. I must travel my dark road alone, and it will lead me where it will. From day to day, sometimes from hour to hour, I do not see the way before my guilty feet. This is the earthly punishment I have brought upon myself. I bear it, and I hide it."

Even in the thinking of her endurance, she drew her habitual air of proud indifference about her like a veil, though she soon cast it off again.

"I must keep this secret, if by any means it can be kept, not wholly for myself. I have a husband, wretched and dishonouring creature that I am!"

These words she uttered with a suppressed cry of despair, more terrible in its sound than any shriek. Covering her face with her hands, she shrunk down in my embrace as if she were unwilling that I should touch her ; nor could I, by my utmost persuasions, or by any endearments I could use, prevail upon her to rise. She said, No, no, no, she could only speak to me so ; she must be proud and disdainful everywhere else ; she would be humbled and ashamed there, in the only natural moments of her life.

My unhappy mother told me that in my illness she had been nearly frantic. She had but then known that her child was living. She could not have suspected me to be that child before. She had followed me down here, to speak to me but once in all her life. We never could associate, never could communicate, never probably from that time forth could interchange another word, on earth. She put into my hands a letter she had written for my reading only ; and said, when I had read it, and destroyed it—but not so much for her sake, since she asked nothing, as for her husband's and my own—I must evermore consider her as dead. If I could believe that she loved me, in this agony in which I saw her, with a mother's love, she asked me to do that ; for then I might think of her with a greater pity, imagining what she suffered. She had put herself beyond all hope, and beyond all help. Whether she preserved her secret until death, or it came to be discovered and she brought dishonour and disgrace upon the name she had taken, it was her solitary struggle always ; and no affection could come near her, and no human creature could render her any aid.

"But is the secret safe so far ?" I asked. "Is it safe now, dearest mother ?"

"No," replied my mother. "It has been very near discovery. It was saved by an accident. It may be lost by another accident—to-morrow, any day."

"Do you dread a particular person ?"

"Hush ! Do not tremble and cry so much for me. I am not worthy of these tears," said my mother, kissing my hands. "I dread one person very much."

"An enemy ?"

"Not a friend. One who is too passionless to be either. He is Sir Leicester Dedlock's lawyer ; mechanically faithful without attachment, and very jealous of the profit, privilege, and reputation of being master of the mysteries of great houses."

"Has he any suspicions ?"

"Many."

"Not of you ?" I said, alarmed.

"Yes ! He is always vigilant, and always near me. I may keep him at a standstill, but I can never shake him off."

"Has he so little pity or compunction ?"

"He has none, and no anger. He is indifferent to everything but his calling. His calling is the acquisition of secrets, and the holding possession of such power as they give him, with no sharer or opponent in it."

"Could you trust in him ?"

"I shall never try. The dark road I have trodden for so many years will end where it will. I follow it alone to the end, whatever the end be. It may be near, it may be distant; while the road lasts, nothing turns me."

"Dear mother, are you so resolved?"

"I *am* resolved. I have long outbidden folly with folly, pride with pride, scorn with scorn, insolence with insolence, and have outlived many vanities with many more. I will outlive this danger, and outdie it, if I can. It has closed around me, almost as awfully as if these woods of Chesney Wold had closed around the house; but my course through it is the same. I have but one; I can have but one."

"Mr. Jarndyce—" I was beginning, when my mother hurriedly inquired: "Does *he* suspect?"

"No," said I. "No, indeed! Be assured that he does not!" And I told her what he had related to me as his knowledge of my story. "But he is so good and sensible," said I, "that perhaps if he knew——"

My mother, who until this time had made no change in her position, raised her hand up to my lips, and stopped me.

"Confide fully in him," she said, after a little while. "You have my free consent— a small gift from such a mother to her injured child!—but do not tell me of it. Some pride is left in me, even yet."

I explained, as nearly as I could then, or can recall now—for my agitation and distress throughout were so great that I scarcely understood myself, though every word that was uttered in the mother's voice, so unfamiliar and so melancholy to me; which in my childhood I had never learned to love and recognise, had never been sung to sleep with, had never heard a blessing from, had never had a hope inspired by; made an enduring impression on my memory—I say I explained, or tried to do it, how I had only hoped that Mr. Jarndyce, who had been the best of fathers to me, might be able to afford some counsel and support to her. But my mother answered no, it was impossible; no one could help her. Through the desert that lay before her, she must go alone.

"My child, my child!" she said. "For the last time! These kisses for the last time! These arms upon my neck for the last time! We shall meet no more. To hope to do what I seek to do, I must be what I have been so long. Such is my reward and doom. If you hear of Lady Dedlock, brilliant, prosperous, and flattered; think of your wretched mother, conscience-stricken, underneath that mask! Think that the reality is in her suffering, in her useless remorse, in her murdering within her breast the only love and truth of which it is capable! And then forgive her, if you can; and cry to Heaven to forgive her, which it never can!"

We held one another for a little space yet, but she was so firm, that she took my hands away, and put them back against my breast, and, with a last kiss as she held them there, released them, and went from me into the wood. I was alone; and, calm and quiet below me in the sun and shade, lay the old house, with its terraces and turrets, on which there had seemed to me to be such complete repose when I first saw it, but which now looked like the obdurate and unpitying watcher of my mother's misery.

Stunned as I was, as weak and helpless at first as I had ever been in my sick chamber, the necessity of guarding against the danger of discovery, or even of the remotest suspicion, did me service. I took such precautions as I could to hide from Charley that I had been crying; and I constrained myself to think of every sacred obligation that there was upon me to be careful and collected. It was not a little while before I could succeed, or could even restrain bursts of grief; but after an hour or so, I was better, and felt that I might return. I went home very slowly, and told Charley, whom I found at the gate looking for me, that I had been tempted to extend my walk after Lady Dedlock had left me, and that I was over-tired, and would lie down. Safe in my own room, I read the letter. I clearly derived from it—and that was much then—that I had not been abandoned by my mother. Her elder and only sister, the godmother of my childhood, discovering signs of life in me when I had been laid aside as dead, had, in her stern sense of duty, with no desire or willingness that I should live, reared me in rigid secrecy, and had never again beheld my mother's face from within a few hours of my birth. So strangely did I hold my place in this world, that, until within a short time back, I had never, to my own mother's knowledge, breathed —had been buried—had never been endowed with life—had never borne a name. When she had first seen me in the church, she had been startled; and had thought of what would have been like me, if it had ever lived, and had lived on; but that was all, then.

What more the letter told me, needs not to be repeated here. It has its own times and places in my story.

My first care was to burn what my mother had written, and to consume even its ashes. I hope it may not appear very unnatural or bad in me, that I then became heavily sorrowful to think I had ever been reared. That I felt as if I knew it would have been better and happier for many people, if indeed I had never breathed. That I had a terror of myself, as the danger and the possible disgrace of my own mother, and of a proud family name. That I was so confused and shaken, as to be possessed by a belief that it was right, and had been intended, that I should die in my birth; and that it was wrong, and not intended, that I should be then alive.

These are the real feelings that I had. I fell asleep, worn out; and when I awoke, I cried afresh to think that I was back in the world, with my load of trouble for others. I was more than ever frightened of myself, thinking anew of her, against whom I was a witness; of the owner of Chesney Wold; of the new and terrible meaning of the old words, now moaning in my ear like a surge upon the shore, "Your mother, Esther, was your disgrace, and you are hers. The time will come—and soon enough—when you will understand this better, and will feel it too, as no one save a woman can." With them, those other words returned, "Pray daily that the sins of others be not visited upon your head." I could not disentangle all that was about me; and I felt as if the blame and the shame were all in me, and the visitation had come down.

The day waned into a gloomy evening, overcast and sad, and I still contended with the same distress. I went out alone; and, after walking a little in the park, watching the dark shades falling on the trees, and the fitful flight of the bats, which sometimes almost touched me, was attracted to the house for the first time. Perhaps I might not have gone near it, if I had been in a stronger frame of mind. As it was, I took the path that led close by it.

I did not dare to linger or to look up, but I passed before the terrace garden with its fragrant odours, and its broad walks, and its well-kept beds and smooth turf; and I saw how beautiful and grave it was, and how the old stone balustrades and parapets, and wide flights of shallow steps, were seamed by time and weather; and how the trained moss and ivy grew about them, and around the old stone pedestal of the sun-dial; and I heard the fountain falling. Then the way went by long lines of dark windows, diversified by turreted towers, and porches, of eccentric shapes, where old stone lions and grotesque monsters bristled outside dens of shadow, and snarled at the evening gloom over the escutcheons they held in their grip. Thence the path wound underneath a gateway, and through a courtyard where the principal entrance was (I hurried quickly on), and by the stables where none but deep voices seemed to be, whether in the murmuring of the wind through the strong mass of ivy holding to a high red wall, or in the low complaining of the weathercock, or in the barking of the dogs, or in the slow striking of a clock. So, encountering presently a sweet smell of limes, whose rustling I could hear, I turned with the turning of the path, to the south front; and there, above me, were the balustrades of the Ghost's Walk, and one lighted window that might be my mother's.

The way was paved here, like the terrace overhead, and my footsteps from being noiseless made an echoing sound upon the flags. Stopping to look at nothing, but seeing all I did see as I went, I was passing quickly on, and in a few moments should have passed the lighted window, when my echoing footsteps brought it suddenly into my mind that there was a dreadful truth in the legend of the Ghost's Walk; that it was I, who was to bring calamity upon the stately house; and that my warning feet were haunting it even then. Seized with an augmented terror of myself which turned me cold, I ran from myself and everything, retraced the way by which I had come, and never paused until I had gained the lodge-gate, and the park lay sullen and black behind me.

Not before I was alone in my own room for the night, and had again been dejected and unhappy there, did I begin to know how wrong and thankless this state was. But, from my darling who was coming on the morrow, I found a joyful letter, full of such loving anticipation that I must have been of marble if it had not moved me; from my guardian, too, I found another letter, asking me to tell Dame Durden, if I should see that little woman anywhere, that they had moped most pitiably without her, that the housekeeping was going to rack and ruin, that nobody else could manage the keys, and that everybody in and about the house declared that it was not the same house, and was becoming rebellious for her return. Two such letters together made me think how far beyond my deserts I was beloved, and how happy I ought to be. That made me think of all my past life ; and that brought me, as it ought to have done before, into a better condition.

For, I saw very well that I could not have been intended to die, or I should never have lived ; not to say should never have been reserved for such a happy life. I saw very well how many things had worked together for my welfare; and that if the sins of the fathers were sometimes visited upon the children, the phrase did not mean what I had in the morning feared it meant. I knew I was as innocent of my birth as a queen of hers ; and that before my Heavenly Father I should not be punished for birth, nor a queen rewarded for it. I had had experience, in the shock of that very day, that I could, even thus soon, find comforting reconcilements to the change that had fallen on me. I renewed my resolutions, and prayed to be strengthened in them ; pouring out my heart for myself, and for my unhappy mother, and feeling that the darkness of the morning was passing away. It was not upon my sleep ; and when the next day's light awoke me, it was gone.

My dear girl was to arrive at five o'clock in the afternoon. How to help myself through the intermediate time better than by taking a long walk along the road by which she was to come, I did not know ; so Charley and I and Stubbs—Stubbs, saddled, for we never drove him after the one great occasion—made a long expedition along that road, and back. On our return, we held a great review of the house and garden ; and saw that everything was in its prettiest condition, and had the bird out ready as an important part of the establishment.

There were more than two full hours yet to elapse, before she could come ; and in that interval, which seemed a long one, I must confess I was nervously anxious about my altered looks. I loved my darling so well that I was more concerned for their effect on her than on any one. I was not in this slight distress because I at all repined—I am quite certain I did not, that day—but, I thought, would she be wholly prepared ? When she first saw me, might she not be a little shocked and disappointed ? Might it not prove a little worse than she had expected ? Might she not look for her old Esther, and not find her ? Might she not have to grow used to me, and to begin all over again ?

I knew the various expressions of my sweet girl's face so well, and it was such an honest face in its loveliness, that I was sure, beforehand, she could not hide that first look from me. And I considered whether, if it should signify any one of these meanings, which was so very likely, could I quite answer for myself?

Well, I thought I could. After last night, I thought I could. But to wait and wait, and expect and expect, and think and think, was such bad preparation, that I resolved to go along the road again, and meet her.

So I said to Charley, "Charley, I will go by myself and walk along the road until she comes." Charley highly approving of anything that pleased me, I went, and left her at home.

But before I got to the second milestone I had been in so many palpitations from seeing dust in the distance (though I knew it was not, and could not be the coach, yet), that I resolved to turn back and go home again. And when I had turned, I was in such fear of the coach coming up behind me (though I still knew that it neither would, nor could, do any such thing), that I ran the greater part of the way, to avoid being overtaken.

Then, I considered, when I had got safe back again, this was a nice thing to have done! Now I was hot, and had made the worst of it, instead of the best.

At last, when I believed there was at least a quarter of an hour more yet, Charley all at once cried out to me as I was trembling in the garden, "Here she comes, miss! Here she is!"

I did not mean to do it, but I ran upstairs into my room, and hid myself behind the door. There I stood, trembling, even when I heard my darling calling as she came upstairs, "Esther, my dear, my love, where are you? Little woman, dear Dame Durden!"

She ran in, and was running out again when she saw me. Ah, my angel girl! the old dear look, all love, all fondness, all affection. Nothing else in it—no, nothing, nothing!

Oh how happy I was, down upon the floor, with my sweet beautiful girl down upon the floor too, holding my scarred face to her lovely cheek, bathing it with tears and kisses, rocking me to and fro like a child, calling me by every tender name that she could think of, and pressing me to her faithful heart.

CHAPTER XXXVII

JARNDYCE AND JARNDYCE

IF the secret that I had to keep had been mine, I must have confided it to Ada before we had been long together. But it was not mine; and I did not feel that I had a right to tell it, even to my guardian, unless some great emergency arose. It was a weight to bear alone; still my present duty appeared to be plain, and, blessed in the attachment of my dear, I did not want an impulse and encouragement to do it. Though often when she was asleep, and all was quiet, the remembrance of my mother kept me waking, and made the night sorrowful, I did not yield to it at another time; and Ada found me what I used to be—except, of course, in that particular of which I have said enough, and which I have no intention of mentioning any more, just now, if I can help it.

The difficulty that I felt in being quite composed that first evening, when Ada asked me, over our work, if the family were at the house, and when I was obliged to answer yes, I believed so, for Lady Dedlock had spoken to me in the woods the day before yesterday, was great. Greater still, when Ada asked me what she had said, and when I replied that she had been kind and interested; and when Ada, while admitting her beauty and elegance, remarked upon her proud manner, and her imperious chilling air. But Charley helped me through unconsciously, by telling us that Lady Dedlock had only stayed at the House two nights, on her way from London to visit at some other great house in the next county; and that she had left early on the morning after we had seen her at our view, as we called it. Charley verified the adage about little pitchers, I am sure; for she heard of more sayings and doings, in a day, than would have come to my ears in a month.

We were to stay a month at Mr. Boythorn's. My pet had scarcely been there a bright week, as I recollect the time, when one evening after we had finished helping the gardener in watering his flowers, and just as the candles were lighted, Charley, appearing with a very important air behind Ada's chair, beckoned me mysteriously out of the room.

"Oh! if you please, miss," said Charley in a whisper, with her eyes at their roundest and largest. "You're wanted at the Dedlock Arms."

"Why, Charley," said I, "who can possibly want me at the public-house?"

"I don't know, miss," returned Charley, putting her head forward, and folding her hands tight upon the band of her little apron; which she always did, in the enjoyment of anything mysterious or confidential; "but it's a gentleman, miss, and his compliments, and will you please to come without saying anything about it."

"Whose compliments, Charley?"

"His'n, miss," returned Charley: whose grammatical education was advancing, but not very rapidly.

"And how do you come to be the messenger, Charley?"

"I am not the messenger, if you please, miss," returned my little maid. "It was W. Grubble, miss."

"And who is W. Grubble, Charley?"

"Mister Grubble, miss," returned Charley. "Don't you know, miss? The Dedlock Arms, by W. Grubble," which Charley delivered as if she were slowly spelling out the sign.

"Ay? The landlord, Charley?"

"Yes, miss. If you please, miss, his wife is a beautiful woman, but she broke her ankle, and it never joined. And her brother's the sawyer, that was put in the cage, miss, and they expect he'll drink himself to death entirely on beer," said Charley.

Not knowing what might be the matter, and being easily apprehensive now, I thought it best to go to this place by myself. I bade Charley be quick with my bonnet and veil, and my shawl; and having put them on, went away down the little hilly street, where I was as much at home as in Mr. Boythorn's garden.

Mr. Grubble was standing in his shirt sleeves at the door of his very clean little tavern, waiting for me. He lifted off his hat with both hands when he saw me coming, and carrying it so, as if it were an iron vessel (it looked as heavy) preceded me along the sanded passage to his best parlour: a neat carpeted room, with more plants in it than were quite convenient, a coloured print of Queen Caroline, several shells, a good many tea-trays, two stuffed and dried fish in glass cases, and either a curious egg or a curious pumpkin (but I don't know which, and I doubt if many people did) hanging from the ceiling. I knew Mr. Grubble very well by sight, from his often standing at his door. A pleasant-looking, stoutish, middle-aged man, who never seemed to consider himself cosily dressed for his own fireside without his hat and top-boots, but who never wore a coat except at church.

He snuffed the candle, and backing away a little to see how it looked, backed out of the room—unexpectedly to me, for I was going to ask him by whom he had been sent. The door of the opposite parlour being then opened, I heard some voices, familiar in my ears, I thought, which stopped. A quick light step approached the room in which I was, and who should stand before me, but Richard!

"My dear Esther!" he said, "my best friend!" and he really was so warm-hearted and earnest, that in the first surprise and pleasure of his brotherly greeting, I could scarcely find breath to tell him that Ada was well.

"Answering my very thoughts—always the same dear girl!" said Richard, leading me to a chair, and seating himself beside me.

I put my veil up, but not quite.

"Always the same dear girl!" said Richard, just as heartily as before.

I put my veil up altogether, and laying my hand on Richard's sleeve, and looking in his face, told him how much I thanked him for his kind welcome, and how greatly I rejoiced to see him; the more so, because of the determination I had made in my illness, which I now conveyed to him.

"My love," said Richard, "there is no one with whom I have a greater wish to talk than you, for I want you to understand me."

"And I want you, Richard," said I, shaking my head, "to understand some one else."

"Since you refer so immediately to John Jarndyce," said Richard—"I suppose you mean him?"

"Of course I do."

"Then, I may say at once that I am glad of it, because it is on that subject that I am anxious to be understood. By you, mind—you, my dear! I am not accountable to Mr. Jarndyce, or Mr. Anybody."

I was pained to find him taking this tone, and he observed it.

"Well, well, my dear," said Richard, "we won't go into that now. I want to appear quietly in your country house here, with you under my arm, and give my charming cousin a surprise. I suppose your loyalty to John Jarndyce will allow that?"

"My dear Richard," I returned, "you know you would be heartily welcome at his house—your home, if you will but consider it so; and you are as heartily welcome here!"

"Spoken like the best of little women!" cried Richard gaily.

I asked him how he liked his profession?

"Oh, I like it well enough!" said Richard. "It's all right. It does as well as anything else, for a time. I don't know that I shall care about it when I come to be settled; but I can sell out then, and—however, never mind all that botheration at present."

So young and handsome, and in all respects so perfectly the opposite of Miss Flite! And yet, in the clouded, eager, seeking look that passed over him, so dreadfully like her!

"I am in town on leave, just now," said Richard.

"Indeed?"

"Yes. I have run over to look after my—my Chancery interests, before the long vacation," said Richard, forcing a careless laugh. "We are beginning to spin along with that old suit at last, I promise you."

No wonder I shook my head!

"As you say, it's not a pleasant subject." Richard spoke with the same shade crossing his face as before. "Let it go to the four winds for to-night.—Puff? Gone!—Who do you suppose is with me?"

"Was it Mr. Skimpole's voice I heard?"

"That's the man! He does me more good than anybody. What a fascinating child it is!"

I asked Richard if any one knew of their coming down together? He answered, No, nobody. He had been to call upon the dear old infant—so he called Mr. Skimpole—and the dear old infant had told him where we were, and he had told the dear old infant he was bent on coming to see us, and the dear old infant had directly wanted to come too; and so he had brought him. "And he is worth—not to say his sordid expenses—but thrice his weight in gold," said Richard. "He is such a cheery fellow. No worldliness about him. Fresh and green-hearted!"

I certainly did not see the proof of Mr. Skimpole's unworldliness in his having his expenses paid by Richard; but I made no remark about that. Indeed, he came in, and turned our conversation. He was charmed to see me; said he had been shedding delicious tears of joy and sympathy, at intervals for six weeks, on my account; had never been so happy as in hearing of my progress; began to understand the mixture of good and evil in the world now; felt that he appreciated health the more, when somebody else was ill; didn't know but what it might be in the scheme of things that A should squint to make B happier in looking straight; or that C should carry a wooden leg, to make D better satisfied with his flesh and blood in a silk stocking.

"My dear Miss Summerson, here is our friend Richard," said Mr. Skimpole, "full of the brightest visions of the future, which he evokes out of the darkness of Chancery- Now that's delightful, that's inspiriting, that's full of poetry! In old times, the woods and solitudes were

made joyous to the shepherd by the imaginary piping and dancing of
Pan and the Nymphs. This present shepherd, our pastoral Richard,
brightens the dull Inns of Court by making Fortune and her train sport
through them to the melodious notes of a judgment from the bench,
That's very pleasant, you know! Some ill-conditioned, growling fellow
may say to me, 'What's the use of these legal and equitable abuses?
How do you defend them?' I reply, 'My growling friend, I *don't* defend
them, but they are very agreeable to me. There is a shepherd-youth, a
friend of mine, who transmutes them into something highly fascinating
to my simplicity. I don't say it is for this that they exist—for I am a
child among you worldly grumblers, and not called upon to account to
you or myself for anything—but it may be so.'"

I began seriously to think that Richard could scarcely have found a
worse friend than this. It made me uneasy that at such a time, when
he most required some right principle and purpose, he should have this
captivating looseness and putting-off of everything, this airy dispensing
with all principle and purpose, at his elbow. I thought I could understand how such a nature as my guardian's, experienced in the world,
and forced to contemplate the miserable evasions and contentions of the
family misfortune, found an immense relief in Mr. Skimpole's avowal of
his weaknesses and display of guileless candour; but I could not satisfy
myself that it was as artless as it seemed; or that it did not serve Mr.
Skimpole's idle turn quite as well as any other part, and with less trouble.

They both walked back with me; and Mr. Skimpole leaving us at the
gate, I walked softly in with Richard, and said, "Ada, my love, I have
brought a gentleman to visit you." It was not difficult to read the
blushing startled face. She loved him dearly, and he knew it, and I
knew it. It was a very transparent business, that meeting as cousins
only.

I almost mistrusted myself, as growing quite wicked in my suspicions,
but I was not so sure that Richard loved her dearly. He admired her
very much—any one must have done that—and, I dare say, would have
renewed their youthful engagement with great pride and ardour, but that
he knew how she would respect her promise to my guardian. Still, I
had a tormenting idea that the influence upon him extended even here:
that he was postponing his best truth and earnestness, in this as in
all things, until Jarndyce and Jarndyce should be off his mind. Ah
me! what Richard would have been without that blight, I never shall
know now!

He told Ada, in his most ingenuous way, that he had not come to
make any secret inroad on the terms she had accepted (rather too implicitly and confidingly, he thought) from Mr. Jarndyce; that he had
come openly to see her, and to see me, and to justify himself for the
present terms on which he stood with Mr. Jarndyce. As the dear old
infant would be with us directly, he begged that I would make an
appointment for the morning, when he might set himself right, through
the means of an unreserved conversation with me. I proposed to walk

with him in the park at seven o'clock, and this was arranged. Mr. Skimpole soon afterwards appeared, and made us merry for an hour. He particularly requested to see Little Coavinses (meaning Charley), and told her, with a patriarchal air, that he had given her late father all the business in his power; and that if one of her little brothers would make haste to get set-up in the same profession, he hoped he should still be able to put a good deal of employment in his way.

"For I am constantly being taken in these nets," said Mr. Skimpole, looking beamingly at us over a glass of wine-and-water, "and am constantly being bailed out—like a boat. Or paid off—like a ship's company. Somebody always does it for me. *I* can't do it, you know, for I never have any money. But Somebody does it. I get out by Somebody's means; I am not like the starling; I get out. If you were to ask me who Somebody is, upon my word I couldn't tell you. Let us drink to Somebody. God bless him!"

Richard was a little late in the morning, but I had not to wait for him long, and we turned into the park. The air was bright and dewy, and the sky without a cloud. The birds sang delightfully; the sparkles in the fern, the grass, and trees, were exquisite to see; the richness of the woods seemed to have increased twenty-fold since yesterday, as if, in the still night, when they had looked so massively hushed in sleep, Nature, through all the minute details of every wonderful leaf, had been more wakeful than usual for the glory of that day.

"This is a lovely place," said Richard, looking round. "None of the jar and discord of law-suits here!"

But there was other trouble.

"I tell you what, my dear girl," said Richard, "when I get affairs in general settled, I shall come down here, I think, and rest."

"Would it not be better to rest now?" I asked.

"Oh, as to resting *now*," said Richard, "or as to doing anything very definite *now*, that's not easy. In short, it can't be done; *I* can't do it at least."

"Why not?" said I.

"You know why not, Esther. If you were living in an unfinished house, liable to have the roof put on or taken off—to be from top to bottom pulled down or built up—to-morrow, next day, next week, next month, next year—you would find it hard to rest or settle. So do I. Now? There's no now for us suitors."

I could almost have believed in the attraction on which my poor little wandering friend had expatiated, when I saw again the darkened look of last night. Terrible to think, it had in it also, a shade of that unfortunate man who had died.

"My dear Richard," said I, "this is a bad beginning of our conversation."

"I knew you would tell me so, Dame Durden."

"And not I alone, dear Richard. It was not I who cautioned you once, never to found a hope or expectation on the family curse."

"There you come back to John Jarndyce!" said Richard impatiently. "Well! We must approach him sooner or later, for he is the staple of what I have to say; and it's as well at once. My dear Esther, how can you be so blind? Don't you see that he is an interested party, and that it may be very well for him to wish me to know nothing of the suit, and care nothing about it, but that it may not be quite so well for me?"

"O Richard," I remonstrated, "is it possible that you can ever have seen him and heard him, that you can ever have lived under his roof and known him, and can yet breathe, even to me in this solitary place where there is no one to hear us, such unworthy suspicions?"

He reddened deeply, as if his natural generosity felt a pang of reproach. He was silent for a little while, before he replied in a subdued voice:

"Esther, I am sure you know that I am not a mean fellow, and that I have some sense of suspicion and distrust being poor qualities in one of my years."

"I know it very well," said I. "I am not more sure of anything."

"That's a dear girl!" retorted Richard, "and like you, because it gives me comfort. I had need to get some scrap of comfort out of all this business, for it's a bad one at the best, as I have no occasion to tell you."

"I know perfectly," said I, "I know as well, Richard—what shall I say? as well as you do—that such misconstructions are foreign to your nature. And I know, as well as you know, what so changes it."

"Come, sister, come," said Richard, a little more gaily, "you will be fair with me at all events. If I have the misfortune to be under that influence, so has he. If it has a little twisted me, it may have a little twisted him, too. I don't say that he is not an honourable man, out of all this complication and uncertainty; I am sure he is. But it taints everybody. You know it taints everybody. You have heard him say so fifty times. Then why should *he* escape?"

"Because," said I, "his is an uncommon character, and he has resolutely kept himself outside the circle, Richard."

"Oh, because and because!" replied Richard, in his vivacious way. "I am not sure, my dear girl, but that it may be wise and specious to preserve that outward indifference. It may cause other parties interested to become lax about their interests; and people may die off, and points may drag themselves out of memory, and many things may smoothly happen that are convenient enough."

I was so touched with pity for Richard, that I could not reproach him any more, even by a look. I remembered my guardian's gentleness towards his errors, and with what perfect freedom from resentment he had spoken of them.

"Esther," Richard resumed, "you are not to suppose that I have come here to make underhanded charges against John Jarndyce. I have only come to justify myself. What I say is, it is all very well, and we got on very well, while I was a boy, utterly regardless of this same suit; but as soon as I began to take an interest in it, and to look into it, then it was quite another thing. Then John Jarndyce discovers that Ada and I must break off, and that if I don't amend that very objectionable course, I am not fit for her. Now, Esther, I don't mean to amend that very objectionable course : I will not hold John Jarndyce's favour on those unfair terms of compromise, which he has no right to dictate. Whether it pleases him or displeases him, I must maintain my rights, and Ada's. I have been thinking about it a good deal, and this is the conclusion I have come to."

Poor dear Richard! He had indeed been thinking about it a good deal. His face, his voice, his manner, all showed that, too plainly.

" So I tell him honourably (you are to know I have written to him about all this) that we are at issue, and that we had better be at issue openly than covertly. I thank him for his goodwill and his protection, and he goes his road, and I go mine. The fact is, our roads are not the same. Under one of the wills in dispute, I should take much more than he. I don't mean to say that it is the one to be established ; but there it is, and it has its chance."

"I have not to learn from you, my dear Richard," said I, "of your letter. I had heard of it already, without an offended or angry word."

" Indeed ? " replied Richard, softening. " I am glad I said he was an honourable man, out of all this wretched affair. But I always say that, and have never doubted it. Now, my dear Esther, I know these views of mine appear extremely harsh to you, and will to Ada when you tell her what has passed between us. But if you had gone into the case as I have, if you had only applied yourself to the papers as I did when I was at Kenge's, if you only knew what an accumulation of charges and counter-charges, and suspicions and cross-suspicions, they involve, you would think me moderate in comparison."

"Perhaps so," said I. "But do you think that, among those many papers, there is much truth and justice, Richard ? "

"There is truth and justice somewhere in the case, Esther——"

"Or was once, long ago," said I.

"Is—is—must be somewhere," pursued Richard impetuously, "and must be brought out. To allow Ada to be made a bribe and hush-money of, is not the way to bring it out. You say the suit is changing me ; John Jarndyce says it changes, has changed, and will change, everybody who has any share it it. Then the greater right I have on my side, when I resolve to do all I can to bring it to an end."

"All you can, Richard ! Do you think that in these many years no others have done all they could ? Has the difficulty grown easier because of so many failures ? "

"It can't last for ever," returned Richard, with a fierceness kindling in him which again presented to me that last sad reminder. "I am young and earnest ; and energy and determination have done wonders many a time. Others have only half thrown themselves into it. I devote myself to it. I make it the object of my life."

2 c

"Oh, Richard, my dear, so much the worse, so much the worse!"

"No, no, no, don't you be afraid for me," he returned affectionately. "You're a dear, good, wise, quiet, blessed girl; but you have your pre-possessions. So I come round to John Jarndyce. I tell you, my good Esther, when he and I were on those terms which he found so convenient, we were not on natural terms."

"Are division and animosity your natural terms, Richard?"

"No, I don't say that. I mean that all this business puts us on un-natural terms, with which natural relations are incompatible. See another reason for urging it on! I may find out, when it's over, that I have been mistaken in John Jarndyce. My head may be clearer when I am free of it, and I may then agree with what you say to-day. Very well. Then I shall acknowledge it, and make him reparation."

Everything postponed to that imaginary time! Everything held in confusion and indecision until then!

"Now, my best of confidantes," said Richard, "I want my cousin, Ada, to understand that I am not captious, fickle, and wilful about John Jarndyce; but that I have this purpose and reason at my back. I wish to represent myself to her through you, because she has a great esteem and respect for her cousin John; and I know you will soften the course I take, even though you disapprove of it; and—and in short," said Richard, who had been hesitating through these words, "I—I don't like to represent myself in this litigious, contentious, doubting character, to a confiding girl like Ada."

I told him that he was more like himself in those latter words, than in anything he had said yet.

"Why," acknowledged Richard, "that may be true enough, my love. I rather feel it to be so. But I shall be able to give myself fair-play by-and-by. I shall come all right again, then, don't you be afraid."

I asked him if this were all he wished me to tell Ada?

"Not quite," said Richard. "I am bound not to withhold from her that John Jarndyce answered my letter in his usual manner, addressing me as 'My dear Rick,' trying to argue me out of my opinions, and telling me that they should make no difference in him. (All very well of course, but not altering the case.) I also want Ada to know, that if I see her seldom just now, I am looking after her interests as well as my own—we two being in the same boat exactly—and that I hope she will not suppose, from any flying rumours she may hear, that I am at all light-headed or imprudent; on the contrary, I am always looking forward to the termi-nation of the suit, and always planning in that direction. Being of age now, and having taken the step I have taken, I consider myself free from any accountability to John Jarndyce; but Ada being still a ward of the court, I don't yet ask her to renew our engagement. When she is free to act for herself, I shall be myself once more, and we shall both be in very different worldly circumstances, I believe. If you will tell her all this with the advantage of your considerate way, you will do me a very great and a very kind service, my dear Esther; and I shall knock Jarndyce and Jarndyce on the head with greater vigour. Of course I ask for no secrecy at Bleak House."

"Richard," said I, "you place great confidence in me, but I fear you will not take advice from me?"

"It's impossible that I can on this subject, my dear girl. On any other, readily."

As if there were any other in his life! As if his whole career and character were not being dyed one colour!

"But I may ask you a question, Richard?"

"I think so," said he, laughing. "I don't know who may not, if you may not."

"You say, yourself, you are not leading a very settled life?"

"How can I, my dear Esther, with nothing settled?"

"Are you in debt again?"

"Why of course I am," said Richard, astonished at my simplicity.

"Is it of course?"

"My dear child, certainly. I can't throw myself into an object so completely, without expense. You forget, or perhaps you don't know, that under either of the wills Ada and I take something. It's only a question between the larger sum and the smaller. I shall be within the mark, any way. Bless your heart, my excellent girl," said Richard, quite amused with me, "I shall be all right! I shall pull through, my dear!"

I felt so deeply sensible of the danger in which he stood, that I tried, in Ada's name, in my guardian's, in my own, by every fervent means that I could think of, to warn him of it, and to show him some of his mistakes. He received everything I said with patience and gentleness, but it all rebounded from him without taking the least effect. I could not wonder at this, after the reception his pre-occupied mind had given to my guardian's letter; but I determined to try Ada's influence yet.

So, when our walk brought us round to the village again, and I went home to breakfast, I prepared Ada for the account I was going to give her, and told her exactly what reason we had to dread that Richard was losing himself, and scattering his whole life to the winds. It made her very unhappy, of course; though she had a far, far greater reliance on his correcting his errors than I could have—which was so natural and loving in my dear!—and she presently wrote him this little letter:

MY DEAREST COUSIN,—Esther has told me all you said to her this morning. I write this, to repeat most earnestly for myself all that she said to you, and to let you know how sure I am that you will sooner or later find our cousin John a pattern of truth, sincerity, and goodness, when you will deeply, deeply grieve to have done him (without intending it) so much wrong.

I do not quite know how to write what I wish to say next, but I trust you will understand it as I mean it. I have some fears, my dearest cousin, that it may be partly for my sake you are now laying up so much unhappiness for yourself, and, if for yourself, for me. In case this should be so, or in case you should entertain much thought of me in what you are doing, I most earnestly entreat and beg you to desist. You can do nothing for my sake that will make me half so happy, as for ever turning your back upon the shadow in which we both were born. Do not be angry with me for saying this. Pray, pray, dear Richard, for my sake, and for your own, and in a natural repugnance for that source of trouble which had its share in making us both orphans when we were very young, pray, pray, let it go for ever. We have reason to know, by this time, that there is no good in it, and no hope; that there is nothing to be got from it but sorrow.

My dearest cousin, it is needless for me to say that you are quite free, and that it is very likely you may find some one whom you will love much better than your first fancy. I am quite sure, if you will let me say so, that the object of your choice would greatly prefer to follow your fortunes far and wide, however moderate or poor, and see you happy, doing your duty and pursuing your chosen way; than to have the hope of being, or even to be, very rich with you (if such a thing were possible), at the cost of dragging years of procrastination and anxiety, and of your indifference to other aims. You may wonder at my saying this so confidently with so little knowledge or experience, but I know it for a certainty from my own heart. Ever, my dearest cousin, your most affectionate,   ADA.

This note brought Richard to us very soon; but it made little change in him, if any. We would fairly try, he said, who was right and who was wrong—he would show us—we should see! He was animated and glowing, as if Ada's tenderness had gratified him; but I could only hope, with a sigh, that the letter might have some stronger effect upon his mind on re-perusal, than it assuredly had then.

As they were to remain with us that day, and had taken their places to return by the coach next morning, I sought an opportunity of speaking to Mr. Skimpole. Our out-of-door life easily threw one in my way; and I delicately said, that there was a responsibility in encouraging Richard.

"Responsibility, my dear Miss Summerson?" he repeated, catching at the word with the pleasantest smile, "I am the last man in the world for such a thing. I never was responsible in my life—I can't be."

"I am afraid everybody is obliged to be," said I, timidly enough: he being so much older and more clever than I.

"No, really?" said Mr. Skimpole, receiving this new light with a most agreeable jocularity of surprise. "But every man's not obliged to be solvent? I am not. I never was. See, my dear Miss Summerson," he took a handful of loose silver and halfpence from his pocket, "there's so much money. I have not an idea how much. I have not the power of counting. Call it four and ninepence—call it four pound nine. They tell me I owe more than that. I dare say I do. I dare say I owe as much as good-natured people will let me owe. If they don't stop, why should I? There you have Harold Skimpole in little. If that's responsibility, I am responsible."

The perfect ease of manner with which he put the money up again, and looked at me with a smile on his refined face, as if he had been mentioning a curious little fact about somebody else, almost made me feel as if he really had nothing to do with it.

"Now when you mention responsibility," he resumed, "I am disposed to say, that I never had the happiness of knowing any one whom I should consider so refreshingly responsible as yourself. You appear to me to be the very touchstone of responsibility. When I see you, my dear Miss Summerson, intent upon the perfect working of the whole little orderly system of which you are the centre, I feel inclined to say to myself—in fact I do say to myself, very often—*that's* responsibility!"

It was difficult, after this, to explain what I meant; but I persisted so far as to say, that we all hoped he would check and not confirm Richard in the sanguine views he entertained just then.

"Most willingly," he retorted, "if I could. But, my dear Miss Summerson, I have no art, no disguise. If he takes me by the hand, and leads me through Westminster Hall in an airy procession after Fortune, I must go. If he says, 'Skimpole, join the dance!' I must join it. Common sense wouldn't, I know; but I have *no* common sense."

"It was very unfortunate for Richard," I said.

"Do you think so!" returned Mr. Skimpole. "Don't say that, don't say that. Let us suppose him keeping company with Common Sense—an excellent man—a good deal wrinkled—dreadfully practical—change for a ten-pound note in every pocket—ruled account-book in his hand—say, upon the whole, resembling a tax-gatherer. Our dear Richard, sanguine, ardent, overleaping obstacles, bursting with poetry like a young bud, says to this highly respectable companion, 'I see a golden prospect before me; it's very bright, it's very beautiful, it's very joyous; here I go, bounding over the landscape to come at it!' The respectable companion instantly knocks him down with the ruled account-book; tells him, in a literal prosaic way, that he sees no such thing; shows him it's nothing but fees, fraud, horsehair wigs, and black gowns. Now you know that's a painful change;—sensible in the last degree, I have no doubt, but disagreeable. *I* can't do it. I haven't got the ruled account-book, I have none of the tax-gathering elements in my composition, I am not at all respectable, and I don't want to be. Odd perhaps, but so it is!"

It was idle to say more; so I proposed that we should join Ada and Richard, who were a little in advance, and I gave up Mr. Skimpole in despair. He had been over the Hall in the course of the morning, and whimsically described the family pictures as we walked. There were such portentous shepherdesses among the Ladies Dedlock dead and gone, he told us, that peaceful crooks became weapons of assault in their hands. They tended their flocks severely in buckram and powder, and put their sticking-plaster patches on to terrify commoners, as the chiefs of some other tribes put on their war-paint. There was a Sir Somebody Dedlock, with a battle, a sprung-mine, volumes of smoke, flashes of lightning, a town on fire, and a stormed fort, all in full action between his horse's two hind legs : showing, he supposed, how little a Dedlock made of such trifles. The whole race he represented as having evidently been, in life, what he called "stuffed people,"—a large collection, glassy eyed, set up in the most approved manner on their various twigs and perches, very correct, perfectly free from animation, and always in glass cases.

I was not so easy now, during any reference to the name, but that I felt it a relief when Richard, with an exclamation of surprise, hurried away to meet a stranger, whom he first descried coming slowly towards us.

"Dear me !" said Mr. Skimpole. "Vholes !"

We asked if that were a friend of Richard's ?

"Friend and legal adviser," said Mr. Skimpole. "Now, my dear Miss Summerson, if you want common sense, responsibility, and respectability, all united—if you want an exemplary man—Vholes is *the* man."

We had not known, we said, that Richard was assisted by any gentleman of that name.

"When he emerged from legal infancy," returned Mr. Skimpole, "he parted from our conversational friend Kenge, and took up, I believe, with Vholes.   Indeed, I know he did, because I introduced him to Vholes."

"Had you known him long ?" asked Ada.

"Vholes ? My dear Miss Clare, I had had that kind of acquaintance with him which I have had with several gentlemen of his profession.   He had done something or other, in a very agreeable, civil manner—taken proceedings, I think, is the expression—which ended in the proceeding of his taking *me*.   Somebody was so good as to step in and pay the money —something and fourpence was the amount ; I forget the pounds and shillings, but I know it ended with fourpence, because it struck me at the time as being so odd that I could owe anybody fourpence—and after that, I brought them together.   Vholes asked me for the introduction, and I gave it.   Now I come to think of it," he looked inquiringly at us with his frankest smile as he made the discovery, "Vholes bribed me, perhaps ? He gave me something, and called it commission.   Was it a five-pound note ?   Do you know, I think it *must* have been a five-pound note !"

His further consideration of the point was prevented by Richard's coming back to us in an excited state, and hastily presenting Mr. Vholes —a sallow man with pinched lips that looked as if they were cold, a red eruption here and there upon his face, tall and thin, about fifty years of age, high-shouldered and stooping.   Dressed in black, black-gloved, and buttoned to the chin, there was nothing so remarkable in him as a lifeless manner, and a slow fixed way he had of looking at Richard.

"I hope I don't disturb you, ladies," said Mr. Vholes ; and now I observed that he was further remarkable for an inward manner of speaking. "I arranged with Mr. Carstone that he should always know when his cause was in the Chancellor's paper, and being informed by one of my clerks last night, after post time, that it stood, rather unexpectedly, in the paper for to-morrow, I put myself into the coach early this morning and came down to confer with him."

"Yes!" said Richard, flushed, and looking triumphantly at Ada and me, "we don't do these things in the old slow way, now. We spin along, now! Mr. Vholes, we must hire something to get over to the post town in, and catch the mail to-night, and go up by it!"

"Anything you please, sir," returned Mr. Vholes. "I am quite at your service."

"Let me see," said Richard, looking at his watch. "If I run down to the Dedlock, and get my portmanteau fastened up, and order a gig, or a chaise, or whatever's to be got, we shall have an hour then before starting. I'll come back to tea. Cousin Ada, will you and Esther take care of Mr. Vholes while I am gone?"

He was away directly, in his heat and hurry, and was soon lost in the dusk of evening. We who were left walked on towards the house.

"Is Mr. Carstone's presence necessary to-morrow, sir?" said I. "Can it do any good?"

"No, miss," Mr. Vholes replied. "I am not aware that it can."

Both Ada and I expressed our regret that he should go, then, only to be disappointed.

"Mr. Carstone has laid down the principle of watching his own interests," said Mr. Vholes, "and when a client lays down his own principle, and it is not immoral, it devolves upon me to carry it out. I wish in business to be exact and open. I am a widower with three daughters —Emma, Jane, and Caroline—and my desire is so to discharge the duties of life as to leave them a good name. This appears to be a pleasant spot, miss."

The remark being made to me, in consequence of my being next him as we walked, I assented, and enumerated its chief attractions.

"Indeed?" said Mr. Vholes. "I have the privilege of supporting an aged father in the Vale of Taunton—his native place—and I admire that country very much. I had no idea there was anything so attractive here."

To keep up the conversation, I asked Mr. Vholes if he would like to live altogether in the country?

"There, miss," said he, "you touch me on a tender string. My health is not good (my digestion being much impaired), and if I had only myself to consider, I should take refuge in rural habits; especially as the cares of business have prevented me from ever coming much into contact with general society, and particularly with ladies' society, which I have most wished to mix in. But with my three daughters, Emma, Jane, and Caroline—and my aged father—I cannot afford to be selfish. It is true, I have no longer to maintain a dear grandmother who died in her hundred-and-second year; but enough remains to render it indispensable that the mill should be always going."

It required some attention to hear him, on account of his inward speaking and his lifeless manner.

"You will excuse my having mentioned my daughters," he said. "They

are my weak point.   I wish to leave the poor girls some little independence, as well as a good name."

We now arrived at Mr Boythorn's house, where the tea-table, all prepared, was awaiting us.   Richard came in, restless and hurried, shortly
afterwards, and leaning over Mr. Vholes's chair, whispered something in
his ear.   Mr. Vholes replied aloud—or as nearly aloud I suppose as he
ever replied to anything—"You will drive me, will you, sir?   It is all
the same to me, sir.   Anything you please.   I am quite at your service."

We understood from what followed that Mr. Skimpole was to be left
until the morning to occupy the two places which had been already paid
for.   As Ada and I were both in low spirits concerning Richard, and
very sorry so to part with him, we made it as plain as we politely could
that we should leave Mr. Skimpole to the Dedlock Arms, and retire when
the night-travellers were gone.

Richard's high spirits carrying everything before them, we all went out
together to the top of the hill above the village, where he had ordered a
gig to wait ; and where we found a man with a lantern standing at the
head of the gaunt pale horse that had been harnessed to it.

I never shall forget those two seated side by side in the lantern's light ;
Richard, all flush and fire and laughter, with the reins in his hand ; Mr.
Vholes, quite still, black-gloved, and buttoned up, looking at him as if he
were looking at his prey and charming it.   I have before me the whole
picture of the warm dark night, the summer lightning, the dusky track of
road closed in by hedgerows and high trees, the gaunt pale horse with his
ears pricked up, and the driving away at speed to Jarndyce and Jarndyce.

My dear girl told me, that night, how Richard's being thereafter
prosperous or ruined, befriended or deserted, could only make this difference to her, that the more he needed love from one unchanging heart,
the more love that unchanging heart would have to give him ; how he
thought of her through his present errors, and she would think of him at
all times ; never of herself, if she could devote herself to him : never of
her own delights, if she could minister to his.

And she kept her word?

I look along the road before me, where.the distance already shortens and
the journey's end is growing visible ; and, true and good above the dead
sea of the Chancery suit, and all the ashey fruit it casts ashore, I think I
see my darling.

CHAPTER XXXVIII

A STRUGGLE

WHEN our time came for returning to Bleak House again, we were
punctual to the day, and were received with an overpowering
welcome.   I was perfectly restored to health and strength ; and
finding my housekeeping keys laid ready for me in my room, rang myself
in as if I had been a new year, with a merry little peal.   "Once more,

duty, duty, Esther," said I; "and if you are not overjoyed to do it, more than cheerfully and contentedly, through anything and everything, you ought to be. That's all I have to say to *you*, my dear!"

The first few mornings were mornings of so much bustle and business, devoted to such settlements of accounts, such repeated journeys to and fro between the Growlery and all other parts of the house, so many re-arrangements of drawers and presses, and such a general new beginning altogether, that I had not a moment's leisure. But when these arrangements were completed, and everything was in order, I paid a visit of a few hours to London, which something in the letter I had destroyed at Chesney Wold had induced me to decide upon in my own mind.

I made Caddy Jellyby—her maiden name was so natural to me that I always called her by it—the pretext for this visit; and wrote her a note previously, asking the favour of her company on a little business expedition. Leaving home very early in the morning, I got to London by stage-coach in such good time, that I got to Newman Street with the day before me.

Caddy, who had not seen me since her wedding-day, was so glad and so affectionate that I was half-inclined to fear I should make her husband jealous. But he was, in his way, just as bad—I mean as good; and in short it was the old story, and nobody would leave me any possibility of doing anything meritorious.

The elder Mr. Turveydrop was in bed, I found, and Caddy was milling his chocolate, which a melancholy little boy who was an apprentice—it seemed such a curious thing to be apprenticed to the trade of dancing—was waiting to carry upstairs. Her father-in-law was extremely kind and considerate, Caddy told me, and they lived most happily together. (When she spoke of their living together, she meant that the old gentleman had all the good things and all the good lodging, while she and her husband had what they could get, and were poked into two corner rooms over the Mews.)

"And how is your mamma, Caddy?" said I.

"Why, I hear of her, Esther," replied Caddy, "through Pa; but I see very little of her. We are good friends, I am glad to say; but Ma thinks there is something absurd in my having married a dancing-master, and she is rather afraid of its extending to her."

It struck me that if Mrs. Jellyby had discharged her own natural duties and obligations, before she swept the horizon with a telescope in search of others, she would have taken the best precautions against becoming absurd; but I need scarcely observe that I kept this to myself.

"And your papa, Caddy?"

"He comes here every evening," returned Caddy, "and is so fond of sitting in the corner there, that it's a treat to see him."

Looking at the corner, I plainly perceived the mark of Mr. Jellyby's head against the wall. It was consolatory to know that he had found such a resting-place for it.

"And you, Caddy," said I, "you are always busy, I'll be bound?"

"Well, my dear," returned Caddy, "I am indeed; for to tell you a grand secret, I am qualifying myself to give lessons. Prince's health is not strong, and I want to be able to assist him. What with schools, and classes here, and private pupils, *and* the apprentices, he really has too much to do, poor fellow!"

The notion of the apprentices was still so odd to me, that I asked Caddy, if there were many of them?

"Four," said Caddy. "One indoor, and three out. They are very good children; only when they get together they *will* play—children-like—instead of attending to their work. So the little boy you saw just now waltzes by himself in the empty kitchen, and we distribute the others over the house as well as we can."

"That is only for their steps, of course?" said I.

"Only for their steps," said Caddy. "In that way they practise, so many hours at a time, whatever steps they happen to be upon. They dance in the academy; and at this time of year we do Figures at five every morning."

"Why, what a laborious life!" I exclaimed.

"I assure you, my dear," returned Caddy, smiling, "when the out-door apprentices ring us up in the morning (the bell rings into our room, not to disturb old Mr. Turveydrop), and when I put up the window, and see them standing on the door-step with their little pumps under their arms, I am actually reminded of the Sweeps."

All this presented the art to me in a singular light, to be sure. Caddy enjoyed the effect of her communication, and cheerfully recounted the particulars of her own studies.

"You see, my dear, to save expense, I ought to know something of the Piano, and I ought to know something of the Kit too, and consequently I have to practise those two instruments as well as the details of our profession. If Ma had been like anybody else, I might have had some little musical knowledge to begin upon. However, I hadn't any; and that part of the work is, at first, a little discouraging, I must allow. But I have a very good ear, and I am used to drudgery—I have to thank Ma for that, at all events—and where there's a will there's a way, you know, Esther, the world over." Saying these words, Caddy laughingly sat down at a little jingling square piano, and really rattled off a quadrille with great spirit. Then she good-humouredly and blushingly got up again, and while she still laughed herself, said, "Don't laugh at me, please; that's a dear girl!"

I would sooner have cried, but I did neither. I encouraged her, and praised her with all my heart. For I conscientiously believed, dancing-master's wife though she was, and dancing-mistress, though in her limited ambition she aspired to be, she had struck out a natural, wholesome, loving course of industry and perseverance that was quite as good as a Mission.

"My dear," said Caddy, delighted, "you can't think how you cheer me. I shall owe you, you don't know how much. What changes,

Esther, even in my small world! You recollect that first night, when I was so unpolite and inky? Who would have thought, then, of my ever teaching people to dance, of all other possibilities and impossibilities!"

Her husband, who had left us while we had this chat, now coming back, preparatory to exercising the apprentices in the ball-room, Caddy informed me she was quite at my disposal. But it was not my time yet, I was glad to tell her; for I should have been vexed to take her away then. Therefore we three adjourned to the apprentices together, and I made one in the dance.

The apprentices were the queerest little people. Besides the melancholy boy, who, I hoped, had not been made so by waltzing alone in the empty kitchen, there were two other boys, and one dirty little limp girl in a gauzy dress. Such a precocious little girl, with such a dowdy bonnet on (that, too, of a gauzy texture), who brought her sandalled shoes in an old threadbare velvet reticule. Such mean little boys, when they were not dancing, with string, and marbles, and cramp-bones in their pockets, and the most untidy legs and feet—and heels particularly.

I asked Caddy what had made their parents choose this profession for them? Caddy said she didn't know; perhaps they were designed for teachers; perhaps for the stage. They were all people in humble circumstances, and the melancholy boy's mother kept a ginger-beer shop.

We danced for an hour with great gravity; the melancholy child doing wonders with his lower extremities, in which there appeared to be some sense of enjoyment, though it never rose above his waist. Caddy, while she was observant of her husband, and was evidently founded upon him, had acquired a grace and self-possession of her own, which, united to her pretty face and figure, was uncommonly agreeable. She already relieved him of much of the instruction of these young people; and he seldom interfered, except to walk his part in the figure if he had anything to do in it. He always played the tune. The affectation of the gauzy child, and her condescension to the boys, was a sight. And thus we danced an hour by the clock.

When the practice was concluded, Caddy's husband made himself ready to go out of town to a school, and Caddy ran away to get ready to go out with me. I sat in the ball-room in the interval, contemplating the apprentices. The two outdoor boys went upon the staircase to put on their half-boots, and pull the indoor boy's hair: as I judged from the nature of his objections. Returning with their jackets buttoned, and their pumps stuck in them, they then produced packets of cold bread and meat, and bivouacked under a painted lyre on the wall. The little gauzy child, having whisked her sandals into the reticule and put on a trodden-down pair of shoes, shook her head into the dowdy bonnet at one shake; and answering my inquiry whether she liked dancing, by replying, "Not with boys," tied it across her chin and went home contemptuous.

"Old Mr. Turveydrop is so sorry," said Caddy, "that he has not finished dressing yet, and cannot have the pleasure of seeing you before you go. You are such a favourite of his, Esther."

I expressed myself much obliged to him, but did not think it necessary to add that I readily dispensed with this attention.

"It takes him a long time to dress," said Caddy, "because he is very much looked up to in such things, you know, and has a reputation to support. You can't think how kind he is to Pa. He talks to Pa, of an evening, about the Prince Regent, and I never saw Pa so interested."

There was something in the picture of Mr. Turveydrop bestowing his Deportment on Mr. Jellyby, that quite took my fancy. I asked Caddy if he brought her papa out much?

"No," said Caddy, "I don't know that he does that; but he talks to Pa, and Pa greatly admires him, and listens, and likes it. Of course I am aware that Pa has hardly any claims to Deportment, but they get on together delightfully. You can't think what good companions they make. I never saw Pa take snuff before in my life; but he takes one pinch out of Mr. Turveydrop's box regularly, and keeps putting it to his nose and taking it away again, all the evening."

That old Mr. Turveydrop should ever, in the chances and changes of life, have come to the rescue of Mr. Jellyby from Borrioboola-Gha, appeared to me to be one of the pleasantest of oddities.

"As to Peepy," said Caddy, with a little hesitation, "whom I was most afraid of—next to having any family of my own, Esther—as an inconvenience to Mr. Turveydrop, the kindness of the old gentleman to that child is beyond everything. He asks to see him, my dear! He lets him take the newspaper up to him in bed; he gives him the crusts of his toast to eat; he sends him on little errands about the house; he tells him to come to me for sixpences. In short," said Caddy cheerily, "and not to prose, I am a very fortunate girl, and ought to be very grateful. Where are we going, Esther?"

"To the Old Street Road," said I; "where I have a few words to say to the solicitor's clerk, who was sent to meet me at the coach-office on the very day when I came to London, and first saw you, my dear. Now I think of it, the gentleman who brought us to your house."

"Then, indeed, I seem to be naturally the person to go with you," returned Caddy.

To the Old Street Road we went, and there inquired at Mrs. Guppy's residence for Mrs. Guppy. Mrs. Guppy, occupying the parlours, and having indeed been visibly in danger of cracking herself like a nut in the front parlour-door by peeping out before she was asked for, immediately presented herself, and requested us to walk in. She was an old lady in a large cap, with rather a red nose and rather an unsteady eye, but smiling all over. Her close little sitting-room was prepared for a visit; and there was a portrait of her son in it, which, I had almost written here, was more like than life; it insisted upon him with such obstinacy, and was so determined not to let him off.

Not only was the portrait there, but we found the original there too.

He was dressed in a great many colours, and was discovered at a table reading law-papers with his forefinger to his forehead.

"Miss Summerson," said Mr. Guppy, rising, "this is indeed an Oasis. Mother, will you be so good as to put a chair for the other lady, and get out of the gangway?"

Mrs. Guppy, whose incessant smiling gave her quite a waggish appearance, did as her son requested; and then sat down in a corner, holding her pocket-handkerchief to her chest, like a fomentation, with both hands.

I presented Caddy, and Mr. Guppy said that any friend of mine was more than welcome. I then proceeded to the object of my visit.

"I took the liberty of sending you a note, sir," said I.

Mr. Guppy acknowledged its receipt by taking it out of his breast-pocket, putting it to his lips, and returning it to his pocket with a bow. Mr. Guppy's mother was so diverted that she rolled her head as she smiled, and made a silent appeal to Caddy with her elbow.

"Could I speak to you alone for a moment?" said I.

Anything like the jocoseness of Mr. Guppy's mother, just now, I think I never saw. She made no sound of laughter; but she rolled her head, and shook it, and put her handkerchief to her mouth, and appealed to Caddy with her elbow, and her hand, and her shoulder, and was so unspeakably entertained altogether that it was with some difficulty she could marshal Caddy through the little folding-door into her bedroom adjoining.

"Miss Summerson," said Mr. Guppy, "you will excuse the waywardness of a parent ever mindful of a son's appiness. My mother, though highly exasperating to the feelings, is actuated by maternal dictates."

I could hardly have believed that anybody could in a moment have turned so red, or changed so much, as Mr. Guppy did when I now put up my veil.

"I asked the favour of seeing you for a few moments here," said I, "in preference to calling at Mr. Kenge's, because, remembering what you said on an occasion when you spoke to me in confidence, I feared I might otherwise cause you some embarrassment, Mr. Guppy."

I caused him embarrassment enough as it was, I am sure. I never saw such faltering, such confusion, such amazement and apprehension.

"Miss Summerson," stammered Mr. Guppy, "I—I—beg your pardon, but in our profession—we—we—find it necessary to be explicit. You have referred to an occasion, miss, when I—when I did myself the honour of making a declaration which——"

Something seemed to rise in his throat that he could not possibly swallow. He put his hand there, coughed, made faces, tried again to swallow it, coughed again, made faces again, looked all round the room, and fluttered his papers.

"A kind of giddy sensation has come upon me, miss," he explained, "which rather knocks me over. I—er—a little subject to this sort of thing—er—By George!"

I gave him a little time to recover. He consumed it in putting his hand to his forehead and taking it away again, and in backing his chair into the corner behind him.

"My intention was to remark, miss," said Mr. Guppy, "—dear me—something bronchial, I think—hem!—to remark that you was so good on that occasion as to repel and repudiate that declaration. You—you wouldn't perhaps object to admit that? Though no witnesses are present, it might be a satisfaction to—to your mind—if you was to put in that admission."

"There can be no doubt," said I, "that I declined your proposal without any reservation or qualification whatever, Mr. Guppy."

"Thank you, miss," he returned, measuring the table with his troubled hands. "So far that's satisfactory, and it does you credit. Er—this is certainly bronchial!—must be in the tubes—er—you wouldn't perhaps be offended if I was to mention—not that it's necessary, for your own good sense or any person's sense must show 'em that—if I was to mention that such declaration on my part was final, and there terminated?"

"I quite understand that," said I.

"Perhaps—er—it may not be worth the form, but it might be a satisfaction to your mind—perhaps you wouldn't object to admit that, miss?" said Mr. Guppy.

"I admit it most fully and freely," said I.

"Thank you," returned Mr. Guppy. "Very honourable, I am sure. I regret that my arrangements in life, combined with circumstances over which I have no control, will put it out of my power ever to fall back upon that offer, or to renew it in any shape or form whatever; but it will ever be a retrospect entwined—er—with friendship's bowers." Mr. Guppy's bronchitis came to his relief, and stopped his measurement of the table.

"I may now perhaps mention what I wished to say to you?" I began.

"I shall be honoured, I am sure," said Mr. Guppy. "I am so persuaded that your own good sense and right feeling, miss, will—will keep you as square as possible—that I can have nothing but pleasure, I am sure, in hearing any observations you may wish to offer."

"You were so good as to imply, on that occasion——"

"Excuse me, miss," said Mr. Guppy, "but we had better not travel out of the record into implication. I cannot admit that I implied anything."

"You said on that occasion," I recommenced, "that you might possibly have the means of advancing my interests, and promoting my fortunes, by making discoveries of which I should be the subject. I presume that you founded that belief upon your general knowledge of my being an orphan girl, indebted for everything to the benevolence of Mr. Jarndyce. Now, the beginning and the end of what I have come to beg of you is, Mr. Guppy, that you will have the kindness to relinquish all idea of so serving me. I have thought of this sometimes, and I have thought of it most lately—since I have been ill. At length I have decided, in case you should at any time recall that purpose, and act upon it in any way, to come to you, and assure you that you are altogether mistaken. You could make no discovery in reference to me that would do me the least service, or give me the least pleasure. I am acquainted with my personal history; and I have it in my power to assure you that you never can advance my welfare by such means. You may, perhaps, have abandoned this project a long time. If so, excuse my giving you unnecessary trouble. If not, I entreat you, on the assurance I have given you, henceforth to lay it aside. I beg of you to do this, for my peace."

"I am bound to confess," said Mr. Guppy, "that you express yourself, miss, with that good sense and right feeling for which I gave you credit. Nothing can be more satisfactory than such right feeling, and if I mistook any intentions on your part just now, I am prepared to tender a full apology. I should wish to be understood, miss, as hereby offering that apology—limiting it, as your own good sense and right feeling will point out the necessity of, to the present proceedings."

I must say for Mr. Guppy that the shuffling manner he had had upon him improved very much. He seemed truly glad to be able to do something I asked, and he looked ashamed

"If you will allow me to finish what I have to say at once, so that I may have no occasion to resume," I went on, seeing him about to speak, "you will do me a kindness, sir. I come to you as privately as possible, because you announced this impression of yours to me in a confidence which I have really wished to respect—and which I always have respected, as you remember. I have mentioned my illness. There really is no reason why I should hesitate to say that I know very well that any little delicacy I might have had in making a request to you, is quite removed. Therefore I make the entreaty I have now preferred; and I hope you will have sufficient consideration for me to accede to it."

I must do Mr. Guppy the further justice of saying that he had looked more and more ashamed, and that he looked most ashamed, and very earnest, when he now replied with a burning face:

"Upon my word and honour, upon my life, upon my soul, Miss Summerson, as I am a living man, I'll act according to your wish! I'll never go another step in opposition to it. I'll take my oath to it, if it will be any satisfaction to you. In what I promise at this present time touching the matters now in question," continued Mr. Guppy rapidly, as if he were repeating a familiar form of words, "I speak the truth, the whole truth, and nothing but the truth, so——"

"I am quite satisfied," said I, rising at this point, "and I thank you very much. Caddy, my dear, I am ready!"

Mr. Guppy's mother returned with Caddy (now making me the recipient of her silent laughter and her nudges), and we took our leave. Mr. Guppy saw us to the door with the air of one who was either imperfectly awake or walking in his sleep; and we left him there, staring.

But in a minute he came after us down the street without any hat, and with his long hair all blown about, and stopped us, saying fervently :

"Miss Summerson, upon my honour and soul, you may depend upon me !"

"I do," said I, "quite confidently."

"I beg your pardon, miss," said Mr. Guppy, going with one leg and staying with the other, "but this lady being present—your own witness —it might be a satisfaction to your mind (which I should wish to set at rest) if you was to repeat those admissions."

"Well, Caddy," said I, turning to her, "perhaps you will not be surprised when I tell you, my dear, that there never has been any engagement——"

"No proposal or promise of marriage whatsoever," suggested Mr. Guppy.

"No proposal or promise of marriage whatsoever," said I, "between this gentleman——"

"William Guppy of Penton Place, Pentonville, in the county of Middlesex," he murmured.

"Between this gentleman, Mr. William Guppy, of Penton Place, Pentonville, in the county of Middlesex, and myself."

"Thank you, miss," said Mr. Guppy. "Very full—er—excuse me— lady's name, Christian and surname both ?"

I gave them.

"Married woman, I believe ?" said Mr. Guppy. "Married woman. Thank you. Formerly Caroline Jellyby, spinster, then of Thavies' Inn, within the city of London, but extra-parochial ; now of Newman Street, Oxford Street. Much obliged."

He ran home and came running back again.

"Touching that matter, you know, I really and truly am very sorry that my arrangements in life, combined with circumstances over which I have no control, should prevent a renewal of what was wholly terminated some time back," said Mr. Guppy to me, forlornly and despondently, "but it couldn't be. Now *could* it, you know ? I only put it to you."

I replied it certainly could not. The subject did not admit of a doubt. He thanked me, and ran to his mother's again—and back again.

"It's very honourable of you, miss, I am sure," said Mr. Guppy. "If an altar could be erected in the bowers of friendship—but, upon my soul, you may rely upon me in every respect, save and except the tender passion only !"

The struggle in Mr. Guppy's breast, and the numerous oscillations it occasioned him between his mother's door and us, were sufficiently conspicuous in the windy street (particularly as his hair wanted cutting), to make us hurry away. I did so with a lightened heart ; but when we last looked back, Mr. Guppy was still oscillating in the same troubled state of mind.

CHAPTER XXXIX

ATTORNEY AND CLIENT

THE name of MR. VHOLES, preceded by the legend GROUND FLOOR, is inscribed upon a door-post in Symond's Inn, Chancery Lane : a little, pale, wall-eyed, woe-begone inn, like a large dust-bin of two compartments and a sifter. It looked as if Symond were a sparing man in his day, and constructed his inn of old building materials, which took kindly to the dry rot and to dirt and all things decaying and dismal, and perpetuated Symond's memory with congenial shabbiness. Quartered in this dingy hatchment, commemorative of Symond, are the legal bearings of Mr. Vholes.

Mr. Vholes's office, in disposition retiring and in situation retired, is squeezed up in a corner, and blinks at a dead wall. Three feet of knotty floored dark passage bring the client to Mr. Vholes's jet black door, in an angle profoundly dark on the brightest midsummer morning, and encumbered by a black bulk-head of cellarage staircase, against which belated civilians generally strike their brows. Mr. Vholes's chambers are on so small a scale, that one clerk can open the door without getting off his stool, while the other who elbows him at the same desk has equal facilities for poking the fire. A smell as of unwholesome sheep, blending with the smell of must and dust, is referable to the nightly (and often daily) consumption of mutton fat in candles, and to the fretting of parchment forms and skins in greasy drawers. The atmosphere is otherwise stale and close. The place was last painted or whitewashed beyond the memory of man, and the two chimneys smoke, and there is a loose outer surface of soot everywhere, and the dull cracked windows in their heavy frames have but one piece of character in them, which is a determination to be always dirty, and always shut, unless coerced. This accounts for the phenomenon of the weaker of the two usually having a bundle of firewood thrust between its jaws in hot weather.

Mr. Vholes is a very respectable man. He has not a large business, but he is a very respectable man. He is allowed by the greater attorneys who have made good fortunes, or are making them, to be a most respectable man. He never misses a chance in his practice ; which is a mark of respectability. He never takes any pleasure ; which is another mark of respectability. He is reserved and serious ; which is another mark of respectability. His digestion is impaired, which is highly respectable. And he is making hay of the grass which is flesh, for his three daughters. And his father is dependent on him in the Vale of Taunton.

The one great principle of the English law is, to make business for itself. There is no other principle distinctly, certainly, and consistently maintained through all its narrow turnings. Viewed by this light it becomes a coherent scheme, and not the monstrous maze the laity are apt to think it. Let them but once clearly perceive that its grand principle is to make business for itself at their expense, and surely they will cease to grumble.

But, not perceiving this quite plainly—only seeing it by halves in a confused way—the laity sometimes suffer in peace and pocket, with a bad grace, and *do* grumble very much. Then this respectability of Mr. Vholes is brought into powerful play against them. "Repeal this statute, my good sir?" says Mr. Kenge, to a smarting client, "repeal it, my dear sir? Never, with my consent. Alter this law, sir, and what will be the effect of your rash proceeding on a class of practitioners, very worthily represented, allow me to say to you, by the opposite attorney in the case, Mr. Vholes? Sir, that class of practitioners would be swept from the face of the earth. Now you cannot afford—I would say, the social system cannot afford—to lose an order of men like Mr. Vholes. Diligent, persevering, steady, acute in business. My dear sir, I understand your present feelings against the existing state of things, which I grant to be a little hard in your case; but I can never raise my voice for the demolition of a class of men like Mr. Vholes." The respectability of Mr. Vholes has even been cited with crushing effect before Parliamentary committees, as in the following blue minutes of a distinguished attorney's evidence. "Question (number five hundred and seventeen thousand eight hundred and sixty-nine). If I understand you, these forms of practice indisputably occasion delay? Answer. Yes, some delay. Question. And great expense? Answer. Most assuredly they cannot be gone through for nothing. Question. And unspeakable vexation? Answer. I am not prepared to say that. They have never given *me* any vexation; quite the contrary. Question. But you think that their abolition would damage a class of practitioners? Answer. I have no doubt of it. Question. Can you instance any type of that class? Answer. Yes. I would unhesitatingly mention Mr. Vholes. He would be ruined. Question. Mr. Vholes is considered, in the profession, a respectable man? Answer"—which proved fatal to the inquiry for ten years—"Mr. Vholes is considered, in the profession, a *most* respectable man."

So in familiar conversation, private authorities no less disinterested will remark that they don't know what this age is coming to; that we are plunging down precipices; that now here is something else gone; that these changes are death to people like Vholes: a man of undoubted respectability, with a father in the Vale of Taunton, and three daughters at home. Take a few steps more in this direction, say they, and what is to become of Vholes's father? Is he to perish? And of Vholes's daughters? Are they to be shirt-makers, or governesses? As though, Mr. Vholes and his relations being minor cannibal chiefs, and it being proposed to abolish cannibalism, indignant champions were to put the case thus: Make man-eating unlawful, and you starve the Vholeses!

In a word, Mr. Vholes, with his three daughters and his father in the Vale of Taunton, is continually doing duty, like a piece of timber, to shore up some decayed foundation that has become a pitfall and a nuisance.

And with a great many people, in a great many instances, the question is never one of a change from Wrong to Right (which is quite an extraneous consideration), but is always one of injury or advantage to that eminently respectable legion, Vholes.

The Chancellor is, within these ten minutes, "up" for the long vacation. Mr. Vholes and his young client, and several blue bags hastily stuffed, out of all regularity of form, as the larger sort of serpents are in their first gorged state, have returned to the official den. Mr. Vholes, quiet and unmoved, as a man of so much respectability ought to be, takes off his close black gloves as if he were skinning his hands, lifts off his tight hat as if he were scalping himself, and sits down at his desk. The client throws his hat and gloves upon the ground—tosses them anywhere, without looking after them or caring where they go; flings himself into a chair, half sighing and half groaning; rests his aching head upon his hand, and looks the portrait of Young Despair.

"Again nothing done!" says Richard. "Nothing, nothing done!"

"Don't say nothing done, sir," returns the placid Vholes. "That is scarcely fair, sir, scarcely fair!"

"Why, what *is* done?" says Richard, turning gloomily upon him.

"That may not be the whole question," returns Vholes. "The question may branch off into what is doing, what is doing?"

"And what is doing?" asks the moody client.

Vholes, sitting with his arms on his desk, quietly bringing the tips of his five right fingers to meet the tips of his five left fingers, and quietly separating them again, and fixedly and slowly looking at his client, replies:

"A good deal is doing, sir. We have put our shoulders to the wheel, Mr. Carstone, and the wheel is going round."

"Yes, with Ixion on it. How am I to get through the next four or five accursed months?" exclaims the young man, rising from his chair and walking about the room.

"Mr. C.," returns Vholes, following him close with his eyes wherever he goes, "your spirits are hasty, and I am sorry for it on your account. Excuse me if I recommend you not to chafe so much, not to be so impetuous, not to wear yourself out so. You should have more patience. You should sustain yourself better."

"I ought to imitate you, in fact, Mr. Vholes?" says Richard, sitting down again with an impatient laugh, and beating the Devil's Tattoo with his boot on the patternless carpet.

"Sir," returns Vholes, always looking at the client, as if he were making a lingering meal of him with his eyes as well as with his professional appetite. "Sir," returns Vholes, with his inward manner of speech and his bloodless quietude; "I should not have had the presumption to propose myself as a model, for your imitation or any man's. Let me but leave the good name to my three daughters, and that is enough for me; I am not a self-seeker. But, since you mention me so pointedly, I will acknowledge that I should like to impart to you a little of my—come, sir, you are disposed to call it insensibility, and

I am sure I have no objection—say insensibility—a little of my insensibility."

"Mr. Vholes," explains the client, somewhat abashed, "I had no intention to accuse you of insensibility."

"I think you had, sir, without knowing it," returns the equable Vholes. "Very naturally. It is my duty to attend to your interests with a cool head, and I can quite understand that to your excited feelings I may appear, at such times as the present, insensible. My daughters may know me better; my aged father may know me better. But they have known me much longer than you have, and the confiding eye of affection is not the distrustful eye of business. Not that I complain, sir, of the eye of business being distrustful; quite the contrary. In attending to your interests, I wish to have all possible checks upon me; it is right that I should have them; I court inquiry. But your interests demand that I should be cool and methodical, Mr. Carstone; and I cannot be otherwise—no, sir, not even to please you."

Mr. Vholes, after glancing at the official cat who is patiently watching a mouse's hole, fixes his charmed gaze again on his young client, and proceeds in his buttoned-up half-audible voice, as if there were an unclean spirit in him that will neither come out nor speak out:

"What are you to do, sir, you inquire, during the vacation. I should hope you gentlemen of the army may find many means of amusing yourselves, if you give your minds to it. If you had asked me what *I* was to do, during the vacation, I could have answered you more readily. I am to attend to your interests. I am to be found here, day by day, attending to your interests. That is my duty, Mr. C.; and term-time or vacation makes no difference to me. If you wish to consult me as to your interests, you will find me here at all times alike. Other professional men go out of town. I don't. Not that I blame them for going; I merely say, I don't go. This desk is your rock, sir!"

Mr. Vholes gives it a rap, and it sounds as hollow as a coffin. Not to Richard, though. There is encouragement in the sound to him. Perhaps Mr. Vholes knows there is.

"I am perfectly aware, Mr. Vholes," says Richard, more familiarly and good-humouredly, "that you are the most reliable fellow in the world; and that to have to do with you, is to have to do with a man of business who is not to be hoodwinked. But put yourself in my case, dragging on this dislocated life, sinking deeper and deeper into difficulty every day, continually hoping and continually disappointed, conscious of change upon change for the worse in myself, and of no change for the better in anything else; and you will find it a dark-looking case sometimes, as I do."

"You know," says Mr. Vholes, "that I never give hopes, sir. I told you from the first, Mr. C., that I never give hopes. Particularly in a case like this, where the greater part of the costs comes out of the estate, I should not be considerate of my good name, if I gave hopes. It might seem as if costs were my object. Still, when you say there is no change for the better, I must, as a bare matter of fact, deny that."

"Ay?" returns Richard, brightening. "But how do you make it out?"

"Mr. Carstone, you are represented by——"

"You said just now—a rock."

"Yes, sir," says Mr. Vholes, gently shaking his head and rapping the hollow desk, with a sound as if ashes were falling on ashes, and dust on dust, "a rock. That's something. You are separately represented, and no longer hidden and lost in the interests of others. *That's* something. The suit does not sleep; we wake it up, we air it, we walk it about. *That's* something. It's not all Jarndyce, in fact as well as in name. *That's* something. Nobody has it all his own way now, sir. And *that's* something, surely."

Richard, his face flushing suddenly, strikes the desk with his clenched hand.

"Mr. Vholes! If any man had told me, when I first went to John Jarndyce's house, that he was anything but the disinterested friend he seemed—that he was what he has gradually turned out to be—I could have found no words strong enough to repel the slander; I could not have defended him too ardently. So little did I know of the world! Whereas, now, I do declare to you that he becomes to me the embodiment of the suit; that, in place of its being an abstraction, it is John Jarndyce; that the more I suffer, the more indignant I am with him; that every new delay, and every new disappointment, is only a new injury from John Jarndyce's hand."

"No, no," says Vholes. "Don't say so. We ought to have patience, all of us. Besides, I never disparage, sir. I never disparage."

"Mr. Vholes," returns the angry client. "You know as well as I, that he would have strangled the suit if he could."

"He was not active in it," Mr. Vholes admits, with an appearance of reluctance. "He certainly was not active in it. But however, but however, he might have had amiable intentions. Who can read the heart, Mr. C.!"

"You can," returns Richard.

"I, Mr. C.?"

"Well enough to know what his intentions were. Are, or are not, our interests conflicting? Tell—me—that?" says Richard, accompanying his last three words with three raps on his rock of trust.

"Mr. C.," returns Vholes, immovable in attitude and never winking his hungry eyes, "I should be wanting in my duty as your professional adviser, I should be departing from my fidelity to your interests, if I represented those interests as identical with the interests of Mr. Jarndyce. They are no such thing, sir. I never impute motives; I both have, and am, a father, and I never impute motives. But I must not shrink from a professional duty, even if it sows dissension in families. I understand you to be now consulting me professionally, as to your interests? You are so? I reply then, they are not identical with those of Mr. Jarndyce."

"Of course they are not!" cries Richard. "You found that out, long ago."

"Mr. C.," returns Vholes, "I wish to say no more of any third party than is necessary. I wish to leave my good name unsullied, together with any little property of which I may become possessed through industry and perseverance, to my daughters Emma, Jane, and Caroline. I also desire to live in amity with my professional brethren. When Mr. Skimpole did me the honour, sir—I will not say the very high honour, for I never stoop to flattery—of bringing us together in this room, I mentioned to you that I could offer no opinion or advice as to your interests, while those interests were entrusted to another member of the profession. And I spoke in such terms as I was bound to speak, of Kenge and Carboy's office, which stands high. You, sir, thought fit to withdraw your interests from that keeping nevertheless, and to offer them to me. You brought them with clean hands, sir, and I accepted them with clean hands. Those interests are now paramount in this office. My digestive functions, as you may have heard me mention, are not in a good state, and rest might improve them; but I shall not rest, sir, while I am your representative. Whenever you want me, you will find me here. Summon me anywhere, and I will come. During the long vacation, sir, I shall devote my leisure to studying your interests more and more closely, and to making arrangements for moving heaven and earth (including, of course, the Chancellor) after Michaelmas term; and when I ultimately congratulate you, sir," says Mr. Vholes, with the severity of a determined man, "when I ultimately congratulate you, sir, with all my heart, on your accession to fortune—which, but that I never give hopes, I might say something further about—you will owe me nothing, beyond whatever little balance may be then outstanding of the costs as between solicitor and client, not included in the taxed costs allowed out of the estate. I pretend to no claim upon you, Mr. C., but for the zealous and active discharge—not the languid and routine discharge, sir : that much credit I stipulate for—of my professional duty. My duty prosperously ended, all between us is ended."

Vholes finally adds, by way of rider to this declaration of his principles, that as Mr. Carstone is about to rejoin his regiment, perhaps Mr. C. will favour him with an order on his agent for twenty pounds on account.

"For there have been many little consultations and attendances of late, sir," observes Vholes, turning over the leaves of his Diary, "and these things mount up, and I don't profess to be a man of capital. When we first entered on our present relations, I stated to you openly—it is a principle of mine that there never can be too much openness between solicitor and client—that I was not a man of capital; and that if capital was your object, you had better leave your papers in Kenge's office. No, Mr. C., you will find none of the advantages, or disadvantages, of capital here, sir. This," Vholes gives the desk one hollow blow again, "is your rock; it pretends to be nothing more."

The client, with his dejection insensibly relieved, and his vague hopes rekindled, takes pen and ink and writes the draft; not without perplexed consideration and calculation of the date it may bear, implying

scant effects in the agent's hands. All the while, Vholes, buttoned up
in body and mind, looks at him attentively. All the while, Vholes's
official cat watches the mouse's hole.

Lastly, the client, shaking hands, beseeches Mr. Vholes, for Heaven's
sake and Earth's sake, to do his utmost, to "pull him through" the
Court of Chancery. Mr. Vholes, who never gives hopes, lays his palm
upon the client's shoulder, and answers with a smile, "Always here,
sir. Personally, or by letter, you will always find me here, sir, with
my shoulder to the wheel." Thus they part; and Vholes, left alone,
employs himself in carrying sundry little matters out of his Diary into
his draft bill book, for the ultimate behoof of his three daughters. So
might an industrious fox, or bear, make up his account of chickens or
stray travellers with an eye to his cubs; not to disparage by that word
the three raw-visaged, lank, and buttoned-up maidens, who dwell with
the parent Vholes in an earthly cottage situated in a damp garden at
Kennington.

Richard, emerging from the heavy shade of Symond's Inn into the
sunshine of Chancery Lane—for there happens to be sunshine there to-
day—walks thoughtfully on, and turns into Lincoln's Inn, and passes
under the shadow of the Lincoln's Inn trees. On many such loungers
have the speckled shadows of those trees often fallen; on the like bent
head, the bitten nail, the lowering eye, the lingering step, the purpose-
less and dreamy air, the good consuming and consumed, the life turned
sour. This lounger is not shabby yet, but that may come. Chancery,
which knows no wisdom but in Precedent, is very rich in such Precedents; and why should one be different from ten thousand?

Yet the time is so short since his depreciation began, that as he
saunters away, reluctant to leave the spot for some long months together, though he hates it, Richard himself may feel his own case as if
it were a startling one. While his heart is heavy with corroding care,
suspense, distrust, and doubt, it may have room for some sorrowful
wonder when he recalls how different his first visit there, how different
he, how different all the colours of his mind. But injustice breeds
injustice; the fighting with shadows and being defeated by them, neces-
sitates the setting up of substances to combat; from the impalpable suit
which no man alive can understand, the time for that being long gone
by, it has become a gloomy relief to turn to the palpable figure of the
friend who would have saved him from this ruin, and make *him* his
enemy. Richard has told Vholes the truth. Is he in a hardened or a
softened mood, he still lays his injuries equally at that door; he was
thwarted, in that quarter, of a set purpose, and that purpose could only
originate in the one subject that is resolving his existence into itself;
besides, it is a justification to him in his own eyes to have an embodied
antagonist and oppressor.

Is Richard a monster in all this—or would Chancery be found rich in
such Precedents too, if they could be got for citation from the Recording
Angel?

Two pairs of eyes not unused to such people look after him, as, biting his nails and brooding, he crosses the square, and is swallowed up by the shadow of the southern gateway. Mr. Guppy and Mr. Weevle are the possessors of those eyes, and they have been leaning in conversation against the low stone parapet under the trees. He passed close by them, seeing nothing but the ground.

"William," says Mr. Weevle, adjusting his whiskers; "there's combustion going on there! It's not a case of Spontaneous, but it's smouldering combustion it is."

"Ah!" says Mr. Guppy, "he wouldn't keep out of Jarndyce, and I suppose he's over head and ears in debt. I never knew much of him. He was as high as the Monument when he was on trial at our place. A good riddance to me, whether as clerk or client! Well, Tony, that as I was mentioning is what they're up to."

Mr. Guppy, refolding his arms, resettles himself against the parapet, as resuming a conversation of interest.

"They are still up to it, sir," says Mr. Guppy, "still taking stock, still examining papers, still going over the heaps and heaps of rubbish. At this rate they'll be at it these seven years."

"And Small is helping?"

"Small left us at a week's notice. Told Kenge, his grandfather's business was too much for the old gentleman, and he could better himself by undertaking it. There had been a coolness between myself and Small on account of his being so close. But he said you and I began it; and as he had me there—for we did—I put our acquaintance on the old footing. That's how I come to know what they're up to."

"You haven't looked in at all?"

"Tony," says Mr. Guppy, a little disconcerted, "to be unreserved with you, I don't greatly relish the house, except in your company, and therefore I have not; and therefore I proposed this little appointment for our fetching away your things. There goes the hour by the clock! Tony;" Mr. Guppy becomes mysteriously and tenderly eloquent; "it is necessary that I should impress upon your mind once more, that circumstances over which I have no control, have made a melancholy alteration in my most cherished plans, and in that unrequited image which I formerly mentioned to you as a friend. That image is shattered, and that idol is laid low. My only wish now, in connection with the objects which I had an idea of carrying out in the court, with your aid as a friend, is to let 'em alone and bury 'em in oblivion. Do you think it possible, do you think it at all likely (I put it to you, Tony, as a friend), from your knowledge of that capricious and deep old character who fell a prey to the—Spontaneous element; do you, Tony, think it at all likely that, on second thoughts, he put those letters away anywhere, after you saw him alive, and that they were not destroyed that night?"

Mr. Weevle reflects for some time. Shakes his head. Decidedly thinks not.

"Tony," says Mr. Guppy, as they walk towards the court, "once again understand me, as a friend. Without entering into further explanations, I may repeat that the idol is down. I have no purpose to serve now, but burial in oblivion. To that I have pledged myself. I owe it to myself, and I owe it to the shattered image, as also to the circumstances over which I have no control. If you was to express to me by a gesture, by a wink, that you saw lying anywhere in your late lodgings, any papers that so much as looked like the papers in question, I would pitch them into the fire, sir, on my own responsibility."

Mr. Weevle nods. Mr. Guppy, much elevated in his own opinion by having delivered these observations, with an air in part forensic and in part romantic—this gentleman having a passion for conducting anything in the form of an examination, or delivering anything in the form of a summing up or a speech—accompanies his friend with dignity to the court.

Never since it has been a court, has it had such a Fortunatus's purse of gossip as in the proceedings at the rag and bottle shop. Regularly, every morning at eight, is the elder Mr. Smallweed brought down to the corner and carried in, accompanied by Mrs. Smallweed, Judy, and Bart; and regularly, all day, do they all remain there until nine at night, solaced by gipsy dinners, not abundant in quantity, from the cook's shop; rummaging and searching, digging, delving, and diving among the treasures of the late lamented. What those treasures are, they keep so secret, that the court is maddened. In its delirium it imagines guineas pouring out of teapots, crown-pieces overflowing punch-bowls, old chairs and mattresses stuffed with Bank of England notes. It possesses itself of the sixpenny history (with highly-coloured folding frontispiece) of Mr. Daniel Dancer and his sister, and also of Mr. Elwes, of Suffolk, and transfers all the facts from those authentic narratives of Mr. Krook. Twice when the dustman is called in to carry off a cartload of old paper, ashes, and broken bottles, the whole court assembles and pries into the baskets as they come forth. Many times the two gentlemen who write with the ravenous little pens on the tissue paper are seen prowling in the neighbourhood—shy of each other, their late partnership being dissolved. The Sol skilfully carries a vein of the prevailing interest through the Harmonic nights. Little Swills, in what are professionally known as "patter" allusions to the subject, is received with loud applause; and the same vocalist "gags" in the regular business like a man inspired. Even Miss M. Melvilleson, in the revived Caledonian melody of "We're a' nodding," points the sentiment that "the dogs love broo" (whatever the nature of that refreshment may be) with such archness, and such a turn of the head towards next door, that she is immediately understood to mean, Mr. Smallweed loves to find money, and is nightly honoured with a double encore. For all this, the court discovers nothing; and, as Mrs. Piper and Mrs. Perkins now communicate to the late lodger, whose appearance is the signal for a general rally, it is in one continual ferment to discover everything, and more.

Mr. Weevle and Mr. Guppy, with every eye in the court's head upon them, knock at the closed door of the late lamented's house, in a high state of popularity. But, being, contrary to the court's expectation, admitted, they immediately become unpopular, and are considered to mean no good.

The shutters are more or less closed all over the house, and the ground-floor is sufficiently dark to require candles. Introduced into the backshop by Mr. Smallweed the younger, they, fresh from the sunlight, can at first see nothing save darkness and shadows; but they gradually discern the elder Mr. Smallweed, seated in his chair upon the brink of a well or grave of waste paper; the virtuous Judy groping therein, like a female sexton; and Mrs. Smallweed on the level ground in the vicinity, snowed up in a heap of paper fragments, print and manuscript, which would appear to be the accumulated compliments that have been sent flying at her in the course of the day. The whole party, Small included, are blackened with dust and dirt, and present a fiendish appearance not relieved by the general aspect of the room. There is more litter and lumber in it than of old, and it is dirtier if possible; likewise, it is ghostly with traces of its dead inhabitant, and even with his chalked writing on the wall.

On the entrance of visitors, Mr. Smallweed and Judy simultaneously fold their arms and stop in their researches.

"Aha!" croaks the old gentleman. "How de do, gentlemen, how de do! Come to fetch your property, Mr. Weevle! That's well, that's well. Ha! ha! We should have been forced to sell you up, sir, to pay your warehouse room, if you had left it here much longer. You feel quite at home here, again, I dare say? Glad to see you, glad to see you!"

Mr. Weevle, thanking him, casts an eye about. Mr. Guppy's eye follows Mr. Weevle's eye. Mr. Weevle's eye comes back without any new intelligence in it. Mr. Guppy's eye comes back, and meets Mr. Smallweed's eye. That engaging old gentleman is still murmuring, like some wound-up instrument running down, "How de do, sir—how de—how——." And then having run down, he lapses into grinning silence, as Mr. Guppy starts at seeing Mr. Tulkinghorn standing in the darkness opposite, with his hands behind him.

"Gentleman so kind as to act as my solicitor," says Grandfather Smallweed. "I am not the sort of client for a gentleman of such note; but he is so good!"

Mr. Guppy slightly nudging his friend to take another look, makes a shuffling bow to Mr. Tulkinghorn, who returns it with an easy nod. Mr. Tulkinghorn is looking on as if he had nothing else to do, and were rather amused by the novelty.

"A good deal of property here, sir, I should say," Mr. Guppy observes to Mr. Smallweed.

"Principally rags and rubbish, my dear friend! rags and rubbish! Me and Bart, and my grand-daughter Judy, are endeavouring to make out an inventory of what's worth anything to sell. But we haven't come to much as yet, we—haven't—come—to—hah!"

Mr. Smallweed has run down again; while Mr. Weevle's eye, attended by Mr. Guppy's eye, has again gone round the room and come back.

"Well, sir," says Mr. Weevle. "We won't intrude any longer, if you'll allow us to go upstairs."

"Anywhere, my dear sir, anywhere! You're at home. Make yourself so, pray!"

As they go upstairs, Mr. Guppy lifts his eyebrows inquiringly, and looks at Tony. Tony shakes his head. They find the old room very dull and dismal, with the ashes of the fire that was burning on that memorable night yet in the discoloured grate. They have a great disinclination to touch any object, and carefully blow the dust from it first. Nor are they desirous to prolong their visit: packing the few movables with all possible speed, and never speaking above a whisper.

"Look here," says Tony, recoiling. "Here's that horrible cat coming in!"

Mr. Guppy retreats behind a chair. "Small told me of her. She went leaping and bounding and tearing about, that night, like a Dragon, and got out on the house-top, and roamed about up' there for a fortnight, and then came tumbling down the chimney very thin. Did you ever see such a brute? Looks as if she knew all about it, don't she? Almost looks as if she was Krook. Shoohoo! Get out, you goblin!"

Lady Jane in the doorway, with her tiger-snarl from ear to ear, and her club of a tail, shows no intention of obeying; but Mr. Tulkinghorn stumbling over her, she spits at his rusty legs, and swearing wrathfully, takes her arched back upstairs. Possibly to roam the house-tops again, and return by the chimney.

"Mr. Guppy," says Mr. Tulkinghorn, "could I have a word with you?"

Mr. Guppy is engaged in collecting the Galaxy Gallery of British Beauty from the wall, and depositing those works of art in their old ignoble bandbox. "Sir," he returns, reddening, "I wish to act with courtesy towards every member of the profession, and especially, I am sure, towards a member of it so well known as yourself—I will truly add, sir, so distinguished as yourself. Still, Mr. Tulkinghorn, sir, I must stipulate that if you have any word with me, that word is spoken in the presence of my friend."

"Oh, indeed?" says Mr. Tulkinghorn.

"Yes, sir. My reasons are not of a personal nature at all; but they are amply sufficient for myself."

"No doubt, no doubt." Mr. Tulkinghorn is as imperturbable as the hearthstone to which he has quietly walked. "The matter is not of that consequence that I need put you to the trouble of making any conditions, Mr. Guppy." He pauses here to smile, and his smile is as dull and rusty as his pantaloons. "You are to be congratulated, Mr. Guppy; you are a fortunate young man, sir."

"Pretty well so, Mr. Tulkinghorn; I don't complain."

"Complain? High friends, free admission to great houses, and access to elegant ladies! Why, Mr. Guppy, there are people in London who would give their ears to be you."

Mr. Guppy, looking as if he would give his own reddening and still reddening ears to be one of those people at present instead of himself, replies, "Sir, if I attend to my profession, and do what is right by Kenge and Carboy, my friends and acquaintances are of no consequence to them, nor to any member of the profession, not excepting Mr. Tulkinghorn of the Fields. I am not under any obligation to explain myself further; and with all respect for you, sir, and without offence—I repeat, without offence——"

"Oh, certainly!"

"—I don't intend to do it."

"Quite so," says Mr. Tulkinghorn, with a calm nod. "Very good: I see by these portraits that you take a strong interest in the fashionable great, sir?"

He addresses this to the astounded Tony, who admits the soft impeachment.

"A virtue in which few Englishmen are deficient," observes Mr. Tulkinghorn. He has been standing on the hearthstone, with his back to the smoked chimney-piece, and now turns round, with his glasses to his eyes. "Who is this? 'Lady Dedlock.' Ha! A very good likeness in its way, but it wants force of character. Good day to you, gentlemen; good day!"

When he has walked out, Mr. Guppy, in a great perspiration, nerves himself to the hasty completion of the taking down of the Galaxy Gallery, concluding with Lady Dedlock.

"Tony," he says hurriedly to his astonished companion, "let us be quick in putting the things together, and in getting out of this place. It were in vain longer to conceal from you, Tony, that between myself and one of the members of a swanlike aristocracy whom I now hold in my hand, there has been undivulged communication and association. The time might have been, when I might have revealed it to you. It never will be more. It is due alike to the oath I have taken, alike to the shattered idol, and alike to circumstances over which I have no control, that the whole should be buried in oblivion. I charge you as a friend, by the interest you have ever testified in the fashionable intelligence, and by any little advances with which I may have been able to accommodate you, so to bury it without a word of inquiry!"

This charge Mr. Guppy delivers in a state little short of forensic lunacy, while his friend shows a dazed mind in his whole head of hair, and even in his cultivated whiskers.

CHAPTER XL

NATIONAL AND DOMESTIC

ENGLAND has been in a dreadful state for some weeks. Lord Coodle would go out, Sir Thomas Doodle wouldn't come in, and there being nobody in Great Britain (to speak of) except Coodle and Doodle, there has been no Government. It is a mercy that the hostile meeting between those two great men, which at one time seemed inevitable, did not come off; because if both pistols had taken effect, and Coodle and Doodle had killed each other, it is to be presumed that England must have waited to be governed until young Coodle and young Doodle, now in frocks and long stockings, were grown up. This stupendous national calamity, however, was averted by Lord Coodle's making the timely discovery, that if in the heat of debate he had said that he scorned and despised the whole ignoble career of Sir Thomas Doodle, he had merely meant to say that party differences should never induce him to withhold from it the tribute of his warmest admiration; while it as opportunely turned out, on the other hand, that Sir Thomas Doodle had in his own bosom expressly booked Lord Coodle to go down to posterity as the mirror of virtue and honour. Still England has been some weeks in the dismal strait of having no pilot (as was well observed by Sir Leicester Dedlock) to weather the storm; and the marvellous part of the matter is, that England has not appeared to care very much about it, but has gone on eating and drinking and marrying and giving in marriage, as the old world did in the days before the flood. But Coodle knew the danger, and Doodle knew the danger, and all their followers and hangers-on had the clearest possible perception of the danger. At last Sir Thomas Doodle has not only condescended to come in, but has done it handsomely, bringing in with him all his nephews, all his male cousins, and all his brothers-in-law. So there is hope for the old ship yet.

Doodle has found that he must throw himself upon the country—chiefly in the form of sovereigns and beer. In this metamorphosed state he is available in a good many places simultaneously, and can throw himself upon a considerable portion of the country at one time. Britannia being much occupied in pocketing Doodle in the form of sovereigns, and swallowing Doodle in the form of beer, and in swearing herself black in the face that she does neither—plainly to the advancement of her glory and morality—the London season comes to a sudden end, through all the Doodleites and Coodleites dispersing to assist Britannia in those religious exercises.

Hence Mrs. Rouncewell, housekeeper at Chesney Wold, foresees, though no instructions have yet come down, that the family may shortly be expected, together with a pretty large accession of cousins and others who can in any way assist the great Constitutional work. And hence the stately old dame, taking Time by the forelock, leads him up and down the staircases, and along the galleries and passages, and through the rooms, to witness before he grows any older that everything is ready; that floors are rubbed bright, carpets spread, curtains shaken out, beds puffed and patted, still-room and kitchen cleared for action—all things prepared as beseems the Dedlock dignity.

This present summer evening, as the sun goes down, the preparations are complete. Dreary and solemn the old house looks, with so many appliances of habitation, and with no inhabitants except the pictured forms upon the walls. So did these come and go, a Dedlock in possession might have ruminated passing along; so did they see this gallery hushed and quiet, as I see it now; so think, as I think, of the gap that they would make in this domain when they were gone; so find it, as I find it, difficult to believe that it could be without them; so pass from my world, as I pass from theirs, now closing the reverberating door; so leave no blank to miss them, and so die.

Through some of the fiery windows, beautiful from without, and set, at this sunset hour, not in dull grey stone but in a glorious house of gold, the light excluded at the other windows pours in, rich, lavish, overflowing like the summer plenty in the land. Then do the frozen Dedlocks thaw. Strange movements come upon their features, as the shadows of leaves play there. A dense Justice in a corner is beguiled into a wink. A staring Baronet, with a truncheon, gets a dimple in his chin. Down into the bosom of a stony shepherdess there steals a fleck of light and warmth, that would have done it good, a hundred years ago. One ancestress of Volumnia, in high-heeled shoes, very like her—casting the shadow of that virgin event before her full two centuries—shoots out into a halo and becomes a saint. A maid of honour of the court of Charles the Second, with large round eyes (and other charms to correspond), seems to bathe in glowing water, and it ripples as it glows.

But the fire of the sun is dying. Even now the floor is dusky, and shadow slowly mounts the walls, bringing the Dedlocks down like age and death. And now, upon my lady's picture over the great chimney-piece, a weird shade falls from some old tree, that turns it pale, and flutters it, and looks as if a great arm held a veil or hood, watching an opportunity to draw it over her. Higher and darker rises shadow on the wall—now a red gloom on the ceiling—now the fire is out.

All that prospect, which from the terrace looked so near, has moved solemnly away, and changed—not the first or the last of beautiful things that look so near and will so change—into a distant phantom. Light mists arise, and the dew falls, and all the sweet scents in the garden are heavy in the air. Now, the woods settle into great masses as if they were each one profound tree. And now the moon rises, to separate them, and to glimmer here and there in horizontal lines behind their stems, and to make the avenue a pavement of light among high cathedral arches fantastically broken.

Now, the moon is high; and the great house, needing habitation more than ever, is like a body without life. Now, it is even awful, stealing through it, to think of the live people who have slept in the solitary bedrooms: to say nothing of the dead. Now is the time for shadow, when every corner is a cavern, and every downward step a pit, when the stained glass is reflected in pale and faded hues upon the floors, when anything and everything can be made of the heavy staircase beams excepting their own proper shapes, when the armour has dull lights upon it not easily to be distinguished from stealthy movement, and when barred helmets are frightfully suggestive of heads inside. But, of all the shadows in Chesney Wold, the shadow in the long drawing-room upon my lady's picture is the first to come, the last to be disturbed. At this hour and by this light it changes into threatening hands raised up, and menacing the handsome face with every breath that stirs.

"She is not well, ma'am," says a groom in Mrs. Rouncewell's audience-chamber.

"My Lady not well! What's the matter?"

"Why, my Lady has been but poorly, ma'am, since she was last here —I don't mean with the family, ma'am, but when she was here as a bird of passage-like. My Lady has not been out much, for her, and has kept her room a good deal."

"Chesney Wold, Thomas," rejoins the housekeeper, with proud complacency, "will set my Lady up! There is no finer air, and no healthier soil, in the world!"

Thomas may have his own personal opinions on this subject; probably hints them, in his manner of smoothing his sleek head from the nape of his neck to his temples; but he forbears to express them further, and retires to the servants' hall to regale on cold meat-pie and ale.

This groom is the pilot-fish before the nobler shark. Next evening, down come Sir Leicester and my Lady with their largest retinue, and down come the cousins and others from all the points of the compass. Thenceforth for some weeks, backward and forward rush mysterious men with no names, who fly about all those particular parts of the country on which Doodle is at present throwing himself in an auriferous and malty shower, but who are merely persons of a restless disposition and never do anything anywhere.

On these national occasions, Sir Leicester finds the cousins useful. A better man than the Honourable Bob Stables to meet the Hunt at dinner, there could not possibly be. Better got up gentlemen than the other cousins, to ride over to polling-booths and hustings here and there, and show themselves on the side of England, it would be hard to find. Volumnia is a little dim, but she is of the true descent; and there are many who appreciate her sprightly conversation, her French conundrums so old as to have become in the cycles of time almost new again, the honour of taking the fair Dedlock in to dinner, or even the privilege of her hand in the dance. On these national occasions, dancing may be a patriotic service; and Volumnia is constantly seen hopping about, for the good of an ungrateful and unpensioning country.

My Lady takes no great pains to entertain the numerous guests, and, being still unwell, rarely appears until late in the day. But, at all the dismal dinners, leaden lunches, basilisk balls, and other melancholy pageants, her mere appearance is a relief. As to Sir Leicester, he conceives it utterly impossible that anything can be wanting, in any direction, by any one who has the good fortune to be received under that roof; and in a state of sublime satisfaction, he moves among the company, a magnificent refrigerator.

Daily the cousins trot through dust, and canter over roadside turf, away to hustings and polling-booths (with leather gloves and hunting-whips for the counties, and kid gloves and riding-canes for the boroughs), and daily bring back reports on which Sir Leicester holds forth after dinner. Daily the restless men who have no occupation in life, present the appearance of being rather busy. Daily, Volumnia has a little cousinly talk with Sir Leicester on the state of the nation, from which Sir Leicester is disposed to conclude that Volumnia is a more reflecting woman than he had thought her.

"How are we getting on?" says Miss Volumnia, clasping her hands. "*Are* we safe?"

The mighty business is nearly over by this time, and Doodle will throw himself off the country in a few days more. Sir Leicester has just appeared in the long drawing-room after dinner; a bright particular star, surrounded by clouds of cousins.

"Volumnia," replies Sir Leicester, who has a list in his hand, "we are doing tolerably."

"Only tolerably!"

Although it is summer weather, Sir Leicester always has his own particular fire in the evening. He takes his usual screened seat near it, and repeats, with much firmness and a little displeasure, as who should say, I am not a common man, and when I say tolerably, it must not be understood as a common expression; "Volumnia, we are doing tolerably."

"At least there is no opposition to *you*," Volumnia asserts with confidence.

"No, Volumnia. This distracted country has lost its senses in many respects, I grieve to say, but——"

"It is not so mad as that. I am glad to hear it!"

Volumnia's finishing the sentence restores her to favour. Sir Leicester, with a gracious inclination of his head, seems to say to himself, "A sensible woman this, on the whole, though occasionally precipitate."

In fact, as to this question of opposition, the fair Dedlock's observation was superfluous: Sir Leicester, on these occasions, always delivering in his own candidateship, as a kind of handsome wholesale order to be promptly executed. Two other little seats that belong to him, he treats as retail orders of less importance; merely sending down the men, and signifying to the tradespeople, "You will have the goodness to make these materials into two members of parliament, and to send them home when done."

" I regret to say, Volumnia, that in many places the people have shown a bad spirit, and that this opposition to the Government has been of a most determined and most implacable description."

" W-r-retches ! " says Volumnia.

" Even," proceeds Sir Leicester, glancing at the circumjacent cousins on sofas and ottomans, " even in many—in fact, in most—of those places in which the Government has carried it against a faction——"

(Note, by the way, that the Coodleites are always a faction with the Doodleites, and that the Doodleites occupy exactly the same position towards the Coodleites.)

" —Even in them I am shocked, for the credit of Englishmen, to be constrained to inform you that the Party has not triumphed without being put to an enormous expense. Hundreds," says Sir Leicester, eyeing the cousins with increasing dignity and swelling indignation, " hundreds of thousands of pounds ! "

If Volumnia have a fault, it is the fault of being a trifle too innocent ; seeing that the innocence which would go extremely well with a sash and tucker, is a little out of keeping with rouge and pearl necklace. Howbeit, impelled by innocence, she asks,

" What for ? "

" Volumnia," remonstrates Sir Leicester, with his utmost severity. " Volumnia ! "

" No, no, I don't mean what for," cries Volumnia, with her favourite little scream. " How stupid I am ! I mean what a pity ! "

" I am glad," returns Sir Leicester, " that you do mean what a pity."

Volumnia hastens to express her opinion that the shocking people ought to be tried as traitors, and made to support the Party.

" I am glad, Volumnia," repeats Sir Leicester, unmindful of these mollifying sentiments, " that you do mean what a pity. It is disgraceful to the electors. But as you, though inadvertently, and without intending so unreasonable a question, asked me ' what for ? ' let me reply to you. For necessary expenses. And I trust to your good sense, Volumnia, not to pursue the subject, here or elsewhere."

Sir Leicester feels it incumbent on him to observe a crushing aspect towards Volumnia, because it is whispered abroad that these necessary expenses will, in some two hundred election petitions, be unpleasantly connected with the word bribery ; and because some graceless jokers have consequently suggested the omission from the Church service of the ordinary supplication in behalf of the High Court of Parliament, and have recommended instead that the prayers of the congregation be requested for six hundred and fifty-eight gentlemen in a very unhealthy state.

" I suppose," observes Volumnia, having taken a little time to recover her spirits after her late castigation, " I suppose Mr. Tulkinghorn has been worked to death."

" I don't know," says Sir Leicester, opening his eyes, " why Mr. Tulkinghorn should be worked to death. I don't know what Mr. Tulkinghorn's engagements may be. He is not a candidate."

2 E

Volumnia had thought he might have been employed. Sir Leicester could desire to know by whom, and what for? Volumnia, abashed again, suggests by Somebody—to advise and make arrangements. Sir Leicester is not aware that any client of Mr. Tulkinghorn has been in need of his assistance.

Lady Dedlock, seated at an open window with her arm upon its cushioned ledge and looking out at the evening shadows falling on the park, has seemed to attend since the lawyer's name was mentioned.

A languid cousin with a moustache, in a state of extreme debility, now observes from his couch, that—man told him ya'as'dy that Tulkinghorn had gone down t' that iron place t' give legal 'pinion 'bout something; and that, contest being over, t' day, 'twould be highly jawlly thing if Tulkinghorn should 'pear with news that Coodle man was floored.

Mercury in attendance with coffee informs Sir Leicester, hereupon, that Mr. Tulkinghorn has arrived, and is taking dinner. My Lady turns her head inward, for the moment, then looks out again as before.

Volumnia is charmed to hear that her Delight is come. He is so original, such a stolid creature, such an immense being for knowing all sorts of things and never telling them! Volumnia is persuaded that he must be a Freemason. Is sure he is at the head of a lodge, and wears short aprons, and is made a perfect Idol of, with candlesticks and trowels. These lively remarks the fair Dedlock delivers in her youthful manner, while making a purse.

"He has not been here once," she adds, "since I came. I really had some thoughts of breaking my heart for the inconstant creature. I had almost made up my mind that he was dead."

It may be the gathering gloom of evening, or it may be the darker gloom within herself, but a shade is on my Lady's face, as if she thought, "I would he were!"

"Mr. Tulkinghorn," says Sir Leicester, "is always welcome here, and always discreet wheresoever he is. A very valuable person, and deservedly respected."

The debilitated cousin supposes he is "'normously rich fler."

"He has a stake in the country," says Sir Leicester, "I have no doubt. He is, of course, handsomely paid, and he associates almost on a footing of equality with the highest society."

Everybody starts. For a gun is fired close by.

"Good gracious, what's that?" cries Volumnia with her little withered scream.

"A rat," says my Lady. "And they have shot him."

Enter Mr. Tulkinghorn, followed by Mercuries with lamps and candles.

"No, no," says Sir Leicester, "I think not. My Lady, do you object to the twilight?"

On the contrary, my Lady prefers it.

"Volumnia?"

Oh! nothing is so delicious to Volumnia, as to sit and talk in the dark.

"Then take them away," says Sir Leicester. "Tulkinghorn, I beg your pardon. How do you do?"

Mr. Tulkinghorn with his usual leisurely ease advances, renders his passing homage to my Lady, shakes Sir Leicester's hand, and subsides into the chair proper to him when he has anything to communicate, on the opposite side of the Baronet's little newspaper-table. Sir Leicester is apprehensive that my Lady, not being very well, will take cold at that open window. My Lady is obliged to him, but would rather sit there, for the air. Sir Leicester rises, adjusts her scarf about her, and returns to his seat. Mr. Tulkinghorn in the meanwhile takes a pinch of snuff.

"Now," says Sir Leicester. "How has that contest gone?"

"Oh, hollow from the beginning. Not a chance. They have brought in both their people. You are beaten out of all reason. Three to one."

It is a part of Mr. Tulkinghorn's policy and mastery to have no political opinions; indeed, *no* opinions. Therefore he says "you" are beaten, and not "we."

Sir Leicester is majestically wroth. Volumnia never heard of such a thing. The debilitated cousin holds that it's—sort of thing that's sure tapn slongs votes—giv'n—Mob.

"It's the place, you know," Mr. Tulkinghorn goes on to say in the fast increasing darkness, when there is silence again, "where they wanted to put up Mrs. Rouncewell's son."

"A proposal which, as you correctly informed me at the time, he had the becoming taste and perception," observes Sir Leicester, "to decline. I cannot say that I by any means approve of the sentiments expressed by Mr. Rouncewell, when he was here for some half-hour, in this room; but there was a sense of propriety in his decision which I am glad to acknowledge."

"Ha!" says Mr. Tulkinghorn. "It did not prevent him from being very active in this election, though."

Sir Leicester is distinctly heard to gasp before speaking. "Did I understand you? Did you say that Mr. Rouncewell had been very active in this election?"

"Uncommonly active."

"Against——"

"Oh dear yes, against you. He is a very good speaker. Plain and emphatic. He made a damaging effect, and has great influence. In the business part of the proceedings he carried all before him."

It is evident to the whole company, though nobody can see him, that Sir Leicester is staring majestically.

"And he was much assisted," says Mr. Tulkinghorn, as a wind-up, "by his son."

"By his son, sir?" repeats Sir Leicester, with awful politeness.

"By his son."

"The son who wished to marry the young woman in my Lady's service?"

"That son. He has but one."

"Then, upon my honour," says Sir Leicester, after a terrific pause, during which he has been heard to snort and felt to stare; "then upon my honour, upon my life, upon my reputation and principles, the floodgates of society are burst open, and the waters have—a—obliterated the landmarks of the framework of the cohesion by which things are held together!"

General burst of cousinly indignation. Volumnia thinks it is really high time, you know, for somebody in power to step in and do something strong. Debilitated cousin thinks—Country's going—DAYVLE—steeplechase pace.

"I beg," says Sir Leicester, in a breathless condition, "that we may not comment further on this circumstance. Comment is superfluous. My Lady, let me suggest in reference to that young woman——"

"I have no intention," observes my Lady from her window, in a low but decided tone, "of parting with her."

"That was not my meaning," returns Sir Leicester. "I am glad to hear you say so. I would suggest that as you think her worthy of your patronage, you should exert your influence to keep her from these dangerous hands. You might show her what violence would be done, in such association, to her duties and principles; and you might preserve her for a better fate. You might point out to her that she probably would, in good time, find a husband at Chesney Wold, by whom she would not be—" Sir Leicester adds, after a moment's consideration, "dragged from the altars of her forefathers."

These remarks he offers with his unvarying politeness and deference when he addresses himself to his wife. She merely moves her head in reply. The moon is rising; and where she sits there is a little stream of cold pale light, in which her head is seen.

"It is worthy of remark," says Mr. Tulkinghorn, "however, that these people are, in their way, very proud."

"Proud?" Sir Leicester doubts his hearing.

"I should not be surprised, if they all voluntarily abandoned the girl —yes, lover and all—instead of her abandoning them, supposing she remained at Chesney Wold under such circumstances."

"Well!" says Sir Leicester tremulously, "Well! You should know, Mr. Tulkinghorn. You have been among them."

"Really, Sir Leicester," returns the lawyer, "I state the fact. Why, I could tell you a story—with Lady Dedlock's permission."

Her head concedes it, and Volumnia is enchanted. A story! Oh he is going to tell something at last! A ghost in it, Volumnia hopes?

"No. Real flesh and blood." Mr. Tulkinghorn stops for an instant, and repeats, with some little emphasis grafted upon his usual monotony, "Real flesh and blood, Miss Dedlock. Sir Leicester, these particulars have only lately become known to me. They are very brief. They exemplify what I have said I suppress names for the present. Lady Dedlock will not think me ill-bred, I hope?"

By the light of the fire, which is low, he can be seen looking towards the moonlight. By the light of the moon Lady Dedlock can be seen, perfectly still.

"A townsman of this Mrs. Rouncewell, a man in exactly parallel circumstances, as I am told, had the good fortune to have a daughter who attracted the notice of a great lady. I speak of really a great lady; not merely great to him, but married to a gentleman of your condition, Sir Leicester."

Sir Leicester condescendingly says, "Yes, Mr. Tulkinghorn;" implying that then she must have appeared of very considerable moral dimensions indeed, in the eyes of an ironmaster.

"The lady was wealthy and beautiful, and had a liking for the girl, and treated her with great kindness, and kept her always near her. Now this lady preserved a secret under all her greatness, which she had preserved for many years. In fact, she had in early life been engaged to marry a young rake—he was a captain in the army—nothing connected with whom came to any good. She never did marry him, but she gave birth to a child of which he was the father."

By the light of the fire he can be seen looking towards the moonlight. By the moonlight, Lady Dedlock can be seen in profile, perfectly still.

"The captain in the army being dead, she believed herself safe; but a train of circumstances with which I need not trouble you, led to discovery. As I received the story, they began in an imprudence on her own part one day, when she was taken by surprise; which shows how difficult it is for the firmest of us (she was very firm) to be always guarded. There was great domestic trouble and amazement, you may suppose; I leave you to imagine, Sir Leicester, the husband's grief. But that is not the present point. When Mr. Rouncewell's townsman heard of the disclosure, he no more allowed the girl to be patronised and honoured, than he would have suffered her to be trodden underfoot before his eyes. Such was his pride, that he indignantly took her away, as if from reproach and disgrace. He had no sense of the honour done him and his daughter by the lady's condescension; not the least. He resented the girl's position, as if the lady had been the commonest of commoners. That is the story. I hope Lady Dedlock will excuse its painful nature."

There are various opinions on the merits, more or less conflicting with Volumnia's. That fair young creature cannot believe there ever was any such lady, and rejects the whole history on the threshold. The majority incline to the debilitated cousin's sentiment, which is in few words—"no business—Rouncewell's 'fernal townsman." Sir Leicester generally refers back in his mind to Wat Tyler, and arranges a sequence of events on a plan of his own.

There is not much conversation in all, for late hours have been kept at Chesney Wold since the necessary expenses elsewhere began, and this is the first night in many on which the family have been alone. It is past ten, when Sir Leicester begs Mr. Tulkinghorn to ring for candles. Then the stream of moonlight has swelled into a lake, and then Lady Dedlock for the first time moves, and rises, and comes forward to a table for a glass of water. Winking cousins, bat-like in the candle glare, crowd round to give it; Volumnia (always ready for something better if procurable) takes another, a very mild sip of which contents her; Lady Dedlock, graceful, self-possessed, looked after by admiring eyes, passes away slowly down the long perspective by the side of that Nymph, not at all improving her as a question of contrast.

CHAPTER XLI

IN MR. TULKINGHORN'S ROOM

MR. TULKINGHORN arrives in his turret-room, a little breathed by the journey up, though leisurely performed. There is an expression on his face as if he had discharged his mind of some grave matter, and were, in his close way, satisfied. To say of a man so severely and strictly self-repressed that he is triumphant, would be to do him as great an injustice as to suppose him troubled with love or sentiment, or any romantic weakness. He is sedately satisfied. Perhaps there is a rather increased sense of power upon him, as he loosely grasps one of his venous wrists with his other hand, and holding it behind his back walks noiselessly up and down.

There is a capacious writing-table in the room, on which is a pretty large accumulation of papers. The green lamp is lighted, his reading-glasses lie upon the desk, the easy-chair is wheeled up to it, and it would seem as though he had intended to bestow an hour or so upon these claims on his attention before going to bed. But he happens not to be in a business mind. After a glance at the documents awaiting his notice —with his head bent low over the table, the old man's sight for print or writing being defective at night—he opens the French window and steps out upon the leads. There he again walks slowly up and down, in the same attitude; subsiding, if a man so cool may have any need to subside, from the story he has related downstairs.

The time was once, when men as knowing as Mr. Tulkinghorn would walk on turret-tops in the star-light, and look up into the sky to read their fortunes there. Hosts of stars are visible to-night, though their brilliancy is eclipsed by the splendour of the moon. If he be seeking his own star, as he methodically turns and turns upon the leads, it should be but a pale one to be so rustily represented below. If he be tracing out his destiny, that may be written in other characters nearer to his hand.

As he paces the leads, with his eyes most probably as high above his thoughts as they are high above the earth, he is suddenly stopped in passing the window by two eyes that meet his own. The ceiling of his room is rather low; and the upper part of the door, which is opposite the window, is of glass. There is an inner baize door, too, but the night being warm he did not close it when he came upstairs. These eyes that met his own, are looking in through the glass from the corridor outside. He knows them well. The blood has not flushed into his face so suddenly and redly for many a long year, as when he recognises Lady Dedlock.

He steps into the room, and she comes in too, closing both the doors behind her. There is a wild disturbance—is it fear or anger ?—in her eyes. In her carriage and all else, she looks as she looked downstairs two hours ago.

Is it fear, or is it anger, now ? He cannot be sure. Both might be as pale, both as intent.

" Lady Dedlock ? "

She does not speak at first, nor even when she has slowly dropped into the easy-chair by the table. They look at each other, like two pictures.

" Why have you told my story to so many persons ? "

" Lady Dedlock, it was necessary for me to inform you that I knew it."

" How long have you known it ? "

" I have suspected it a long while—fully known it, a little while."

" Months ? "

" Days."

He stands before her, with one hand on a chair-back and the other in his old-fashioned waistcoat and shirt-frill, exactly as he has stood before her at any time since her marriage. The same formal politeness, the same composed deference that might as well be defiance ; the whole man the same dark, cold object, at the same distance, which nothing has ever diminished.

" Is this true concerning the poor girl ? "

He slightly inclines and advances his head, as not quite understanding the question.

" You know what you related. Is it true ? Do her friends know my story also ? Is it the town-talk yet ? Is it chalked upon the walls and cried in the streets ? "

So ! Anger, and fear, and shame. All three contending. What power this woman has, to keep these raging passions down ! Mr. Tulkinghorn's thoughts take such form as he looks at her, with his ragged grey eyebrows a hair's-breadth more contracted than usual, under her gaze.

" No, Lady Dedlock. That was a hypothetical case, arising out of Sir Leicester's unconsciously carrying the matter with so high a hand. But it would be a real case if they knew—what we know."

" Then they do not know it yet ? "

" No."

" Can I save the poor girl from injury before they know it ? "

" Really, Lady Dedlock," Mr. Tulkinghorn replies, " I cannot give a satisfactory opinion on that point."

And he thinks, with the interest of attentive curiosity, as he watches the struggle in her breast, " The power and force of this woman are astonishing ! "

"Sir," she says, for the moment obliged to set her lips with all the energy she has, that she may speak distinctly, "I will make it plainer. I do not dispute your hypothetical case. I anticipated it, and felt its truth as strongly as you can do, when I saw Mr. Rouncewell here. I knew very well that if he could have had the power of seeing me as I was, he would consider the poor girl tarnished by having for a moment been, although most innocently, the subject of my great and distinguished patronage. But, I have an interest in her; or I should rather say— no longer belonging to this place—I had; and if you can find so much consideration for the woman under your foot as to remember that, she will be very sensible of your mercy."

Mr. Tulkinghorn, profoundly attentive, throws this off with a shrug of self-depreciation, and contracts his eyebrows a little more.

"You have prepared me for my exposure, and I thank you for that too. Is there anything that you require of me? Is there any claim that I can release, or any charge or trouble that I can spare my husband in obtaining *his* release, by certifying to the exactness of your discovery? I will write anything, here and now, that you will dictate. I am ready to do it."

And she would do it! thinks the lawyer, watchful of the firm hand with which she takes the pen!

"I will not trouble you, Lady Dedlock. Pray spare yourself."

"I have long expected this, as you know. I neither wish to spare myself, nor to be spared. You can do nothing worse to me than you have done. Do what remains, now."

"Lady Dedlock, there is nothing to be done. I will take leave to say a few words, when you have finished."

Their need for watching one another should be over now, but they do it all this time, and the stars watch them both through the opened window. Away in the moonlight lie the woodland fields at rest, and the wide house is as quiet as the narrow one. The narrow one! Where are the digger and the spade, this peaceful night, destined to add the last great secret to the many secrets of the Tulkinghorn existence? Is the man born yet, is the spade wrought yet? Curious questions to consider, more curious perhaps not to consider, under the watching stars upon a summer night.

"Of repentance or remorse, or any feeling of mine," Lady Dedlock presently proceeds, "I say not a word. If I were not dumb, you would be deaf. Let that go by. It is not for your ears."

He makes a feint of offering a protest, but she sweeps it away with her disdainful hand.

"Of other and very different things I come to speak to you. My jewels are all in their proper places of keeping. They will be found there. So, my dresses. So, all the valuables I have. Some ready money I had with me, please to say, but no large amount. I did not wear my own dress, in order that I might avoid observation. I went, to be henceforward lost. Make this known. I leave no other charge with you."

"Excuse me, Lady Dedlock," says Mr. Tulkinghorn, quite unmoved. "I am not sure that I understand you. You went?——"

"To be lost to all here. I leave Chesney Wold to-night. I go this hour."

Mr. Tulkinghorn shakes his head. She rises; but he, without removing hand from chair-back or from old-fashioned waistcoat and shirt-frill, shakes his head.

"What? Not go as I have said?"

"No, Lady Dedlock," he very calmly replies.

"Do you know the relief that my disappearance will be? Have you forgotten the stain and blot upon this place, and where it is, and who it is?"

"No, Lady Dedlock, not by any means."

Without deigning to rejoin, she moves to the inner door and has it in her hand, when he says to her, without himself stirring hand or foot, or raising his voice:

"Lady Dedlock, have the goodness to stop and hear me, or before you reach the staircase I shall ring the alarm-bell and rouse the house. And then I must speak out, before every guest and servant, every man and woman, in it."

He has conquered her. She falters, trembles, and puts her hand confusedly to her head. Slight tokens these in any one else; but when so practised an eye as Mr. Tulkinghorn's sees indecision for a moment in such a subject, he thoroughly knows its value.

He promptly says again, "Have the goodness to hear me, Lady Dedlock," and motions to the chair from which she has risen. She hesitates, but he motions again, and she sits down.

"The relations between us are of an unfortunate description, Lady Dedlock; but, as they are not of my making, I will not apologise for them. The position I hold in reference to Sir Leicester is so well known to you, that I can hardly imagine but that I must long have appeared in your eyes the natural person to make this discovery."

"Sir," she returns, without looking up from the ground, on which her eyes are now fixed, "I had better have gone. It would have been far better not to have detained me. I have no more to say."

"Excuse me, Lady Dedlock, if I add, a little more to hear."

"I wish to hear it at the window, then. I can't breathe where I am."

His jealous glance as she walks that way, betrays an instant's misgiving that she may have it in her thoughts to leap over, and dashing against ledge and cornice, strike her life out upon the terrace below. But, a moment's observation of her figure as she stands in the window without any support, looking out at the stars—not up—gloomily out at those stars which are low in the heavens—reassures him. By facing round as she has moved, he stands a little behind her.

"Lady Dedlock, I have not yet been able to come to a decision satisfactory to myself, on the course before me. I am not clear what to do, or how to act next. I must request you, in the meantime, to keep your secret as you have kept it so long, and not to wonder that I keep it too."

He pauses, but she makes no reply

"Pardon me, Lady Dedlock. This is an important subject. You are honouring me with your attention?"

"I am."

"Thank you. I might have known it, from what I have seen of your strength of character. I ought not to have asked the question, but I have the habit of making sure of my ground, step by step, as I go on. The sole consideration in this unhappy case is Sir Leicester."

"Then why," she asks in a low voice, and without removing her gloomy look from those distant stars, "do you detain me in his house?"

"Because he *is* the consideration. Lady Dedlock, I have no occasion to tell you that Sir Leicester is a very proud man; that his reliance upon you is implicit; that the fall of that moon out of the sky, would not amaze him more than your fall from your high position as his wife."

She breathes quickly and heavily, but she stands as unflinchingly as ever he has seen her in the midst of her grandest company.

"I declare to you, Lady Dedlock, that with anything short of this case that I have, I would as soon have hoped to root up, by means of my own strength and my own hands, the oldest tree on this estate, as to shake your hold upon Sir Leicester, and Sir Leicester's trust and confidence in you. And even now, with this case, I hesitate. Not that he could doubt (that, even with him, is impossible), but that nothing can prepare him for the blow."

"Not my flight?" she returned. "Think of it again."

"Your flight, Lady Dedlock, would spread the whole truth, and a hundred times the whole truth, far and wide. It would be impossible to save the family credit for a day. It is not to be thought of."

There is a quiet decision in his reply, which admits of no remonstrance.

"When I speak of Sir Leicester being the sole consideration, he and the family credit are one. Sir Leicester and the baronetcy, Sir Leicester and Chesney Wold, Sir Leicester and his ancestors and his patrimony;" Mr. Tulkinghorn very dry here; "are, I need not say to you, Lady Dedlock, inseparable."

"Go on!"

"Therefore," says Mr. Tulkinghorn, pursuing his case in his jog-trot style, "I have much to consider. This is to be hushed up, if it can be. How can it be, if Sir Leicester is driven out of his wits, or laid upon a death-bed? If I inflicted this shock upon him to-morrow morning, how could the immediate change in him be accounted for? What could have caused it? What could have divided you? Lady Dedlock, the wall-chalking and the street-crying would come on directly; and you are to remember that it would not affect you merely (whom I cannot at all consider in this business), but your husband, Lady Dedlock, your husband."

He gets plainer as he gets on, but not an atom more emphatic or animated.

"There is another point of view," he continues, "in which the case presents itself. Sir Leicester is devoted to you almost to infatuation. He might not be able to overcome that infatuation, even knowing what we know. I am putting an extreme case, but it might be so. If so, it were better that he knew nothing. Better for common sense, better for him, better for me. I must take all this into account, and it combines to render a decision very difficult."

She stands looking out at the same stars, without a word. They are beginning to pale, and she looks as if their coldness froze her.

"My experience teaches me," says Mr. Tulkinghorn, who has by this time got his hands in his pockets, and is going on in his business consideration of the matter, like a machine. "My experience teaches me, Lady Dedlock, that most of the people I know would do far better to leave marriage alone. It is at the bottom of three-fourths of their troubles. So I thought when Sir Leicester married, and so I always have thought since. No more about that. I must now be guided by circumstances. In the meanwhile I must beg you to keep your own counsel, and I will keep mine."

"I am to drag my present life on, holding its pains at your pleasure, day by day?" she asks, still looking at the distant sky.

"Yes, I am afraid so, Lady Dedlock."

"It is necessary, you think, that I should be so tied to the stake?"

"I am sure that what I recommend is necessary."

"I am to remain upon this gaudy platform, on which my miserable deception has been so long acted, and it is to fall beneath me when you give the signal?" she says slowly.

"Not without notice, Lady Dedlock. I shall take no step without forewarning you."

She asks all her questions as if she were repeating them from memory, or calling them over in her sleep.

"We are to meet as usual?"

"Precisely as usual, if you please."

"And I am to hide my guilt, as I have done so many years?"

"As you have done so many years. I should not have made that reference myself, Lady Dedlock, but I may now remind you that your secret can be no heavier to you than it was, and is no worse and no better than it was. *I* know it certainly, but I believe we have never wholly trusted each other."

She stands absorbed in the same frozen way for some little time, before asking:

"Is there anything more to be said to-night?"

"Why," Mr. Tulkinghorn returns methodically, as he softly rubs his hands, "I should like to be assured of your acquiescence in my arrangements, Lady Dedlock."

"You may be assured of it."

"Good. And I would wish in conclusion to remind you, as a business precaution, in case it should be necessary to recall the fact in any communication with Sir Leicester, that throughout our interview I have expressly stated my sole consideration to be Sir Leicester's feelings and honour, and the family reputation. I should have been happy to have made Lady Dedlock a prominent consideration, too, if the case had admitted of it; but unfortunately it does not."

"I can attest your fidelity, sir."

Both before and after saying it, she remains absorbed, but at length moves, and turns, unshaken in her natural and acquired presence, towards the door. Mr. Tulkinghorn opens both the doors exactly as he would have done yesterday, or as he would have done ten years ago, and makes his old-fashioned bow as she passes out. It is not an ordinary look that he receives from the handsome face as it goes into the darkness, and it is not an ordinary movement, though a very slight one, that acknowledges his courtesy. But, as he reflects when he is left alone, the woman has been putting no common constraint upon herself.

He would do it all the better, if he saw the woman pacing her own rooms with her hair wildly thrown from her flung-back face, her hands clasped behind her head, her figure twisted as if by pain. He would think so all the more, if he saw the woman thus hurrying up and down for hours, without fatigue, without intermission, followed by the faithful step upon the Ghost's Walk. But he shuts out the now chilled air, draws the window-curtain, goes to bed, and falls asleep. And truly, when the stars go out and the wan day peeps into the turret-chamber, finding him at his oldest, he looks as if the digger and the spade were both commissioned, and would soon be digging.

The same wan day peeps in at Sir Leicester pardoning the repentant country in a majestically condescending dream; and at the cousins entering on various public employments, principally receipt of salary; and at the chaste Volumnia, bestowing a dower of fifty thousand pounds upon a hideous old General, with a mouth of false teeth like a pianoforte too full of keys, long the admiration of Bath and the terror of every other community. Also into rooms high in the roof, and into offices in courtyards and over stables, where humbler ambition dreams of bliss, in keepers' lodges, and in holy matrimony with Will or Sally. Up comes the bright sun, drawing everything up with it—the Wills and Sallys, the latent vapour in the earth, the drooping leaves and flowers, the birds and beasts and creeping things, the gardeners to sweep the dewy turf and unfold emerald velvet where the roller passes, the smoke of the great kitchen fire wreathing itself straight and high into the lightsome air. Lastly, up comes the flag over Mr. Tulkinghorn's unconscious head, cheerfully proclaiming that Sir Leicester and Lady Dedlock are in their happy home, and that there is hospitality at the place in Lincolnshire.

CHAPTER XLII

IN MR. TULKINGHORN'S CHAMBERS

FROM the verdant undulations and the spreading oaks of the Dedlock property, Mr. Tulkinghorn transfers himself to the stale heat and dust of London. His manner of coming and going between the two places, is one of his impenetrabilities. He walks into Chesney Wold as if it were next door to his chambers, and returns to his chambers as if he had never been out of Lincoln's Inn Fields. He neither changes his dress before the journey, nor talks of it afterwards. He melted out of his turret-room this morning, just as now, in the late twilight, he melts into his own square.

Like a dingy London bird among the birds at roost in these pleasant fields, where the sheep are all made into parchment, the goats into wigs, and the pasture into chaff, the lawyer, smoke-dried and faded, dwelling among mankind but not consorting with them, aged without experience of genial youth, and so long used to make his cramped nest in holes and corners of human nature that he has forgotten its broader and better range, comes sauntering home. In the oven made by the hot pavements and hot buildings, he has baked himself drier than usual; and he has, in his thirsty mind, his mellowed port-wine half-a-century old.

The lamplighter is skipping up and down his ladder on Mr. Tulkinghorn's side of the Fields, when that high-priest of noble mysteries arrives at his own dull courtyard. He ascends the doorsteps, and is gliding into the dusky hall, when he encounters, on the top step, a bowing and propitiatory little man.

"Is that Snagsby?"

"Yes sir. I hope you are well sir. I was just giving you up sir, and going home."

"Ay? What is it? What do you want with me?"

"Well sir," says Mr. Snagsby, holding his hat at the side of his head, in his deference towards his best customer, "I was wishful to say a word to you, sir."

"Can you say it here?"

"Perfectly sir."

"Say it then." The lawyer turns, leans his arms on the iron railing at the top of the steps, and looks at the lamplighter lighting the courtyard.

"It is relating," says Mr. Snagsby, in a mysterious low voice; "it is relating—not to put too fine a point upon it—to the foreigner sir?"

Mr. Tulkinghorn eyes him with some surprise. "What foreigner?"

"The foreign female sir. French, if I don't mistake? I am not acquainted with that language myself, but I should judge from her manners and appearance that she was French; anyways, certainly foreign. Her that was upstairs sir, when Mr. Bucket and me had the honour of wait-ing upon you with the sweeping-boy that night."

"Oh! yes, yes.   Mademoiselle Hortense."

"Indeed sir?"   Mr. Snagsby coughs his cough of submission behind his hat.   "I am not acquainted myself with the names of foreigners in general, but I have no doubt it *would* be that."   Mr. Snagsby appears to have set out in this reply with some desperate design of repeating the name; but on reflection coughs again to excuse himself.

"And what can you have to say, Snagsby," demands Mr. Tulkinghorn, "about her?"

"Well sir," returns the stationer, shading his communication with his hat, "it falls a little hard upon me.   My domestic happiness is very great—at least, it's as great as can be expected, I'm sure—but my little woman is rather given to jealousy.   Not to put too fine a point upon it, she is very much given to jealousy.   And you see, a foreign female of that genteel appearance coming into the shop, and hovering—I should be the last to make use of a strong expression, if I could avoid it, but hover-ing sir—in the court—you know it is—now ain't it?   I only put it to yourself sir?"

Mr. Snagsby having said this in a very plaintive manner, throws in a cough of general application to fill up all the blanks.

"Why, what do you mean?" asks Mr. Tulkinghorn.

"Just so sir," returns Mr. Snagsby; "I was sure you would feel it yourself, and would excuse the reasonableness of *my* feelings when coupled with the known excitableness of my little woman.   You see, the foreign female—which you mentioned her name just now, with quite a native sound I am sure—caught up the word Snagsby that night, being uncommon quick, and made inquiry, and got the direction and come at dinner-time. Now Guster, our young woman, is timid and has fits, and she, taking fright at the foreigner's looks—which are fierce—and at a grinding manner that she has of speaking—which is calculated to alarm a weak mind—gave way to it, instead of bearing up against it, and tumbled down the kitchen stairs out of one into another, such fits as I do sometimes think are never gone into, or come out of, in any house but ours.   Consequently there was by good fortune ample occupation for my little woman, and only me to answer the shop.   When she *did* say Mr. Tulkinghorn, being always denied to her by his Employer (which I had no doubt at the time was a foreign mode of viewing a clerk), she would do herself the pleasure of continually calling at my place until she was let in here.   Since then she has been, as I began by saying, hovering—Hovering sir," Mr. Snagsby repeats the word with pathetic emphasis, "in the court.   The effects of which movement it is impossible to calculate.   I shouldn't wonder if it might have already given rise to the painfullest mistakes even in the neighbours' minds, not mentioning (if such a thing was possible) my little woman.   Whereas, Goodness knows," says Mr. Snagsby, shaking his head, "I never had an idea of a foreign female, except as being formerly connected with a bunch of brooms and a baby, or at the present time with a tambourine and earrings. I never had, I do assure you sir ! "

Mr. Tulkinghorn had listened gravely to this complaint, and inquires, when the stationer has finished, " And that's all, is it, Snagsby ? "

" Why yes sir, that's all," says Mr. Snagsby, ending with a cough that plainly adds, " and it's enough too—for me."

" I don't know what Mademoiselle Hortense may want or mean, unless she is mad," says the lawyer.

" Even if she was, you know sir," Mr. Snagsby pleads, " it wouldn't be a consolation to have some weapon or another in the form of a foreign dagger, planted in the family."

" No," says the other. " Well, well ! This shall be stopped. I am sorry you have been inconvenienced. If she comes again, send her here."

Mr. Snagsby, with much bowing and short apologetic coughing, takes his leave, lightened in heart. Mr. Tulkinghorn goes upstairs, saying to himself, " These women were created to give trouble, the whole earth over. The Mistress not being enough to deal with, here's the maid now ! But I will be short with *this* jade at least ! "

So saying he unlocks his door, gropes his way into his murky rooms, lights his candles, and looks about him. It is too dark to see much of allegory overhead there ; but that importunate Roman, who is for ever toppling out of the clouds and pointing, is at his old work pretty distinctly. Not honouring him with much attention, Mr. Tulkinghorn takes a small key from his pocket, unlocks a drawer in which there is another key, which unlocks a chest in which there is another, and so comes to the cellar-key, with which he prepares to descend to the regions of old wine. He is going towards the door with a candle in his hand, when a knock comes.

" Who's this ?—Ay, ay, mistress, it's you, is it ? You appear at a good time. I have just been hearing of you. Now ! What do you want ? "

He stands the candle on the chimney-piece in the clerks' hall, and taps his dry cheek with the key, as he addresses these words of welcome to Mademoiselle Hortense. That feline personage, with her lips tightly shut, and her eyes looking out at him sideways, softly closes the door before replying.

" I have had great deal of trouble to find you, sir."

" *Have* you ! "

" I have been here very often, sir. It has always been said to me, he is not at home, he is engage, he is this and that, he is not for you."

" Quite right, and quite true."

" Not true. Lies ! "

At times, there is a suddenness in the manner of Mademoiselle Hortense so like a bodily spring upon the subject of it, that such subject involuntarily starts and falls back. It is Mr. Tulkinghorn's case at present, though Mademoiselle Hortense, with her eyes almost shut up (but still looking out sideways), is only smiling contemptuously and shaking her head.

"Now, mistress," says the lawyer, tapping the key hastily upon the chimney-piece. "If you have anything to say, say it, say it."

"Sir, you have not use me well. You have been mean and shabby."

"Mean and shabby, eh?" returns the lawyer, rubbing his nose with the key.

"Yes. What is it that I tell you? You know you have. You have attrapped me—catched me—to give you information; you have asked me to show you the dress of mine my Lady must have wore that night, you have prayed me to come in it here to meet that boy—Say! Is it not?" Mademoiselle Hortense makes another spring.

"You are a vixen, a vixen!" Mr. Tulkinghorn seems to meditate, as he looks distrustfully at her; then he replies, "Well, wench, well. I paid you."

"You paid me!" she repeats, with fierce disdain. "Two sovereign! I have not change them, I ref-use them, I des-pise them, I throw them from me!" Which she literally does, taking them out of her bosom as she speaks, and flinging them with such violence on the floor, that they jerk up again into the light before they roll away into corners, and slowly settle down there after spinning vehemently.

"Now!" says Mademoiselle Hortense, darkening her large eyes again. "You have paid me? Eh my God, oh yes!"

Mr. Tulkinghorn rubs his head with the key, while she entertains herself with a sarcastic laugh.

"You must be rich, my fair friend," he composedly observes, " to throw money about in that way!"

"I *am* rich," she returns, "I am very rich in hate. I hate my Lady, of all my heart. You know that."

"Know it? How should I know it?"

"Because you have known it perfectly, before you prayed me to give you that information. Because you have known perfectly that I was en-r-r-r-raged!" It appears impossible for Mademoiselle to roll the letter r sufficiently in this word, notwithstanding that she assists her energetic delivery, by clenching both her hands, and setting all her teeth.

"Oh! I knew that, did I?" says Mr. Tulkinghorn, examining the wards of the key.

"Yes, without doubt. I am not blind. You have made sure of me because you knew that. You had reason! I det-est her." Mademoiselle Hortense folds her arms, and throws this last remark at him over one of her shoulders.

"Having said this, have you anything else to say, Mademoiselle?"

"I am not yet placed. Place me well. Find me a good condition! If you cannot, or do not choose to do that, employ me to pursue her, to chase her, to disgrace and to dishonour her. I will help you well, and with a good will. It is what *you* do. Do I not know that?"

"You appear to know a good deal," Mr. Tulkinghorn retorts.

"Do I not? Is it that I am so weak as to believe, like a child, that I come here in that dress to rec-eive that boy, only to decide a little bet, a wager?—Eh my God, oh yes!" In this reply, down to the word "wager" inclusive, Mademoiselle has been ironically polite and tender; then, as suddenly dashed into the bitterest and most defiant scorn, with her black eyes in one and the same moment very nearly shut, and staringly wide open.

"Now, let us see," says Mr. Tulkinghorn, tapping his chin with the key, and looking imperturbably at her, "how this matter stands."

"Ah! Let us see," Mademoiselle assents, with many angry and tight nods of her head.

"You come here to make a remarkably modest demand, which you have just stated, and it not being conceded, you will come again."

"And again," says Mademoiselle, with more tight and angry nods. "And yet again. And yet again. And many times again. In effect, for ever!"

"And not only here, but you will go to Mr. Snagsby's, too, perhaps? That visit not succeeding either, you will go again, perhaps?"

"And again," repeats Mademoiselle, cataleptic with determination. "And yet again. And yet again. And many times again. In effect, for ever!"

"Very well. Now, Mademoiselle Hortense, let me recommend you to take the candle and pick up that money of yours. I think you will find it behind the clerk's partition in the corner yonder."

She merely throws a laugh over her shoulder, and stands her ground with folded arms.

"You will not, eh?"

"No, I will not!"

"So much the poorer you; so much the richer I? Look, mistress, that is the key of my wine-cellar. It is a large key, but the keys of prisons are larger. In this city there are houses of correction (where the treadmills are, for women), the gates of which are very strong and heavy, and no doubt the keys too. I am afraid a lady of your spirit and activity would find it an inconvenience to have one of those keys turned upon her for any length of time. What do you think?"

"I think," Mademoiselle replies, without any action, and in a clear obliging voice, "that you are a miserable wretch."

"Probably," returns Mr. Tulkinghorn, quietly blowing his nose. "But I don't ask what you think of myself: I ask what you think of the prison."

"Nothing. What does it matter to me?"

"Why it matters this much, mistress," says the lawyer, deliberately putting away his handkerchief, and adjusting his frill, "the law is so despotic, here, that it interferes to prevent any of our good English citizens from being troubled, even by a lady's visits, against his desire. And, on his complaining that he is so troubled, it takes hold of the troublesome lady, and shuts her up in prison under hard discipline. Turns the key upon her, mistress." Illustrating with the cellar key.

"Truly?" returns Mademoiselle, in the same pleasant voice. "That is droll! But—my faith!—still what does it matter to me?"

"My fair friend," says Mr. Tulkinghorn, "make another visit here, or at Mr. Snagsby's, and you shall learn."

"In that case you will send Me to the prison, perhaps?"

"Perhaps."

It would be contradictory for one in Mademoiselle's state of agreeable jocularity to foam at the mouth, otherwise a tigerish expansion thereabouts might look as if a very little more would make her do it.

"In a word, mistress," says Mr. Tulkinghorn, "I am sorry to be unpolite, but if you ever present yourself uninvited here——or there—— again, I will give you over to the police. Their gallantry is great, but they carry troublesome people through the streets in an ignominious manner; strapped down on a board, my good wench."

"I will prove you," whispers Mademoiselle, stretching out her hand, "I will try if you dare to do it!"

"And if," pursues the lawyer, without minding her, "I place you in that good condition of being locked up in jail, it will be some time before you find yourself at liberty again."

"I will prove you," repeats Mademoiselle in her former whisper.

"And now," proceeds the lawyer, still without minding her, "you had better go. Think twice, before you come here again."

"Think you," she answers, "twice two hundred times!"

"You were dismissed by your lady, you know," Mr. Tulkinghorn observes, following her out upon the staircase, "as the most implacable and unmanageable of women. Now turn over a new leaf, and take warning by what I say to you. For what I say, I mean; and what I threaten, I will do, mistress."

She goes down without answering or looking behind her. When she is gone, he goes down too; and returning with his cobweb-covered bottle, devotes himself to a leisurely enjoyment of its contents: now and then, as he throws his head back in his chair, catching sight of the pertinacious Roman pointing from the ceiling.

CHAPTER XLIII

ESTHER'S NARRATIVE

IT matters little now, how much I thought of my living mother who had told me evermore to consider her dead. I could not venture to approach her, or to communicate with her in writing, for my sense of the peril in which her life was passed was only to be equalled by my fears of increasing it. Knowing that my mere existence as a living creature was an unforeseen danger in her way, I could not always conquer that terror of myself which had seized me when I first knew the secret. At no time did I dare to utter her name. I felt as if I did not even dare to hear it. If the conversation anywhere, when I was present, took that direction, as it sometimes naturally did, I tried not to hear—I mentally counted, repeated something that I knew, or went out of the room. I am conscious, now, that I often did these things when there can have been no danger of her being spoken of; but I did them in the dread I had of hearing anything that might lead to her betrayal, and to her betrayal through me.

It matters little now how often I recalled the tones of my mother's voice, wondered whether I should ever hear it again as I so longed to do, and thought how strange and desolate it was that it should be so new to me. It matters little that I watched for every public mention of my mother's name; that I passed and repassed the door of her house in town, loving it, but afraid to look at it; that I once sat in the theatre when my mother was there and saw me, and when we were so wide asunder, before the great company of all degrees, that any link or confidence between us seemed a dream. It is all, all over. My lot has been so blest that I can relate little of myself which is not a story of goodness and generosity in others. I may well pass that little, and go on.

When we were settled at home again, Ada and I had many conversations with my guardian, of which Richard was the theme. My dear girl was deeply grieved that he should do their kind cousin so much wrong; but she was so faithful to Richard, that she could not bear to blame him, even for that. My guardian was assured of it, and never coupled his name with a word of reproof. " Rick is mistaken, my dear," he would say to her. " Well, well ! we have all been mistaken over and over again. We must trust to you and time to set him right."

We knew afterwards what we suspected then ; that he did not trust to time until he had often tried to open Richard's eyes. That he had written to him, gone to him, talked with him, tried every gentle and persuasive art his kindness could devise. Our poor devoted Richard was deaf and blind to all. If he were wrong, he would make amends when the Chancery suit was over. If he were groping in the dark, he could not do better than do his utmost to clear away those clouds in which so much was confused and obscured. Suspicion and misunderstanding were the fault of the suit? Then let him work the suit out, and come through it to his right mind. This was his unvarying reply. Jarndyce and Jarndyce had obtained such possession of his whole nature, that it was impossible to place any consideration before him which he did not—with a distorted kind of reason—make a new argument in favour of his doing what he did. " So that it is even more mischievous," said my guardian once to me, " to remonstrate with the poor dear fellow, than to leave him alone."

I took one of these opportunities of mentioning my doubts of Mr. Skimpole as a good adviser for Richard.

" Adviser ? " returned my guardian, laughing. " My dear, who would advise with Skimpole ? "

" Encourager would perhaps have been a better word," said I.

" Encourager ! " returned my guardian again. " Who could be encouraged by Skimpole ? "

"Not Richard?" I asked.

"No," he replied. "Such an unworldly, uncalculating, gossamer creature is a relief to him, and an amusement. But as to advising or encouraging, or occupying a serious station towards anybody or anything, it is simply not to be thought of in such a child as Skimpole."

"Pray, cousin John," said Ada, who had just joined us, and now looked over my shoulder, "what made him such a child?"

"What made him such a child?" inquired my guardian, rubbing his head, a little at a loss.

"Yes, cousin John."

"Why," he slowly replied, roughening his head more and more, "he is all sentiment, and—and susceptibility, and—and sensibility—and—and imagination. And these qualities are not regulated in him, somehow. I suppose the people who admired him for them in his youth, attached too much importance to them, and too little to any training that would have balanced and adjusted them; and so he became what he is. Hey?" said my guardian, stopping short, and looking at us hopefully. "What do you think, you two?"

Ada glancing at me, said she thought it was a pity he should be an expense to Richard.

"So it is, so it is," returned my guardian hurriedly. "That must not be. We must arrange that. I must prevent it. That will never do."

And I said I thought it was to be regretted that he had ever introduced Richard to Mr. Vholes, for a present of five pounds.

"Did he?" said my guardian, with a passing shade of vexation on his face. "But there you have the man. There you have the man! There is nothing mercenary in that, with him. He has no idea of the value of money. He introduces Rick; and then he is good friends with Mr. Vholes, and borrows five pounds of him. He means nothing by it, and thinks nothing of it. He told you himself, I'll be bound, my dear?"

"Oh yes!" said I.

"Exactly!" cried my guardian, quite triumphant. "There you have the man! If he had meant any harm by it, or was conscious of any harm in it, he wouldn't tell it. He tells it as he does it, in mere simplicity. But you shall see him in his own home, and then you'll understand him better. We must pay a visit to Harold Skimpole, and caution him on these points. Lord bless you, my dears, an infant, an infant!"

In pursuance of this plan, we went into London on an early day, and presented ourselves at Mr. Skimpole's door.

He lived in a place called the Polygon, in Somers Town, where there were at that time a number of poor Spanish refugees walking about in cloaks, smoking little paper cigars. Whether he was a better tenant than one might have supposed, in consequence of his friend Somebody always paying his rent at last, or whether his inaptitude for business rendered it particularly difficult to turn him out, I don't know; but he had occupied the same house some years. It was in a state of dilapidation quite equal to our expectation. Two or three of the area railings were gone; the water-butt was broken; the knocker was loose; the bell-handle had been pulled off a long time, to judge from the rusty state of the wire; and dirty footprints on the steps were the only signs of its being inhabited.

À slatternly full-blown girl, who seemed to be bursting out at the rents in her gown, and the cracks in her shoes, like an over-ripe berry, answered our knock by opening the door a very little way, and stopping up the gap with her figure. As she knew Mr. Jarndyce (indeed Ada and I both thought that she evidently associated him with the receipt of her wages), she immediately relented and allowed us to pass in. The lock of the door being in a disabled condition, she then applied herself to securing it with a chain, which was not in good action either, and said would we go upstairs?

We went upstairs to the first floor, still seeing no other furniture than the dirty footprints. Mr. Jarndyce, without further ceremony, entered a room there, and we followed. It was dingy enough, and not at all clean; but furnished with an odd kind of shabby luxury, with a large footstool, a sofa, and plenty of cushions, an easy-chair, and plenty of pillows, a piano, books, drawing materials, music, newspapers, and a few sketches and pictures. A broken pane of glass in one of the dirty windows was papered and wafered over; but there was a little plate of hothouse nectarines on the table, and there was another of grapes, and another of sponge-cakes, and there was a bottle of light wine. Mr. Skimpole himself reclined upon the sofa, in a dressing-gown, drinking some fragrant coffee from an old china cup—it was then about mid-day—and looking at a collection of wallflowers in the balcony.

He was not in the least disconcerted by our appearance, but rose and received us in his usual airy manner.

"Here I am, you see!" he said, when we were seated: not without some little difficulty, the greater part of the chairs being broken. "Here I am! This is my frugal breakfast. Some men want legs of beef and mutton for breakfast; I don't. Give me my peach, my cup of coffee, and my claret; I am content. I don't want them for themselves, but they remind me of the sun. There's nothing solar about legs of beef and mutton. Mere animal satisfaction!"

"This is our friend's consulting-room (or would be, if he ever prescribed), his sanctum, his studio," said my guardian to us.

"Yes," said Mr. Skimpole, turning his bright face about, "this is the bird's cage. This is where the bird lives and sings. They pluck his feathers now and then, and clip his wings; but he sings, he sings!"

He handed us the grapes, repeating in his radiant way, "he sings! Not an ambitious note, but still he sings."

"These are very fine," said my guardian. "A present?"

"No," he answered. "No! Some amiable gardener sells them. His man wanted to know, when he brought them last evening, whether he should wait for the money. 'Really, my friend,' I said, 'I think not—if your time is of any value to you.' I suppose it was, for he went away."

My guardian looked at us with a smile, as though he asked us, "is it possible to be worldly with this baby?"

"This is a day," said Mr. Skimpole, gaily taking a little claret in a tumbler, "that will ever be remembered here. We shall call it the Saint Clare and Saint Summerson day. You must see my daughters. I have a blue-eyed daughter who is my Beauty daughter, I have a Sentiment daughter, and I have a Comedy daughter. You must see them all. They'll be enchanted."

He was going to summon them, when my guardian interposed, and asked him to pause a moment, as he wished to say a word to him first. "My dear Jarndyce," he cheerfully replied, going back to his sofa, "as many moments as you please. Time is no object here. We never know what o'clock it is, and we never care. Not the way to get on in life, you'll tell me? Certainly. But we *don't* get on in life. We don't pretend to do it."

My guardian looked at us again, plainly saying, "You hear him?"

"Now, Harold," he began, "the word I have to say relates to Rick."

"The dearest friend I have!" returned Mr. Skimpole cordially. "I suppose he ought not to be my dearest friend, as he is not on terms with you. But he is, I can't help it; he is full of youthful poetry, and I love him. If you don't like it, I can't help it. I love him."

The engaging frankness with which he made this declaration, really had a disinterested appearance, and captivated my guardian; if not, for the moment, Ada too.

"You are welcome to love him as much as you like," returned Mr. Jarndyce, "but we must save his pocket, Harold."

"Oh!" said Mr. Skimpole. "His pocket? Now, you are coming to what I don't understand." Taking a little more claret, and dipping one of the cakes in it, he shook his head, and smiled at Ada and me with an ingenuous foreboding that he never could be made to understand.

"If you go with him here or there," said my guardian plainly, "you must not let him pay for both."

"My dear Jarndyce," returned Mr. Skimpole, his genial face irradiated by the comicality of this idea, "what am I to do? If he takes me anywhere, I must go. And how can *I* pay? I never have any money. If I had any money, I don't know anything about it. Suppose I say to a man, how much? Suppose the man says to me seven and sixpence? I know nothing about seven and sixpence. It is impossible for me to pursue the subject, with any consideration for the man. I don't go about asking busy people what seven and sixpence is in Moorish—which I don't understand. Why should I go about asking them what seven and sixpence is in Money—which I don't understand?"

"Well," said my guardian, by no means displeased with this artless reply, "if you come to any kind of journeying with Rick, you must borrow the money of me (never breathing the least allusion to that circumstance), and leave the calculation to him."

"My dear Jarndyce," returned Mr. Skimpole, "I will do anything to give you pleasure, but it seems an idle form—a superstition. Besides, I give you my word, Miss Clare and my dear Miss Summerson, I thought Mr. Carstone was immensely rich. I thought he had only to make over something, or to sign a bond, or a draft, or a cheque, or a bill, or to put something on a file somewhere, to bring down a shower of money."

"Indeed it is not so, sir," said Ada. "He is poor."

"No, really?" returned Mr. Skimpole, with his bright smile, "you surprise me."

"And not being the richer for trusting in a rotten reed," said my guardian, laying his hand emphatically on the sleeve of Mr. Skimpole's dressing-gown, "be you very careful not to encourage him in that reliance, Harold."

"My dear good friend," returned Mr. Skimpole, "and my dear Miss Summerson, and my dear Miss Clare, how can I do that? It's business, and I don't know business. It is he who encourages me. He emerges from great feats of business, presents the brightest prospects before me as their result, and calls upon me to admire them. I do admire them— as bright prospects. But I know no more about them, and I tell him so."

The helpless kind of candour with which he presented this before us, the light-hearted manner in which he was amused by his innocence, the fantastic way in which he took himself under his own protection and argued about that curious person, combined with the delightful ease of everything he said exactly to make out my guardian's case. The more I saw of him, the more unlikely it seemed to me, when he was present, that he could design, conceal, or influence anything; and yet the less likely that appeared when he was not present, and the less agreeable it was to think of his having anything to do with any one for whom I cared.

Hearing that his examination (as he called it) was now over, Mr. Skimpole left the room with a radiant face to fetch his daughters (his sons had run away at various times), leaving my guardian quite delighted by the manner in which he had vindicated his childish character. He soon came back, bringing with him the three young ladies and Mrs. Skimpole, who had once been a beauty, but was now a delicate high-nosed invalid, suffering under a complication of disorders.

"This," said Mr. Skimpole, "is my Beauty daughter, Arethusa—plays and sings odds and ends like her father. This is my Sentiment daughter, Laura—plays a little but don't sing. This is my Comedy daughter, Kitty—sings a little but don't play. We all draw a little, and compose a little, and none of us have any idea of time or money."

Mrs. Skimpole sighed, I thought, as if she would have been glad to strike out this item in the family attainments. I also thought that she rather impressed her sigh upon my guardian, and that she took every opportunity of throwing in another.

"It is pleasant," said Mr. Skimpole, turning his sprightly eyes from one to the other of us, "and it is whimsically interesting, to trace peculiarities in families. In this family we are all children, and I am the youngest."

The daughters, who appeared to be very fond of him, were amused by this droll fact; particularly the Comedy daughter.

"My dears, it is true," said Mr. Skimpole, "is it not? So it is, and so it must be, because, like the dogs in the hymn, 'it is our nature to.' Now, here is Miss Summerson with a fine administrative capacity, and a knowledge of details perfectly surprising. It will sound very strange in Miss Summerson's ears, I dare say, that we know nothing about chops in this house. But we don't; not the least. We can't cook anything whatever. A needle and thread we don't know how to use. We admire the people who possess the practical wisdom we want; but we don't quarrel with them. Then why should they quarrel with us? Live, and let live, we say to them. Live upon your practical wisdom, and let us live upon you!"

He laughed, but, as usual, seemed quite candid, and really to mean what he said.

"We have sympathy, my roses," said Mr. Skimpole, "sympathy for everything. Have we not?"

"Oh yes, papa!" cried the three daughters.

"In fact, that is our family department," said Mr. Skimpole, "in this hurly-burly of life. We are capable of looking on and of being interested, and we *do* look on, and we *are* interested. What more can we do? Here is my Beauty daughter, married these three years. Now, I dare say her marrying another child, and having two more, was all wrong in point of political economy; but it was very agreeable. We had our little festivities on those occasions, and exchanged social ideas. She brought her young husband home one day, and they and their young fledgelings have their nest upstairs. I dare say, at some time or other, Sentiment and Comedy will bring *their* husbands home, and have *their* nests upstairs too. So we get on, we don't know how, but somehow."

She looked very young, indeed, to be the mother of two children; and I could not help pitying both her and them. It was evident that the three daughters had grown up as they could, and had had just as little hap-hazard instruction as qualified them to be their father's playthings in his idlest hours. His pictorial tastes were consulted, I observed, in their respective styles of wearing their hair; the Beauty daughter being in the classic manner; the Sentiment daughter luxuriant and flowing; and the Comedy daughter in the arch style, with a good deal of sprightly forehead, and vivacious little curls dotted about the corners of her eyes. They were dressed to correspond, though in a most untidy and negligent way.

Ada and I conversed with these young ladies, and found them wonderfully like their father. In the meanwhile Mr. Jarndyce (who had been rubbing his head to a great extent, and hinting at a change in the wind) talked with Mrs. Skimpole in a corner, where we could not help hearing the chink of money. Mr. Skimpole had previously volunteered to go home with us, and had withdrawn to dress himself for the purpose.

"My roses," he said, when he came back, "take care of mamma. She is poorly to-day. By going home with Mr. Jarndyce for a day or two, I shall hear the larks sing, and preserve my amiability. It has been tried, you know, and would be tried again if I remained at home."

"That bad man!" said the Comedy daughter.

"At the very time when he knew papa was lying down by his wall-flowers, looking at the blue sky," Laura complained.

"And when the smell of hay was in the air!" said Arethusa.

"It showed a want of poetry in the man," Mr. Skimpole assented; but with perfect good-humour. "It was coarse. There was an absence of the finer touches of humanity in it! My daughters have taken great offence," he explained to us, "at an honest man——"

"Not honest, papa. Impossible!" they all three protested.

"At a rough kind of fellow—a sort of human hedgehog rolled up," said Mr. Skimpole, "who is a baker in this neighbourhood, and from whom we borrowed a couple of arm-chairs. We wanted a couple of arm-chairs, and we hadn't got them, and therefore of course we looked to a man who *had* got them, to lend them. Well! this morose person lent them, and we wore them out. When they were worn out, he wanted them back. He had them back. He was contented, you will say. Not at all. He objected to their being worn. I reasoned with him, and pointed out his mistake. I said, 'Can you, at your time of life, be so headstrong, my friend, as to persist that an arm-chair is a thing to put upon a shelf and look at? That it is an object to contemplate, to survey from a distance, to consider from a point of sight? Don't you *know* that these arm-chairs were borrowed to be sat upon?' He was unreasonable and unpersuadable, and used intemperate language. Being as patient as I am at this minute, I addressed another appeal to him. I said, 'Now, my good man, however our business capacities may vary, we are all children of one great mother, Nature. On this blooming summer morning here you see me' (I was on the sofa) 'with flowers before me, fruit upon the table, the cloudless sky above me, the air full of fragrance, contemplating Nature. I entreat you, by our common brotherhood, not to interpose between me and a subject so sublime, the absurd figure of an angry baker!' But he did," said Mr. Skimpole, raising his laughing eyes in playful astonishment; "he did interpose that ridiculous figure, and he does, and he will again. And therefore I am very glad to get out of his way, and to go home with my friend Jarndyce."

It seemed to escape his consideration that Mrs. Skimpole and the daughters remained behind to encounter the baker; but this was so old a story to all of them that it had become a matter of course. He took leave of his family with a tenderness as airy and graceful as any other aspect in which he showed himself, and rode away with us in perfect harmony of mind. We had an opportunity of seeing through some open doors, as we went downstairs, that his own apartment was a palace to the rest of the house.

I could have no anticipation, and I had none, that something very startling to me at the moment, and ever memorable to me in what ensued from it, was to happen before this day was out. Our guest was in such spirits on the way home, that I could do nothing but listen to him and wonder at him; nor was I alone in this, for Ada yielded to the same fascination. As to my guardian, the wind, which had threatened to become fixed in the east when we left Somers Town, veered completely round, before we were a couple of miles from it.

Whether of questionable childishness or not, in any other matters, Mr. Skimpole had a child's enjoyment of change and bright weather. In no way wearied by his sallies on the road, he was in the drawing-room before any of us; and I heard him at the piano while I was yet looking after my housekeeping, singing refrains of barcarolles and drinking songs, Italian and German, by the score.

We were all assembled shortly before dinner, and he was still at the piano idly picking out in his luxurious way little strains of music, and talking between whiles of finishing some sketches of the ruined old Verulam wall, to-morrow, which he had begun a year or two ago and had got tired of; when a card was brought in, and my guardian read aloud in a surprised voice:

" Sir Leicester Dedlock ! "

The visitor was in the room while it was yet turning round with me, and before I had the power to stir. If I had had it, I should have hurried away. I had not even the presence of mind, in my giddiness, to retire to Ada in the window, or to see the window, or to know where it was. I heard my name, and found that my guardian was presenting me, before I could move to a chair.

" Pray be seated, Sir Leicester."

" Mr. Jarndyce," said Sir Leicester in reply, as he bowed and seated himself, " I do myself the honour of calling here——"

" You do *me* the honour, Sir Leicester."

" Thank you—of calling here on my road from Lincolnshire, to express my regret that any cause of complaint, however strong, that I may have against a gentleman who—who is known to you and has been your host, and to whom therefore I will make no farther reference, should have prevented you, still more ladies under your escort and charge, from seeing whatever little there may be to gratify a polite and refined taste, at my house, Chesney Wold."

" You are exceedingly obliging, Sir Leicester, and on behalf of those ladies (who are present) and for myself, I thank you very much."

" It is possible, Mr. Jarndyce, that the gentleman to whom, for the reasons I have mentioned ,I refrain from making further allusion—it is possible, Mr. Jarndyce, that that gentleman may have done me the honour so far as to misapprehend my character, as to induce you to believe that you would not have been received by my local establishment in Lincolnshire with that urbanity, that courtesy, which its members are instructed to show to all ladies and gentlemen who present themselves at that house. I merely beg to observe, sir, that the fact is the reverse."

SIR LESTER DEDLOCK.

My guardian delicately dismissed this remark without making any verbal answer.

"It has given me pain, Mr. Jarndyce," Sir Leicester weightily proceeded. "I assure you, sir, it has given—Me—pain—to learn from the housekeeper at Chesney Wold, that a gentleman who was in your company in that part of the county, and who would appear to possess a cultivated taste for the Fine Arts, was likewise deterred, by some such cause, from examining the family pictures with that leisure, that attention, that care, which he might have desired to bestow upon them, and which some of them might possibly have repaid." Here he produced a card, and read, with much gravity and a little trouble, through his eye-glass, "Mr. Hirrold, — Herald — Harold — Skampling — Skumpling — I beg your pardon,—Skimpole."

"This is Mr. Harold Skimpole," said my guardian, evidently surprised.

"Oh ! " exclaimed Sir Leicester, "I am happy to meet Mr. Skimpole, and to have the opportunity of tendering my personal regrets. I hope, sir, that when you again find yourself in my part of the county, you will be under no similar sense of restraint."

"You are very obliging, Sir Leicester Dedlock. So encouraged, I shall certainly give myself the pleasure and advantage of another visit to your beautiful house. The owners of such places as Chesney Wold," said Mr. Skimpole, with his usual happy and easy air, "are public benefactors. They are good enough to maintain a number of delightful objects for the admiration and pleasure of us poor men ; and not to reap all the admiration and pleasure that they yield, is to be ungrateful to our benefactors."

Sir Leicester seemed to approve of this sentiment highly. "An artist, sir ? "

"No," returned Mr. Skimpole. "A perfectly idle man. A mere amateur."

Sir Leicester seemed to approve of this even more. He hoped he might have the good fortune to be at Chesney Wold when Mr. Skimpole next came down into Lincolnshire. Mr. Skimpole professed himself much flattered and honoured.

"Mr. Skimpole mentioned," pursued Sir Leicester, addressing himself again to my guardian ; "mentioned to the housekeeper, who, as he may have observed, is an old and attached retainer of the family——"

("That is, when I walked through the house the other day, on the occasion of my going down to visit Miss Summerson and Miss Clare," Mr. Skimpole airily explained to us.)

"That the friend with whom he had formerly been staying there, was Mr. Jarndyce." Sir Leicester bowed to the bearer of that name. "And hence I became aware of the circumstance for which I have professed my regret. That this should have occurred to any gentleman, Mr. Jarndyce, but especially a gentleman formerly known to Lady Dedlock, and indeed claiming some distant connection with her, and for whom (as I learn from my Lady herself) she entertains a high respect, does, I assure you, give— Me—pain."

"Pray say no more about it, Sir Leicester," returned my guardian. "I am very sensible, as I am sure we all are, of your consideration. Indeed the mistake was mine, and I ought to apologise for it."

I had not once looked up. I had not seen the visitor, and had not even appeared to myself to hear the conversation. It surprises me to find that I can recall it, for it seemed to make no impression on me as it passed. I heard them speaking, but my mind was so confused, and my instinctive avoidance of this gentleman made his presence so distressing to me, that I thought I understood nothing, through the rushing in my head and the beating of my heart.

"I mentioned the subject to Lady Dedlock," said Sir Leicester, rising, "and my Lady informed me that she had had the pleasure of exchanging a few words with Mr. Jarndyce and his wards, on the occasion of an accidental meeting during their sojourn in the vicinity. Permit me, Mr. Jarndyce, to repeat to yourself, and to these ladies, the assurance I have already tendered to Mr. Skimpole. Circumstances undoubtedly prevent my saying that it would afford me any gratification to hear that Mr. Boythorn had favoured my house with his presence; but those circumstances are confined to that gentleman himself, and do not extend beyond him."

"You know my old opinion of him," said Mr. Skimpole, lightly appealing to us. "An amiable bull, who is determined to make every colour scarlet!"

Sir Leicester Dedlock coughed, as if he could not possibly hear another word in reference to such an individual; and took his leave with great ceremony and politeness. I got to my own room with all possible speed, and remained there until I had recovered my self-command. It had been very much disturbed; but I was thankful to find, when I went downstairs again, that they only rallied me for having been shy and mute before the great Lincolnshire baronet.

By that time I had made up my mind that the period was come when I must tell my guardian what I knew. The possibility of my being brought into contact with my mother, of my being taken to her house,—even of Mr. Skimpole's, however distantly associated with me, receiving kindnesses and obligations from her husband,—was so painful, that I felt I could no longer guide myself without his assistance.

When we had retired for the night, and Ada and I had had our usual talk in our pretty room, I went out at my door again, and sought my guardian among his books. I knew he always read at that hour; and as I drew near, I saw the light shining out into the passage from his reading-lamp.

"May I come in, Guardian?"

"Surely, little woman. What's the matter?"

"Nothing is the matter. I thought I would like to take this quiet time of saying a word to you about myself."

He put a chair for me, shut his book, and put it by, and turned his kind attentive face towards me. I could not help observing that it wore that curious expression I had observed in it once before—on that night when he had said that he was in no trouble which I could readily understand.

"What concerns you, my dear Esther," said he, "concerns us all. You cannot be more ready to speak than I am to hear."

"I know that, Guardian. But I have such need of your advice and support. Oh! you don't know how much need I have to-night."

He looked unprepared for my being so earnest, and even a little alarmed.

"Or how anxious I have been to speak to you," said I, "ever since the visitor was here to-day."

"The visitor, my dear! Sir Leicester Dedlock?"

"Yes."

He folded his arms, and sat looking at me with an air of the profoundest astonishment, awaiting what I should say next. I did not know how to prepare him.

"Why, Esther," said he, breaking into a smile, "our visitor and you are the two last persons on earth I should have thought of connecting together!"

"Oh yes, Guardian, I know it. And I too, but a little while ago."

The smile passed from his face, and he became graver than before. He crossed to the door to see that it was shut (but I had seen to that), and resumed his seat before me.

"Guardian," said I, "do you remember, when we were overtaken by the thunder-storm, Lady Dedlock's speaking to you of her sister?"

"Of course. Of course I do."

"And reminding you that she and her sister had differed; had 'gone their several ways?'"

"Of course."

"Why did they separate, Guardian?"

His face quite altered as he looked at me. "My child, what questions are these? I never knew. No one but themselves ever did know, I believe. Who could tell what the secrets of those two handsome and proud women were? You have seen Lady Dedlock. If you had ever seen her sister, you would know her to have been as resolute and haughty as she."

"Oh, Guardian, I have seen her many and many a time!"

"Seen her?"

He paused a little, biting his lip. "Then, Esther, when you spoke to me long ago of Boythorn, and when I told you that he was all but married once, and that the lady did not die, but died to him, and that that time had had its influence on his later life—did you know it all, and know who the lady was?"

"No, Guardian," I returned, fearful of the light that dimly broke upon me. "Nor do I know yet."

"Lady Dedlock's sister."

"And why," I could scarcely ask him, "why, Guardian, pray tell me why were *they* parted?"

"It was her act, and she kept its motives in her inflexible heart. He afterwards did conjecture (but it was mere conjecture), that some injury which her haughty spirit had received in her cause of quarrel with her sister, had wounded her beyond all reason; but she wrote him that from the date of that letter she died to him—as in literal truth she did—and that the resolution was exacted from her by her knowledge of his proud temper and his strained sense of honour, which were both her nature too. In consideration for those master points in him, and even in consideration for them in herself, she made the sacrifice, she said, and would live in it and die in it. She did both, I fear; certainly he never saw her, never heard of her from that hour. Nor did any one."

"Oh, Guardian, what have I done!" I cried, giving way to my grief; "what sorrow have I innocently caused!"

"You caused, Esther?"

"Yes, Guardian, innocently, but most surely. That secluded sister is my first remembrance."

"No, no!" he cried, starting.

"Yes, Guardian, yes! And *her* sister is my mother!"

I would have told him all my mother's letter, but he would not hear it then. He spoke so tenderly and wisely to me, and he put so plainly before me all I had myself imperfectly thought and hoped in my better state of mind, that, penetrated as I had been with fervent gratitude towards him through so many years, I believed I had never loved him so dearly, never thanked him in my heart so fully, as I did that night. And when he had taken me to my room and kissed me at the door, and when at last I lay down to sleep, my thought was how could I ever be busy enough, how could I ever be good enough, how in my little way could I ever hope to be forgetful enough of myself, devoted enough to him, and useful enough to others, to show him how I blessed and honoured him.

CHAPTER XLIV

THE LETTER AND THE ANSWER

MY guardian called me into his room next morning, and then I told him what had been left untold on the previous night. There was nothing to be done, he said, but to keep the secret, and to avoid another such encounter as that of yesterday. He understood my feeling, and entirely shared it. He charged himself even with restraining Mr. Skimpole from improving his opportunity. One person whom he need not name to me, it was not now possible for him to advise or help. He wished it were; but no such thing could be. If her mistrust of the lawyer whom she had mentioned were well-founded, which he scarcely doubted, he dreaded discovery. He knew something of him, both by sight and by reputation, and it was certain that he was a dangerous man. Whatever happened, he repeatedly impressed upon me with anxious affection and kindness, I was as innocent of, as himself; and as unable to influence.

"Nor do I understand," said he, "that any doubts tend towards you, my dear. Much suspicion may exist without that connection."

"With the lawyer," I returned. "But two other persons have come into my mind since I have been anxious." Then I told him all about Mr. Guppy, who I feared might have had his vague surmises when I little understood his meaning, but in whose silence after our last interview I expressed perfect confidence.

"Well," said my guardian. "Then we may dismiss him for the present. Who is the other?"

I called to his recollection the French maid, and the eager offer of herself she had made to me.

"Ha!" he returned thoughtfully, "that is a more alarming person than the clerk. But after all, my dear, it was but seeking for a new service. She had seen you and Ada a little while before, and it was natural that you should come into her head. She merely proposed herself for your maid, you know. She did nothing more."

"Her manner was strange," said I.

"Yes, and her manner was strange when she took her shoes off, and showed that cool relish for a walk that might have ended in her death-bed," said my guardian. "It would be useless self-distress and torment to reckon up such chances and possibilities. There are very few harmless circumstances that would not seem full of perilous meaning, so considered. Be hopeful, little woman. You can be nothing better than yourself; be that, through this knowledge, as you were before you had it. It is the best you can do, for everybody's sake. I sharing the secret with you——"

"And lightening it, Guardian, so much," said I.

"——Will be attentive to what passes in that family, so far as I can observe it from my distance. And if the time should come when I can stretch out a hand to tender the least service to one whom it is better not to name even here, I will not fail to do it for her dear daughter's sake."

I thanked him with my whole heart. What could I ever do but thank him! I was going out at the door, when he asked me to stay a moment. Quickly turning round, I saw that same expression on his face again; and all at once, I don't know how, it flashed upon me as a new and far off possibility that I understood it.

"My dear Esther," said my guardian, "I have long had something in my thoughts that I have wished to say to you."

"Indeed?"

"I have had some difficulty in approaching it, and I still have. I should wish it to be so deliberately said, and so deliberately considered. Would you object to my writing it?"

"Dear Guardian, how could I object to your writing anything for *me* to read?"

"Then see, my love," said he, with his cheery smile; "am I at this moment quite as plain and easy—do I seem as open, as honest and old-fashioned, as I am at any time?"

I answered, in all earnestness, "Quite." With the strictest truth, for his momentary hesitation was gone (it had not lasted a minute), and his fine, sensible, cordial, sterling manner was restored.

"Do I look as if I suppressed anything, meant anything but what I said, had any reservation at all, no matter what?" said he, with his bright clear eyes on mine.

I answered, most assuredly he did not.

"Can you fully trust me, and thoroughly rely on what I profess, Esther?"

"Most thoroughly," said I, with my whole heart.

"My dear girl," returned my guardian, "give me your hand."

He took it in his, holding me lightly with his arm, and, looking down into my face with the same genuine freshness and faithfulness of manner—the old protecting manner which had made that house my home in a moment—said, "You have wrought changes in me, little woman, since the winter day in the stage-coach. First and last you have done me a world of good, since that time!"

"Ah, Guardian, what have you done for me since that time!"

"But," said he, "that is not to be remembered now."

"It never can be forgotten."

"Yes, Esther," said he, with a gentle seriousness, "it is to be forgotten now; to be forgotten for awhile. You are only to remember now, that nothing can change me as you know me. Can you feel quite assured of that, my dear?"

"I can, and I do," I said.

"That's much," he answered. "That's everything. But I must not take that, at a word. I will not write this something in my thoughts, until you have quite resolved within yourself that nothing can change me as you know me. If you doubt that in the least degree I will never write it. If you are sure of that, on good consideration, send Charley to me this night week—'for the letter.' But if you are not quite certain, never send. Mind, I trust to your truth, in this thing as in everything. If you are not quite certain on that one point, never send!"

"Guardian," said I, "I am already certain. I can no more be changed in that conviction, than you can be changed towards me. I shall send Charley for the letter."

He shook my hand and said no more. Nor was any more said in reference to this conversation, either by him or me, through the whole week. When the appointed night came, I said to Charley as soon as I was alone, "Go and knock at Mr. Jarndyce's door, Charley, and say you have come from me—'for the letter.'" Charley went up the stairs, and down the stairs, and along the passages—the zigzag way about the old-fashioned house seemed very long in my listening ears that night—and so came back, along the passages, and down the stairs, and up the

stairs, and brought the letter. "Lay it on the table, Charley," said I.
So Charley laid it on the table and went to bed, and I sat looking at it
without taking it up, thinking of many things.

I began with my overshadowed childhood, and passed through those
timid days to the heavy time when my aunt lay dead, with her resolute
face so cold and set; and when I was more solitary with Mrs. Rachael,
than if I had had no one in the world to speak to or to look at. I passed
to the altered days when I was so blessed as to find friends in all around
me, and to be beloved. I came to the time when I first saw my dear
girl, and was received into that sisterly affection which was the grace
and beauty of my life. I recalled the first bright gleam of welcome
which had shone out of those very windows upon our expectant faces on
that cold bright night, and which had never paled. I lived my happy
life there over again, I went through my illness and recovery, I thought
of myself so altered and of those around me so unchanged; and all this
happiness shone like a light from one central figure, represented before
me by the letter on the table.

I opened it and read it. It was so impressive in its love for me, and
in the unselfish caution it gave me, and the consideration it showed for
me in every word, that my eyes were too often blinded to read much at
a time. But I read it through three times, before I laid it down. I
had thought beforehand that I knew its purport, and I did. It asked
me, would I be the mistress of Bleak House.

It was not a love-letter though it expressed so much love, but was written
just as he would at any time have spoken to me. I saw his face, and heard
his voice, and felt the influence of his kind protecting manner, in every
line. It addressed me as if our places were reversed : as if all the good
deeds had been mine, and all the feelings they had awakened, his. It
dwelt on my being young, and he past the prime of life ; on his having
attained a ripe age, while I was a child ; on his writing to me with a
silvered head, and knowing all this so well as to set it in full before me
for mature deliberation. It told me that I would gain nothing by such
a marriage, and lose nothing by rejecting it ; for no new relation could
enhance the tenderness in which he held me, and whatever my decision
was, he was certain it would be right. But he had considered this step
anew, since our late confidence, and had decided on taking it ; if it only
served to show me, through one poor instance, that the whole world
would readily unite to falsify the stern prediction of my childhood. I
was the last to know what happiness I could bestow upon him, but of
that he said no more ; for I was always to remember that I owed him
nothing, and that he was my debtor, and for very much. He had often
thought of our future ; and, foreseeing that the time must come, and
fearing that it might come soon, when Ada (now very nearly of age)
would leave us, and when our present mode of life must be broken up,
had become accustomed to reflect on this proposal. Thus he made it. If
I felt that I could ever give him the best right he could have to be my
protector, and if I felt that I could happily and justly become the dear

companion of his remaining life, superior to all lighter chances and changes than Death, even then he could not have me bind myself irrevocably, while this letter was yet so new to me; but, even then, I must have ample time for reconsideration. In that case, or in the opposite case, let him be unchanged in his old relation, in his old manner, in the old name by which I called him. And as to his bright Dame Durden and little housekeeper, she would ever be the same, he knew.

This was the substance of the letter; written throughout with a justice and a dignity, as if he were indeed my responsible guardian, impartially representing the proposal of a friend against whom in his integrity he stated the full case.

But he did not hint to me, that when I had been better-looking, he had had this same proceeding in his thoughts, and had refrained from it. That when my old face was gone from me, and I had no attractions, he could love me just as well as in my fairer days. That the discovery of my birth gave him no shock. That his generosity rose above my disfigurement, and my inheritance of shame. That the more I stood in need of such fidelity, the more firmly I might trust in him to the last.

But *I* knew it, I knew it well now. It came upon me as the close of the benignant history I had been pursuing, and I felt that I had but one thing to do. To devote my life to his happiness was to thank him poorly, and what had I wished for the other night but some new means of thanking him?

Still I cried very much; not only in the fulness of my heart after reading the letter, not only in the strangeness of the prospect—for it was strange though I had expected the contents—but as if something for which there was no name or distinct idea were indefinitely lost to me. I was very happy, very thankful, very hopeful; but I cried very much.

By-and-by I went to my old glass. My eyes were red and swollen, and I said, "O Esther, Esther, can that be you!" I am afraid the face in the glass was going to cry again at this reproach, but I held up my finger at it, and it stopped.

"That is more like the composed look you comforted me with, my dear, when you showed me such a change!" said I, beginning to let down my hair. "When you are mistress of Bleak House, you are to be as cheerful as a bird. In fact, you are always to be cheerful; so let us begin for once and for all."

I went on with my hair now, quite comfortably. I sobbed a little still, but that was because I had been crying; not because I was crying then.

"And so, Esther, my dear, you are happy for life. Happy with your best friends, happy in your old home, happy in the power of doing a great deal of good, and happy in the undeserved love of the best of men."

I thought, all at once, if my guardian had married some one else, how should I have felt, and what should I have done! That would have been a change indeed. It presented my life in such a new and blank form, that I rang my housekeeping keys and gave them a kiss before I laid them down in their basket again.

Then I went on to think, as I dressed my hair before the glass, how often had I considered within myself that the deep traces of my illness, and the circumstances of my birth, were only new reasons why I should be busy, busy, busy—useful, amiable, serviceable, in all honest, unpretending ways. This was a good time, to be sure, to sit down morbidly and cry! As to its seeming at all strange to me at first (if that were any excuse for crying, which it was not) that I was one day to be the mistress of Bleak House, why should it seem strange? Other people had thought of such things, if I had not. "Don't you remember, my plain dear," I asked myself, looking at the glass, "what Mrs. Woodcourt said before those scars were there, about your marrying——"

Perhaps the name brought them to my remembrance. The dried remains of the flowers. It would be better not to keep them now. They had only been preserved in memory of something wholly past and gone, but it would be better not to keep them now.

They were in a book, and it happened to be in the next room—our sitting-room, dividing Ada's chamber from mine. I took a candle, and went softly in to fetch it from its shelf. After I had it in my hand, I saw my beautiful darling, through the open door, lying asleep, and I stole in to kiss her.

It was weak in me, I know, and I could have no reason for crying; but I dropped a tear upon her dear face, and another, and another. Weaker than that, I took the withered flowers out, and put them for a moment to her lips. I thought about her love for Richard; though, indeed, the flowers had nothing to do with that. Then I took them into my own room, and burned them at the candle, and they were dust in an instant.

On entering the breakfast-room next morning, I found my guardian just as usual; quite as frank, as open, and free. There being not the least constraint in his manner, there was none (or I think there was none) in mine. I was with him several times in the course of the morning, in and out, when there was no one there; and I thought it not unlikely that he might speak to me about the letter; but he did not say a word.

So, on the next morning, and the next, and for at least a week; over which time Mr. Skimpole prolonged his stay. I expected, every day, that my guardian might speak to me about the letter; but he never did.

I thought then, growing uneasy, that I ought to write an answer. I tried over and over again in my own room at night, but I could not write an answer that at all began like a good answer; so I thought each night I would wait one more day. And I waited seven more days, and he never said a word.

At last Mr. Skimpole having departed, we three were one afternoon going out for a ride; and I being dressed before Ada, and going down, came upon my guardian, with his back towards me, standing at the drawing-room window looking out.

He turned on my coming in, and said, smiling, "Ay, it's you, little woman, is it?" and looked out again.

I had made up my mind to speak to him now. In short, I had come down on purpose. "Guardian," I said, rather hesitating and trembling, "when would you like to have the answer to the letter Charley came for?"

"When it's ready, my dear," he replied.

"I think it is ready," said I.

"Is Charley to bring it?" he asked pleasantly.

"No. I have brought it myself, Guardian," I returned.

I put my two arms round his neck and kissed him; and he said was this the mistress of Bleak House; and I said yes; and it made no difference presently, and we all went out together, and I said nothing to my precious pet about it.

CHAPTER XLV

IN TRUST

ONE morning when I had done jingling about with my basket of keys, as my beauty and I were walking round and round the garden I happened to turn my eyes towards the house, and saw a long thin shadow going in which looked like Mr. Vholes. Ada had been telling me only that morning, of her hopes that Richard might exhaust his ardour in the Chancery suit by being so very earnest in it; and therefore, not to damp my dear girl's spirits, I said nothing about Mr. Vholes's shadow.

Presently came Charley, lightly winding among the bushes, and tripping along the paths, as rosy and pretty as one of Flora's attendants instead of my maid, saying, "Oh, if you please, miss, would you step and speak to Mr. Jarndyce?"

It was one of Charley's peculiarities, that whenever she was charged with a message she always began to deliver it as soon as she beheld, at any distance, the person for whom it was intended. Therefore I saw Charley, asking me in her usual form of words, to "step and speak" to Mr. Jarndyce, long before I heard her. And when I did hear her, she had said it so often that she was out of breath.

I told Ada I would make haste back, and inquired of Charley, as we went in, whether there was not a gentleman with Mr. Jarndyce? To which Charley, whose grammar, I confess to my shame, never did any credit to my educational powers, replied, "Yes, miss. Him as come down in the country with Mr. Richard."

A more complete contrast than my guardian and Mr. Vholes, I suppose there could not be. I found them looking at one another across a table; the one so open, and the other so close; the one so broad and upright, and the other so narrow and stooping; the one giving out what he had to say in such a rich ringing voice, and the other keeping it in in such a cold-blooded, gasping, fish-like manner; that I thought I never had seen two people so unmatched.

"You know Mr. Vholes, my dear," said my guardian. Not with the greatest urbanity, I must say.

Mr. Vholes rose, gloved and buttoned up as usual, and seated himself again, just as he had seated himself beside Richard in the gig. Not having Richard to look at, he looked straight before him.

"Mr. Vholes," said my guardian, eyeing his black figure, as if he were a bird of ill-omen, "has brought an ugly report of our most unfortunate Rick." Laying a marked emphasis on most unfortunate, as if the words were rather descriptive of his connection with Mr. Vholes.

I sat down between them; Mr. Vholes remained immovable, except that he secretly picked at one of the red pimples on his yellow face with his black glove.

"And as Rick and you are happily good friends, I should like to know," said my guardian, "what you think, my dear. Would you be so good as to—as to speak up, Mr. Vholes?"

Doing anything but that, Mr. Vholes observed:

"I have been saying that I have reason to know, Miss Summerson, as Mr. C.'s professional adviser, that Mr. C.'s circumstances are at the present moment in an embarrassed state. Not so much in point of amount, as owing to the peculiar and pressing nature of liabilities Mr. C. has incurred, and the means he has of liquidating or meeting the same. I have staved off many little matters for Mr. C.; but there is a limit to staving off, and we have reached it. I have made some advances out of pocket to accommodate these unpleasantnesses, but I necessarily look to being repaid, for I do not pretend to be a man of capital, and I have a father to support in the Vale of Taunton, besides striving to realise some little independence for three dear girls at home. My apprehension is, Mr. C.'s circumstances being such, lest it should end in his obtaining leave to part with his commission; which at all events is desirable to be made known to his connections."

Mr. Vholes, who had looked at me while speaking, here emerged into the silence he could hardly be said to have broken, so stifled was his tone; and looked before him again.

"Imagine the poor fellow without even his present resource," said my guardian to me. "Yet what can I do? You know him, Esther. He would never accept of help from me, now. To offer it, or hint at it, would be to drive him to an extremity, if nothing else did."

Mr. Vholes hereupon addressed me again.

"What Mr. Jarndyce remarks, miss, is no doubt the case, and is the difficulty. I do not see that anything is to be done. I do not say that anything is to be done. Far from it. I merely come down here under the seal of confidence and mention it, in order that everything may be openly carried on, and that it may not be said afterwards that everything was not openly carried on. My wish is that everything should be openly carried on. I desire to leave a good name behind me. If I consulted merely my own interests with Mr. C., I should not be here. So insurmountable, as you must well know, would be his objections. This is not a professional attendance. This can be charged to nobody. I have no interest in it, except as a member of society and a father—*and* a son," said Mr. Vholes, who had nearly forgotten that point.

It appeared to us that Mr. Vholes said neither more nor less than the truth, in intimating that he sought to divide the responsibility, such as it was, of knowing Richard's situation. I could only suggest that I should go down to Deal, where Richard was then stationed, and see him, and try if it were possible to avert the worst. Without consulting Mr. Vholes on this point, I took my guardian aside to propose it, while Mr. Vholes gauntly stalked to the fire, and warmed his funeral gloves.

The fatigue of the journey formed an immediate objection on my guardian's part ; but as I saw he had no other, and as I was only too happy to go, I got his consent. We had then merely to dispose of Mr. Vholes.

"Well, sir," said Mr. Jarndyce, "Miss Summerson will communicate with Mr. Carstone, and we can only hope that his position may be yet retrievable. You will allow me to order your lunch after your journey, sir."

"I thank you, Mr. Jarndyce," said Mr. Vholes, putting out his long black sleeve, to check the ringing of the bell, "not any. I thank you, no, not a morsel. My digestion is much impaired, and I am but a poor knife and fork at any time. If I was to partake of solid food at this period of the day, I don't know what the consequences might be. Everything having been openly carried on, sir, I will now with your permission take my leave."

"And I would that you could take your leave, and we could all take our leave, Mr. Vholes," returned my guardian, bitterly, "of a Cause you know of."

Mr. Vholes, whose black dye was so deep from head to foot that it had quite steamed before the fire, diffusing a very unpleasant perfume, made a short one-sided inclination of his head from the neck, and slowly shook it.

"We whose ambition it is to be looked upon in the light of respectable practitioners, sir, can but put our shoulders to the wheel. We do it, sir. At least, I do it myself ; and I wish to think well of my professional brethren, one and all. You are sensible of an obligation not to refer to me, miss, in communicating with Mr. C. ?"

I said I would be careful not to do it.

"Just so, miss. Good morning. Mr. Jarndyce, good morning, sir." Mr. Vholes put his dead glove, which scarcely seemed to have any hand in it, on my fingers, and then on my guardian's fingers, and took his long thin shadow away. I thought of it on the outside of the coach, passing over all the sunny landscape between us and London, chilling the seed in the ground as it glided along.

Of course it became necessary to tell Ada where I was going, and why

I was going; and of course she was anxious and distressed. But she was too true to Richard to say anything but words of pity and words of excuse; and in a more loving spirit still—my dear, devoted girl!—she wrote him a long letter, of which I took charge.

Charley was to be my travelling companion, though I am sure I wanted none, and would willingly have left her at home. We all went to London that afternoon, and finding two places in the mail, secured them. At our usual bed-time, Charley and I were rolling away seaward, with the Kentish letters.

It was a night's journey in those coach times; but we had the mail to ourselves, and did not find the night very tedious. It passed with me as I suppose it would with most people under such circumstances. At one while, my journey looked hopeful, and at another hopeless. Now I thought that I should do some good, and now I wondered how I could ever have supposed so. Now it seemed one of the most reasonable things in the world that I should have come, and now one of the most unreasonable. In what state I should find Richard, what I should say to him, and what he would say to me, occupied my mind by turns with these two states of feeling; and the wheels seemed to play one tune (to which the burden of my guardian's letter set itself) over and over again all night.

At last we came into the narrow streets of Deal; and very gloomy they were, upon a raw misty morning. The long flat beach, with its little irregular houses, wooden and brick, and its litter of capstans, and great boats, and sheds, and bare upright poles with tackle and blocks, and loose gravelly waste places overgrown with grass and weeds, wore as dull an appearance as any place I ever saw. The sea was heaving under a thick white fog; and nothing else was moving but a few early rope-makers, who, with the yarn twisted round their bodies, looked as if, tired of their present state of existence, they were spinning themselves into cordage.

But when we got into a warm room in an excellent hotel, and sat down, comfortably washed and dressed, to an early breakfast (for it was too late to think of going to bed), Deal began to look more cheerful. Our little room was like a ship's cabin, and that delighted Charley very much. Then the fog began to rise like a curtain; and numbers of ships, that we had no idea were near, appeared. I don't know how many sail the waiter told us were then lying in the Downs. Some of these vessels were of grand size: one was a large Indiaman just come home: and when the sun shone through the clouds, making silvery pools in the dark sea, the way in which these ships brightened, and shadowed, and changed, amid a bustle of boats putting off from the shore to them and from them to the shore, and a general life and motion in themselves and everything around them, was most beautiful.

The large Indiaman was our great attraction, because she had come into the Downs in the night. She was surrounded by boats; and we said how glad the people on board of her must be to come ashore.

Charley was curious, too, about the voyage, and about the heat in India, and the serpents and the tigers; and as she picked up such information much faster than grammar, I told her what I knew on those points.   I told her, too, how people in such voyages were sometimes wrecked and cast on rocks, where they were saved by the intrepidity and humanity of one man.   And Charley asking how that could be, I told her how we knew at home of such a case.

I had thought of sending Richard a note, saying I was there, but it seemed so much better to go to him without preparation.   As he lived in barracks I was a little doubtful whether this was feasible, but we went out to reconnoitre.   Peeping in at the gate of the barrack-yard, we found everything very quiet at that time in the morning; and I asked a serjeant standing on the guardhouse-steps, where he lived.   He sent a man before to show me, who went up some bare stairs, and knocked with his knuckles at a door, and left us.

"Now then!" cried Richard from within.   So I left Charley in the little passage, and going on to the half-open door, said, "Can I come in, Richard?   It's only Dame Durden."

He was writing at a table, with a great confusion of clothes, tin cases, books, boots, brushes, and portmanteaus strewn all about the floor.   He was only half-dressed—in plain clothes, I observed, not in uniform—and his hair was unbrushed, and he looked as wild as his room.   All this I saw after he had heartily welcomed me, and I was seated near him, for he started upon hearing my voice, and caught me in his arms in a moment.   Dear Richard!   He was ever the same to me.   Down to—ah, poor poor fellow!—to the end, he never received me but with something of his old merry boyish manner.

"Good Heaven, my dear little woman," said he, "how do you come here?   Who could have thought of seeing you!   Nothing the matter?   Ada is well?"

"Quite well.   Lovelier than ever, Richard!"

"Ah!" he said, leaning back in his chair.   "My poor cousin!   I was writing to you, Esther."

So worn and haggard as he looked, even in the fulness of his handsome youth, leaning back in his chair, and crushing the closely-written sheet of paper in his hand!

"Have you been at the trouble of writing all that, and am I not to read it after all?" I asked.

"Oh my dear," he returned, with a hopeless gesture.   "You may read it in the whole room.   It is all over here."

I mildly entreated him not to be despondent.   I told him that I had heard by chance of his being in difficulty, and had come to consult with him what could best be done.

"Like you, Esther, but useless, and so *not* like you!" said he with a melancholy smile.   "I am away on leave this day—should have been gone in another hour—and that is to smooth it over, for my selling out.   Well!   Let bygones be bygones.   So this calling follows the rest.   I only want to have been in the church, to have made the round of all the professions."

"Richard," I urged, "it is not so hopeless as that?"

"Esther," he returned, "it is indeed. I am just so near disgrace as that those who are put in authority over me (as the catechism goes) would far rather be without me than with me. And they are right. Apart from debts and duns, and all such drawbacks, I am not fit even for this employment. I have no care, no mind, no heart, no soul, but for one thing. Why, if this bubble hadn't broken now," he said, tearing the letter he had written into fragments, and moodily casting them away, by driblets, "how could I have gone abroad? I must have been ordered abroad; but how could I have gone? How could I, with my experience of that thing, trust even Vholes unless I was at his back!"

I suppose he knew by my face what I was about to say, but he caught the hand I had laid upon his arm, and touched my own lips with it to prevent me from going on.

"No, Dame Durden! Two subjects I forbid—must forbid. The first is John Jarndyce. The second, you know what. Call it madness, and I tell you I can't help it now, and can't be sane. But it is no such thing; it is the one object I have to pursue. It is a pity I ever was prevailed upon to turn out of my road for any other. It would be wisdom to abandon it now, after all the time, anxiety, and pains I have bestowed upon it! Oh yes, true wisdom. It would be very agreeable, too, to some people; but I never will."

He was in that mood in which I thought it best not to increase his determination (if anything could increase it) by opposing him. I took out Ada's letter, and put it in his hand.

"Am I to read it now?" he asked.

As I told him yes, he laid it on the table, and, resting his head upon his hand, began. He had not read far, when he rested his head upon his two hands—to hide his face from me. In a little while he rose as if the light were bad, and went to the window. He finished reading it there, with his back towards me; and, after he had finished and had folded it up, stood there for some minutes with the letter in his hand. When he came back to his chair, I saw tears in his eyes.

"Of course, Esther, you know what she says here?" He spoke in a softened voice, and kissed the letter as he asked me.

"Yes, Richard."

"Offers me," he went on, tapping his foot upon the floor, "the little inheritance she is certain of so soon—just as little and as much as I have wasted—and begs and prays me to take it, set myself right with it, and remain in the service."

"I know your welfare to be the dearest wish of her heart," said I. "And oh, my dear Richard, Ada's is a noble heart."

"I am sure it is. I—I wish I was dead!"

He went back to the window, and laying his arm across it, leaned his head down on his arm. It greatly affected me to see him so; but I hoped he might become more yielding, and I remained silent. My experience was very limited; I was not at all prepared for his rousing himself out of this emotion to a new sense of injury.

"And this is the heart that the same John Jarndyce, who is not otherwise to be mentioned between us, stepped in to estrange from me," said he indignantly. "And the dear girl makes me this generous offer from under the same John Jarndyce's roof, and with the same John Jarndyce's gracious consent and connivance, I dare say, as a new means of buying me off."

"Richard!" I cried out, rising hastily, "I will not hear you say such shameful words!" I was very angry with him, indeed, for the first time in my life; but it only lasted a moment. When I saw his worn young face looking at me as if he were sorry, I put my hand on his shoulder, and said, "If you please, my dear Richard, do not speak in such a tone to me. Consider!"

He blamed himself exceedingly; and told me in the most generous manner, that he had been very wrong, and that he begged my pardon a thousand times. At that I laughed, but trembled a little too, for I was rather fluttered after being so fiery.

"To accept this offer, my dear Esther," said he, sitting down beside me, and resuming our conversation,—"once more, pray, pray forgive me; I am deeply grieved—to accept my dearest cousin's offer is, I need not say, impossible. Besides, I have letters and papers that I could show you, which would convince you it is all over here. I have done with the red coat, believe me. But it is some satisfaction, in the midst of my troubles and perplexities, to know that I am pressing Ada's interests in pressing my own. Vholes has his shoulder to the wheel, and he cannot help urging it on as much for her as for me, thank God!"

His sanguine hopes were rising within him, and lighting up his features, but they made his face more sad to me than it had been before.

"No, no!" cried Richard exultingly. "If every farthing of Ada's little fortune were mine, no part of it should be spent in retaining me in what I am not fit for, can take no interest in, and am weary of. It should be devoted to what promises a better return, and should be used where she has a larger stake. Don't be uneasy for me! I shall now have only one thing on my mind, and Vholes and I will work it. I shall not be without means. Free of my commission, I shall be able to compound with some small usurers, who will hear of nothing but their bond now—Vholes says so. I should have a balance in my favour anyway, but that will swell it. Come, come! You shall carry a letter to Ada from me, Esther, and you must both of you be more hopeful of me, and not believe that I am quite cast away just yet, my dear."

I will not repeat what I said to Richard. I know it was tiresome, and nobody is to suppose for a moment that it was at all wise. It only came from my heart. He heard it patiently and feelingly; but I saw that on the two subjects he had reserved, it was at present hopeless to make any representation to him. I saw too, and had experienced in this very interview, the sense of my guardian's remark, that it was even more mischievous to use persuasion with him than to leave him as he was.

Therefore I was driven at last to asking Richard if he would mind convincing me that it really was all over there, as he had said, and that it was not his mere impression. He showed me without hesitation a correspondence making it quite plain that his retirement was arranged. I found, from what he told me, that Mr. Vholes had copies of these papers, and had been in consultation with him throughout. Beyond ascertaining this, and having been the bearer of Ada's letter, and being (as I was going to be) Richard's companion back to London, I had done no good by coming down. Admitting this to myself with a reluctant heart, I [said I would return to the hotel and wait until he joined me there ; so he threw a cloak over his shoulders and saw me to the gate, and Charley and I went back along the beach.

There was a concourse of people in one spot, surrounding some naval officers who were landing from a boat, and pressing about them with unusual interest. I said to Charley this would be one of the great Indiaman's boats now, and we stopped to look.

The gentlemen came slowly up from the waterside, speaking good-humouredly to each other and to the people around, and glancing about them, as if they were glad to be in England again. "Charley, Charley !" said I, "come away !" And I hurried on so swiftly that my little maid was surprised.

It was not until we were shut up in our cabin-room, and I had had time to take breath, that I began to think why I had made such haste. In one of the sunburnt faces I had recognised Mr. Allan Woodcourt, and I had been afraid of his recognising me. I had been unwilling that he should see my altered looks. I had been taken by surprise, and my courage had quite failed me.

But I knew this would not do, and I now said to myself, "My dear, there is no reason—there is and there can be no reason at all—why it should be worse for you now, than it ever has been. What you were last month, you are to-day ; you are no worse, you are no better. This is not your resolution ; call it up, Esther, call it up !" I was in a great tremble—with running—and at first was quite unable to calm myself ; but I got better, and I was very glad to know it.

The party came to the hotel. I heard them speaking on the staircase. I was sure it was the same gentlemen because I knew their voices again —I mean I knew Mr. Woodcourt's. It would still have been a great relief to me to have gone away without making myself known, but I was determined not to do so. "No, my dear, no. No, no, no !"

I untied my bonnet, and put my veil half up—I think I mean half down, but it matters very little—and wrote on one of my cards that I happened to be there with Mr. Richard Carstone ; and I sent it in to Mr. Woodcourt. He came immediately. I told him I was rejoiced to be by chance among the first to welcome him home to England. And I saw that he was very sorry for me.

"You have been in shipwreck and peril since you left us, Mr. Woodcourt," said I, "but we can hardly call that a misfortune which enabled you to be so useful and so brave. We read of it with the truest interest. It first came to my knowledge through your old patient, poor Miss Flite, when I was recovering from my severe illness."

"Ah! little Miss Flite!" he said. "She lives the same life yet?"

"Just the same."

I was so comfortable with myself now, as not to mind the veil, and to be able to put it aside.

"Her gratitude to you, Mr. Woodcourt, is delightful. She is a most affectionate creature, as I have reason to say."

"You—you have found her so?" he returned. "I—I am glad of that." He was so very sorry for me that he could scarcely speak.

"I assure you," said I, "that I was deeply touched by her sympathy and pleasure at the time I have referred to."

"I was grieved to hear that you had been very ill."

"I was very ill."

"But you have quite recovered?"

"I have quite recovered my health and my cheerfulness," said I. "You know how good my guardian is, and what a happy life we lead; and I have everything to be thankful for, and nothing in the world to desire."

I felt as if he had greater commiseration for me than I had ever had for myself. It inspired me with new fortitude, and new calmness, to find that it was I who was under the necessity of reassuring him. I spoke to him of his voyage out and home, and of his future plans, and of his probable return to India. He said that was very doubtful. He had not found himself more favoured by fortune there, than here. He had gone out a poor ship's surgeon, and had come home nothing better. While we were talking, and when I was glad to believe that I had alleviated (if I may use such a term) the shock he had had in seeing me, Richard came in. He had heard downstairs who was with me, and they met with cordial pleasure.

I saw that after their first greetings were over, and when they spoke of Richard's career, Mr. Woodcourt had a perception that all was not going well with him. He frequently glanced at his face, as if there were something in it that gave him pain; and more than once he looked towards me, as though he sought to ascertain whether I knew what the truth was. Yet Richard was in one of his sanguine states, and in good spirits; and was thoroughly pleased to see Mr. Woodcourt again, whom he had always liked.

Richard proposed that we all should go to London together; but Mr. Woodcourt having to remain by his ship a little longer, could not join us. He dined with us, however, at an early hour; and became so much more like what he used to be, that I was still more at peace to think I had been able to soften his regrets. Yet his mind was not relieved of Richard. When the coach was almost ready, and Richard ran down to look after his luggage, he spoke to me about him.

I was not sure that I had a right to lay his whole story open; but I referred in a few words to his estrangement from Mr. Jarndyce, and to his being entangled in the ill-fated Chancery suit. Mr. Woodcourt listened with interest and expressed his regret.

"I saw you observe him rather closely," said I. "Do you think him so changed?"

"He is changed," he returned, shaking his head.

I felt the blood rush into my face for the first time, but it was only an instantaneous emotion. I turned my head aside, and it was gone.

"It is not," said Mr. Woodcourt, "his being so much younger or older, or thinner, or fatter, or paler or ruddier, as there being upon his face such a singular expression. I never saw so remarkable a look in a young person. One cannot say that it is all anxiety, or all weariness; yet it is both, and like ungrown despair."

"You do not think he is ill?" said I.

No. He looked robust in body.

"That he cannot be at peace in mind, we have too much reason to know," I proceeded. "Mr. Woodcourt, you are going to London?"

"To-morrow or the next day."

"There is nothing Richard wants so much, as a friend. He always liked you. Pray see him when you get there. Pray help him sometimes with your companionship, if you can. You do not know of what service it might be. You cannot think how Ada, and Mr. Jarndyce, and even I—how we should all thank you, Mr. Woodcourt!"

"Miss Summerson," he said, more moved than he had been from the first, "before Heaven, I will be a true friend to him! I will accept him as a trust, and it shall be a sacred one!"

"God bless you!" said I, with my eyes filling fast; but I thought they might, when it was not for myself. "Ada loves him—we all love him, but Ada loves him as we cannot. I will tell her what you say. Thank you, and God bless you, in her name!"

Richard came back as we finished exchanging these hurried words, and gave me his arm to take me to the coach.

"Woodcourt," he said, unconscious with what application, "pray let us meet in London!"

"Meet?" returned the other. "I have scarcely a friend there, now, but you. Where shall I find you?"

"Why, I must get a lodging of some sort," said Richard, pondering. "Say at Vholes's, Symond's Inn."

"Good! Without loss of time."

They shook hands heartily. When I was seated in the coach, and Richard was yet standing in the street, Mr. Woodcourt laid his friendly hand on Richard's shoulder, and looked at me. I understood him, and waved mine in thanks.

And in his last look as we drove away, I saw that he was very sorry for me. I was glad to see it. I felt for my old self as the dead may feel if they ever revisit these scenes. I was glad to be tenderly remembered, to be gently pitied, not to be quite forgotten.

CHAPTER XLVI

STOP HIM!

DARKNESS rests upon Tom-all-Alone's. Dilating and dilating since the sun went down last night, it has gradually swelled until it fills every void in the place. For a time there were some dungeon lights burning, as the lamp of Life burns in Tom-all-Alone's, heavily, heavily, in the nauseous air, and winking—as that lamp, too, winks in Tom-all-Alone's—at many horrible things. But they are blotted out. The moon has eyed Tom with a dull cold stare, as admitting some puny emulation of herself in his desert region unfit for life and blasted by volcanic fires; but she has passed on, and is gone. The blackest nightmare in the infernal stables grazes on Tom-all-Alone's, and Tom is fast asleep.

Much mighty speech-making there has been, both in and out of Parliament, concerning Tom, and much wrathful disputation how Tom shall be got right. Whether he shall be put into the main road by constables, or by beadles, or by bell-ringing, or by force of figures, or by correct principles of taste, or by high church, or by low church, or by no church; whether he shall be set to splitting trusses of polemical straws with the crooked knife of his mind, or whether he shall be put to stone-breaking instead. In the midst of which dust and noise, there is but one thing perfectly clear, to wit, that Tom only may and can, or shall and will, be reclaimed according to somebody's theory but nobody's practice. And in the hopeful meantime, Tom goes to perdition head foremost in his old determined spirit.

But he has his revenge. Even the winds are his messengers, and they serve him in these hours of darkness. There is not a drop of Tom's corrupted blood but propagates infection and contagion somewhere. It shall pollute, this very night, the choice stream (in which chemists on analysis would find the genuine nobility) of a Norman house, and his Grace shall not be able to say Nay to the infamous alliance. There is not an atom of Tom's slime, not a cubic inch of any pestilential gas in which he lives, not one obscenity or degradation about him, not an ignorance, not a wickedness, not a brutality of his committing, but shall work its retribution, through every order of society, up to the proudest of the proud, and to the highest of the high. Verily, what with tainting, plundering, and spoiling, Tom has his revenge.

It is a moot point whether Tom-all-Alone's be uglier by day or by night; but on the argument that the more that is seen of it the more shocking it must be, and that no part of it left to the imagination is at all likely to be made so bad as the reality, day carries it. The day begins to break now; and in truth it might be better for the national glory even that the sun should sometimes set upon the British dominions, than that it should ever rise upon so vile a wonder as Tom.

A brown sunburnt gentleman, who appears in some inaptitude for sleep to be wandering abroad rather than counting the hours on a restless pillow, strolls hitherward at this quiet time. Attracted by curiosity, he often pauses and looks about him, up and down the miserable by-ways. Nor is he merely curious, for in his bright dark eye there is compassionate interest; and as he looks here and there, he seems to understand such wretchedness, and to have studied it before.

On the banks of the stagnant channel of mud which is the main street of Tom-all-Alone's, nothing is to be seen but the crazy houses, shut up and silent. No waking creature save himself appears, except in one direction, where he sees the solitary figure of a woman sitting on a doorstep. He walks that way. Approaching, he observes that she has journeyed a long distance, and is footsore and travel-stained. She sits on the doorstep in the manner of one who is waiting, with her elbow on her knee and her head upon her hand. Beside her is a canvas bag, or bundle, she has carried. She is dozing probably, for she gives no heed to his steps as he comes toward her.

The broken footway is so narrow, that when Allan Woodcourt comes to where the woman sits, he has to turn into the road to pass her. Looking down at her face, his eye meets hers, and he stops.

"What is the matter?"

"Nothing, sir."

"Can't you make them hear? Do you want to be let in?"

"I'm waiting till they get up at another house—a lodging-house—not here," the woman patiently returns. "I'm waiting here because there will be sun here presently to warm me."

"I am afraid you are tired. I am sorry to see you sitting in the street."

"Thank you, sir. It don't matter."

A habit in him of speaking to the poor, and of avoiding patronage or condescension, or childishness (which is the favourite device, many people deeming it quite a subtlety to talk to them like little spelling-books), has put him on good terms with the woman easily.

"Let me look at your forehead," he says, bending down. "I am a doctor. Don't be afraid. I wouldn't hurt you for the world."

He knows that by touching her with his skilful and accustomed hand, he can soothe her yet more readily. She makes a slight objection, saying, "It's nothing;" but he has scarcely laid his fingers on the wounded place when she lifts it up to the light.

"Ay! A bad bruise, and the skin sadly broken. This must be very sore."

"It do ache a little, sir," returns the woman, with a started tear upon her cheek.

"Let me try to make it more comfortable. My handkerchief won't hurt you!"

"Oh dear no, sir, I'm sure of that!"

He cleanses the injured place and dries it; and having carefully examined it and gently pressed it with the palm of his hand, takes a small case from his pocket, dresses it, and binds it up. While he is thus employed, he says, after laughing at his establishing a surgery in the street:

"And so your husband is a brickmaker?"

"How do you know that, sir?" asked the woman, astonished.

"Why, I suppose so, from the colour of the clay upon your bag and on your dress. And I know brickmakers go about working at piecework in different places. And I am sorry to say I have known them cruel to their wives too."

The woman hastily lifts up her eyes as if she would deny that her injury is referable to such a cause. But feeling the hand upon her forehead, and seeing his busy and composed face, she quietly drops them again.

"Where is he now?" asks the surgeon.

"He got into trouble last night, sir; but he'll look for me at the lodging-house."

"He will get into worse trouble if he often misuses his large and heavy hand as he has misused it here. But you forgive him, brutal as he is, and I say no more of him, except that I wish he deserved it. You have no young child?"

The woman shakes her head. "One as I calls mine, sir, but it's Liz's."

"Your own is dead. I see! Poor little thing!"

By this time he has finished, and is putting up his case. "I suppose you have some settled home. Is it far from here?" he asks, good-humouredly making light of what he has done, as she gets up and curtseys.

"It's a good two or three-and-twenty mile from here, sir. At Saint Albans. You know Saint Albans, sir? I thought you gave a start like, as if you did?"

"Yes, I know something of it. And now I will ask you a question in return. Have you money for your lodging?"

"Yes, sir," she says, "really and truly." And she shows it. He tells her, in acknowledgment of her many subdued thanks, that she is very welcome, gives her good day, and walks away. Tom-all-Alone's is still asleep, and nothing is astir.

Yes, something is! As he retraces his way to the point from which he descried the woman at a distance sitting on the step, he sees a ragged figure coming very cautiously along, crouching close to the soiled walls —which the wretchedest figure might as well avoid—and furtively thrusting a hand before it. It is the figure of a youth, whose face is hollow, and whose eyes have an emaciated glare. He is so intent on getting along unseen, that even the apparition of a stranger in whole garments does not tempt him to look back. He shades his face with his ragged elbow as he passes on the other side of the way, and goes shrinking and creeping on, with his anxious hand before him, and his shapeless clothes hanging in shreds. Clothes made for what purpose, or of what material, it would be impossible to say. They look, in colour and in substance, like a bundle of rank leaves of swampy growth, that rotted long ago.

Allan Woodcourt pauses to look after him and note all this, with a shadowy belief that he has seen the boy before. He cannot recall how, or where; but there is some association in his mind with such a form. He imagines that he must have seen it in some hospital or refuge; still, cannot make out why it comes with any special force on his remembrance.

He is gradually emerging from Tom-all-Alone's in the morning light, thinking about it, when he hears running feet behind him; and looking round, sees the boy scouring towards him at great speed, followed by the woman.

"Stop him, stop him!" cries the woman, almost breathless. "Stop him, sir!"

He darts across the road into the boy's path, but the boy is quicker than he—makes a curve—ducks—dives under his hands—comes up half-a-dozen yards beyond him, and scours away again. Still, the woman follows, crying, "Stop him, sir, pray stop him!" Allan, not knowing but that he has just robbed her of her money, follows in chase, and runs so hard, that he runs the boy down a dozen times; but each time he repeats the curve, the duck, the dive, and scours away again. To strike at him, on any of these occasions, would be to fell and disable him; but the pursuer cannot resolve to do that; and so the grimly ridiculous pursuit continues. At last the fugitive, hard-pressed, takes to a narrow passage, and a court which has no thoroughfare. Here, against a hoarding of decaying timber, he is brought to bay, and tumbles down, lying gasping at his pursuer, who stands and gasps at him until the woman comes up.

"O you, Jo!" cries the woman. "What? I have found you at last!"

"Jo," repeats Allan, looking at him with attention, "Jo! Stay. To be sure! I recollect this lad some time ago being brought before the coroner."

"Yes, I see you once afore at the Inkwhich," whimpers Jo. "What of that? Can't you never let such an unfortnet as me alone? An't I unfortnet enough for you yet? How unfortnet do you want me fur to be? I've been a chivied and a chivied, fust by one on you and nixt by another on you, till I'm worritted to skins and bones. The Inkwhich warn't *my* fault. *I* done nothink. He wos wery good to me, he wos; he wos the only one I knowed to speak to, as ever come across my crossing. It ain't wery likely I should want him to be Inkwhich'd. I only wish I wos, myself. I don't know why I don't go and make a hole in the water, I'm sure I don't."

He says it with such a pitiable air, and his grimy tears appear so real, and he lies in the corner up against the hoarding so like a growth of fungus or any unwholesome excrescence produced there in neglect and impurity, that Allan Woodcourt is softened towards him. He says to the woman, "Miserable creature, what has he done?"

2 H

To which she only replies, shaking her head at the prostrate figure more amazedly than angrily: "O you Jo, you Jo. I have found you at last!"

"What has he done?" says Allan. "Has he robbed you?"

"No, sir, no. Robbed me? He did nothing but what was kind-hearted by me, and that's the wonder of it."

Allan looks from Jo to the woman, and from the woman to Jo, waiting for one of them to unravel the riddle.

"But he was along with me, sir," says the woman,—"O you Jo!— he was along with me, sir, down at Saint Albans, ill, and a young lady Lord bless her for a good friend to me took pity on him when I durstn't, and took him home——"

Allan shrinks back from him with a sudden horror.

"Yes, sir, yes. Took him home, and made him comfortable, and like a thankless monster he ran away in the night, and never has been seen or heard of since, till I set eyes on him just now. And that young lady that was such a pretty dear, caught his illness, lost her beautiful looks, and wouldn't hardly be known for the same young lady now, if it wasn't for her angel temper, and her pretty shape, and her sweet voice. Do you know it? You ungrateful wretch, do you know that this is all along of you and of her goodness to you?" demands the woman, beginning to rage at him as she recalls it, and breaking into passionate tears.

The boy, in rough sort stunned by what he hears, falls to smearing his dirty forehead with his dirty palm, and to staring at the ground, and to shaking from head to foot until the crazy hoarding against which he leans, rattles.

Allan restrains the woman, merely by a quiet gesture, but effectually.

"Richard told me," he falters, "—I mean, I have heard of this—don't mind me for a moment, I will speak presently."

He turns away, and stands for a while looking out at the covered passage. When he comes back, he has recovered his composure; except that he contends against an avoidance of the boy, which is so very remarkable, that it absorbs the woman's attention.

"You hear what she says. But get up, get up!"

Jo, shaking and chattering, slowly rises, and stands, after the manner of his tribe in a difficulty, sideways against the hoarding, resting one of his high shoulders against it, and covertly rubbing his right hand over his left, and his left foot over his right.

"You hear what she says, and I know it's true. Have you been here ever since?"

"Wishermaydie if I seen Tom-all-Alone's till this blessed morning," replies Jo hoarsely.

"Why have you come here now?"

Jo looks all round the confined court, looks at his questioner no higher than the knees, and finally answers:

"I don't know how to do nothink, and I can't get nothink to do.

I'm wery poor and ill, and I thought I'd come back here when there warn't nobody about, and lay down and hide somewheres as I knows on till arter dark, and then go and beg a trifle of Mr. Sangsby. He wos allus willin fur to give me somethink he wos, though Mrs. Sangsby she was allus a chivying on me—like everybody everywheres."

"Where have you come from?"

Jo looks all round the court again, looks at his questioner's knees again, and concludes by laying his profile against the hoarding in a sort of resignation.

"Did you hear me ask you where you have come from?"

"Tramp then," says Jo.

"Now, tell me," proceeds Allan, making a strong effort to overcome his repugnance, going very near to him, and leaning over him with an expression of confidence, "tell me how it came about that you left that house, when the good young lady had been so unfortunate as to pity you, and take you home."

Jo suddenly comes out of his resignation, and excitedly declares, addressing the woman, that he never known about the young lady, that he never heern about it, that he never went fur to hurt her, that he would sooner have hurt his own self, that he'd sooner have had his unfortnet ed chopped off than ever gone a-nigh her, and that she wos wery good to him, she wos. Conducting himself throughout as if in his poor fashion he really meant it, and winding up with some very miserable sobs.

Allan Woodcourt sees that this is not a sham. He constrains himself to touch him. "Come, Jo. Tell me."

"No. I dustn't," says Jo, relapsing into the profile state. "I dustn't, or I would."

"But I must know," returns the other, "all the same. Come, Jo."

After two or three such abjurations, Jo lifts up his head again, looks round the court again, and says in a low voice, "Well, I'll tell you something. I wos took away. There!"

"Took away? In the night?"

"Ah!" Very apprehensive of being overheard, Jo looks about him, and even glances up some ten feet at the top of the hoarding, and through the cracks in it, lest the object of his distrust should be looking over, or hidden on the other side.

"Who took you away?"

"I dustn't name him," says Jo. "I dustn't do it, sir."

"But I want, in the young lady's name, to know. You may trust me. No one else shall hear."

"Ah, but I don't know," replies Jo, shaking his head fearfully, "as he *don't* hear."

"Why, he is not in this place."

"Oh, ain't he though?" says Jo. "He's in all manner of places, all at wanst."

Allan looks at him in perplexity, but discovers some real meaning and good faith at the bottom of this bewildering reply. He patiently awaits an explicit answer; and Jo, more baffled by his patience than by anything else, at last desperately whispers a name in his ear.

"Ay!" says Allan. "Why, what had you been doing?"

"Nothink, sir. Never done nothink to get myself into no trouble, 'sept in not moving on and the Inkwhich. But I'm a-moving on now. I'm a-moving on to the berryin ground—that's the move as I'm up to."

"No, no, we will try to prevent that. But what did he do with you?"

"Put me in a horsepittle," replied Jo, whispering, "till I was discharged, then giv me a little money—four half bulls, wot you may call half-crowns—and ses 'Hook it! Nobody wants you here,' he ses. 'You hook it. You go and tramp,' he ses. 'You move on,' he ses. 'Don't let me ever see you nowheres within forty mile of London, or you'll repent it.' So I shall, if ever he doos see me, and he'll see me if I'm above ground," concludes Jo, nervously repeating all his former precautions and investigations.

Allan considers a little; then remarks, turning to the woman, but keeping an encouraging eye on Jo: "He is not so ungrateful as you supposed. He had a reason for going away, though it was an insufficient one."

"Thank'ee, sir, thank'ee!" exclaims Jo. "There now! See how hard you wos upon me. But ony you tell the young lady wot the genlmn ses, and it's all right. For *you* wos wery good to me too, and I knows it."

"Now, Jo," says Allan, keeping his eye upon him, "come with me, and I will find you a better place than this to lie down and hide in. If I take one side of the way and you the other to avoid observation, you will not run away, I know very well, if you make me a promise."

"I won't, not unless I wos to see *him* a-coming, sir."

"Very well. I take your word. Half the town is getting up by this time, and the whole town will be broad awake in another hour. Come along. Good day again, my good woman."

"Good day again, sir, and I thank you kindly many times again."

She has been sitting on her bag, deeply attentive, and now rises and takes it up. Jo, repeating, "Ony you tell the young lady as I never went fur to hurt her and wot the genlmn ses!" nods and shambles and shivers, and smears and blinks, and half laughs and half cries, a farewell to her, and takes his creeping way along after Allan Woodcourt, close to the houses on the opposite side of the street. In this order, the two come up out of Tom-all-Alone's into the broad rays of the sunlight and the purer air.

CHAPTER XLVII

JO'S WILL

AS Allan Woodcourt and Jo proceed along the streets, where the high church spires and the distances are so near and clear in the morning light that the city itself seems renewed by rest, Allan revolves in his mind how and where he shall bestow his companion. "It surely is a strange fact," he considers, "that in the heart of a civilised world this creature in human form should be more difficult to dispose of than an unowned dog." But it is none the less a fact because of its strangeness, and the difficulty remains.

At first, he looks behind him often, to assure himself that Joe is still really following. But, look where he will, he still beholds him close to the opposite houses, making his way with his wary hand from brick to brick and from door to door, and often, as he creeps along, glancing over at him, watchfully. Soon satisfied that the last thing in his thoughts is to give him the slip, Allan goes on; considering with a less divided attention what he shall do.

A breakfast-stall at a street corner suggests the first thing to be done. He stops there, looks round, and beckons Jo. Jo crosses, and comes halting and shuffling up, slowly scooping the knuckles of his right hand round and round in the hollowed palm of his left—kneading dirt with a natural pestle and mortar. What is a dainty repast to Jo is then set before him, and he begins to gulp the coffee, and to gnaw the bread-and-butter; looking anxiously about him in all directions as he eats and drinks, like a scared animal.

But he is so sick and miserable, that even hunger has abandoned him. "I thought I was amost a-starvin, sir," says Jo, soon putting down his food; "but I don't know nothink—not even that. I don't care for eating wittles nor yet for drinking on 'em." And Jo stands shivering, and looking at the breakfast wonderingly.

Allan Woodcourt lays his hand upon his pulse, and on his chest. "Draw breath, Jo!" "It draws," says Jo, "as heavy as a cart." He might add, "and rattles like it;" but he only mutters, "I'm a-moving on, sir."

Allan looks about for an apothecary's shop. There is none at hand, but a tavern does as well or better. He obtains a little measure of wine, and gives the lad a portion of it very carefully. He begins to revive, almost as soon as it passes his lips. "We may repeat that dose, Jo," observes Allan, after watching him with his attentive face. "So! Now we will take five minutes' rest, and then go on again."

Leaving the boy sitting on the bench of the breakfast-stall, with his back against an iron railing, Allan Woodcourt paces up and down in the early sunshine, casting an occasional look towards him without appearing to watch him. It requires no discernment to perceive that he is warmed and refreshed. If a face so shaded can brighten, his face brightens somewhat; and, by little and little, he eats the slice of bread he had so hopelessly laid down. Observant of these signs of improvement, Allan engages him in conversation; and elicits to his no small wonder the adventure of the lady in the veil, with all its consequences. Jo slowly munches, as he slowly tells it. When he has finished his story and his bread, they go on again.

Intending to refer his difficulty in finding a temporary place of refuge for the boy, to his old patient, zealous little Miss Flite, Allan leads the way to the court where he and Jo first foregathered. But all is changed at the rag-and-bottle shop; Miss Flite no longer lodges there; it is shut up; and a hard-featured female, much obscured by dust, whose age is a problem—but who is indeed no other than the interesting Judy—is tart and spare in her replies. These sufficing, however, to inform the visitor that Miss Flite and her birds are domiciled with a Mrs. Blinder, in Bell Yard, he repairs to that neighbouring place; where Miss Flite (who rises early that she may be punctual at the Divan of justice held by her excellent friend the Chancellor) comes running downstairs, with tears of welcome and with open arms.

"My dear physician!" cries Miss Flite. "My meritorious, distinguished, honourable officer!" She uses some odd expressions, but is as cordial and full of heart as sanity itself can be—more so than it often is. Allan, very patient with her, waits until she has no more raptures to express; than points out Jo, trembling in a doorway, and tells her how he comes there.

"Where can I lodge him hereabouts for the present? Now you have a fund of knowledge and good sense, and can advise me."

Miss Flite, mighty proud of the compliment, sets herself to consider; but it is long before a bright thought occurs to her. Mrs. Blinder is entirely let, and she herself occupies poor Gridley's room. "Gridley!" exclaims Miss Flite, clapping her hands, after a twentieth repetition of this remark. "Gridley! To be sure! of course! My dear physician! General George will help us out."

It is hopeless to ask for any information about General George, and would be, though Miss Flite had not already run upstairs to put on her pinched bonnet and her poor little shawl, and to arm herself with her reticule of documents. But as she informs her physician, in her disjointed manner, on coming down in full array, that General George, whom she often calls upon, knows her dear Fitz-Jarndyce, and takes a great interest in all connected with her, Allan is induced to think that they may be in the right way. So he tells Jo, for his encouragement, that this walking about will soon be over now; and they repair to the General's. Fortunately it is not far.

From the exterior of George's Shooting Gallery, and the long entry, and the bare perspective beyond it, Allan Woodcourt augurs well. He also descries promise in the figure of Mr. George himself, striding towards them in his morning exercise with his pipe in his mouth, no stock on, and his muscular arms, developed by broadsword and dumb-bell, weightily asserting themselves through his light shirt-sleeves.

"Your servant, sir," says Mr. George, with a military salute. Good-humouredly smiling all over his broad forehead up into his crisp hair, he then defers to Miss Flite, as, with great stateliness, and at some length, she performs the courtly ceremony of presentation. He winds it up with another "Your servant, sir!" and another salute.

",Excuse me, sir. A sailor, I believe?" says Mr. George.

"I am proud to find I have the air of one," returns Allan; "but I am only a sea-going doctor."

"Indeed, sir! I should have thought you was a regular blue-jacket, myself."

Allan hopes Mr. George will forgive his intrusion the more readily on that account, and particularly that he will not lay aside his pipe, which, in his politeness, he has testified some intention of doing. "You are very good, sir," returns the trooper. "As I know, by experience, that it's not disagreeable to Miss Flite, and since it's equally agreeable to your-self—" and finishes the sentence by putting it between his lips again. Allan proceeds to tell him all he knows about Jo; unto which the trooper listens with a grave face.

"And that's the lad, sir, is it?" he inquires, looking along the entry to where Jo stands staring up at the great letters on the whitewashed front, which have no meaning in his eyes.

"That's he," says Allan. "And, Mr. George, I am in this difficulty about him. I am unwilling to place him in a hospital, even if I could procure him immediate admission, because I foresee that he would not stay there many hours, if he could be so much as got there. The same objection applies to a workhouse; supposing I had the patience to be evaded and shirked, and handed about from post to pillar in trying to get him into one—which is a system that I don't take kindly to."

"No man does, sir," returns Mr. George.

"I am convinced that he would not remain in either place, because he is possessed by an extraordinary terror of this person who ordered him to keep out of the way; in his ignorance, he believes this person to be everywhere, and cognisant of everything."

"I ask your pardon, sir," says Mr. George. "But you have not mentioned that party's name. Is it a secret, sir?"

"The boy makes it one. But his name is Bucket."

"Bucket the Detective, sir?"

"The same man."

"The man is known to me, sir," returns the trooper, after blowing out a cloud of smoke, and squaring his chest; "and the boy is so far correct that he undoubtedly is a—rum customer." Mr. George smokes with a profound meaning after this, and surveys Miss Flite in silence.

"Now, I wish Mr. Jarndyce and Miss Summerson at least to know that this Jo, who tells so strange a story, has reappeared; and to have it in their power to speak with him, if they should desire to do so. Therefore I want to get him, for the present moment, into any poor lodging, kept by decent people, where he would be admitted. Decent people and Jo, Mr. George," says Allan, following the direction of the trooper's eyes along the entry, "have not been much acquainted, as you see. Hence the difficulty. Do you happen to know any one in this neighbourhood, who would receive him for a while, on my paying for him beforehand?"

As he puts the question, he becomes aware of a dirty-faced little man, standing at the trooper's elbow, and looking up, with an oddly twisted figure and countenance, into the trooper's face. After a few more puffs at his pipe, the trooper looks down askant at the little man, and the little man winks up at the trooper.

"Well, sir," says Mr. George, "I can assure you that I would willingly be knocked on the head at any time, if it would be at all agreeable to Miss Summerson; and consequently I esteem it a privilege to do that young lady any service, however small. We are naturally in the vagabond way here, sir, both myself and Phil. You see what the place is. You are welcome to a quiet corner of it for the boy, if the same would meet your views. No charge made, except for rations. We are not in a flourishing state of circumstances here, sir. We are liable to be tumbled out neck and crop, at a moment's notice. However, sir, such as the place is, and so long as it lasts, here it is at your service."

With a comprehensive wave of his pipe, Mr. George places the whole building at his visitor's disposal.

"I take it for granted, sir," he adds, "you being one of the medical staff, that there is no present infection about this unfortunate subject?"

Allan is quite sure of it.

"Because, sir," says Mr. George, shaking his head sorrowfully, "we have had enough of that."

His tone is no less sorrowfully echoed by his new acquaintance. "Still, I am bound to tell you," observes Allan, after repeating his former assurance, "that the boy is deplorably low and reduced; and that he may be—I do not say that he is—too far gone to recover."

"Do you consider him in present danger, sir?" inquires the trooper.

"Yes, I fear so."

"Then, sir," returns the trooper, in a decisive manner, "it appears to me—being naturally in the vagabond way myself—that the sooner he comes out of the street, the better. You Phil! Bring him in!"

Mr. Squod tacks out, all on one side, to execute the word of command; and the trooper, having smoked his pipe, lays it by. Jo is brought in. He is not one of Mrs. Pardiggle's Tockahoopo Indians; he is not one of Mrs. Jellyby's lambs, being wholly unconnected with Borrioboola-Gha; he is not softened by distance and unfamiliarity; he is not a genuine foreign-grown savage; he is the ordinary home-made article. Dirty, ugly, disagreeable to all the senses, in body a common creature of the common streets, only in soul a heathen. Homely filth begrimes him, homely parasites devour him, homely sores are in him, homely rags are on him: native ignorance, the growth of English soil and climate, sinks his immortal nature lower than the beasts that perish. Stand forth, Jo, in uncompromising colours! From the sole of thy foot to the crown of thy head, there is nothing interesting about thee.

He shuffles slowly into Mr. George's gallery, and stands huddled together in a bundle, looking all about the floor. He seems to know that they have an inclination to skrink from him, partly for what he is, and partly for what he has caused. He, too, shrinks from them. He is not of the same order of things, not of the same place in creation. He is of no order and no place; neither of the beasts, nor of humanity.

"Look here, Jo!" says Allan. "This is Mr. George."

Jo searches the floor for some time longer, then looks up for a moment, and then down again.

"He is a kind friend to you, for he is going to give you lodging-room here."

Jo makes a scoop with one hand, which is supposed to be a bow. After a little more consideration, and some backing and changing of the foot on which he rests, he mutters that he is "wery thankful."

"You are quite safe here. All you have to do at present is to be obedient, and to get strong. And mind yon tell us the truth here, whatever you do, Jo.

"Wishermaydie if I don't, sir," says Jo, reverting to his favourite declaration. "I never done nothink yit, but wot you knows on, to get myself into no trouble. I never was in no other trouble at all, sir— 'sept not knowin' nothink and starwation."

"I believe it. Now attend to Mr. George. I see he is going to speak to you."

"My intention merely was, sir," observes Mr. George, amazingly broad and upright, "to point out to him where he can lie down, and get a thorough good dose of sleep. Now, look here." As the trooper speaks, he conducts them to the other end of the gallery, and opens one of the little cabins. "There you are, you see! Here is a mattress, and here you may rest, on good behaviour, as long as Mr., I ask your pardon, sir;" he refers apologetically to the card Allan has given him; "Mr. Woodcourt pleases. Don't you be alarmed if you hear shots; they'll be aimed at the target, and not you. Now, there's another thing I would recommend, sir," says the trooper, turning to his visitor. "Phil, come here!"

Phil bears down upon them, according to his usual tactics.

"Here is a man, sir, who was found, when a baby, in the gutter. Consequently, it is to be expected that he takes a natural interest in this poor creature. You do, don't you, Phil?"

"Certainly and surely I do, guv'ner," is Phil's reply.

"Now I was thinking, sir," says Mr. George, in a martial sort of confidence, as if he were giving his opinion in a council of war at a drum-head, "that if this man was to take him to a bath, and was to lay out a few shillings in getting him one or two coarse articles——"

" Mr. George, my considerate friend," returns Allan, taking out his purse, " it is the very favour I would have asked."

Phil Squod and Jo are sent out immediately on this work of improvement. Miss Flite, quite enraptured by her success, makes the best of her way to court; having great fears that otherwise her friend the Chancellor may be uneasy about her, or may give the judgment she has so long expected, in her absence; and observing "which you know, my dear physician, and general, after so many years, would be too absurdly unfortunate ! " Allan takes the opportunity of going out to procure some restorative medicines ; and obtaining them near at hand, soon returns, to find the trooper walking up and down the gallery, and to fall into step and walk with him.

" I take it, sir," says Mr. George, " that you know Miss Summerson pretty well ? "

Yes, it appears.

" Not related to her, sir ? "

No, it appears.

" Excuse the apparent curiosity," says Mr. George. " It seemed to me probable that you might take more than a common interest in this poor creature, because Miss Summerson had taken that unfortunate interest in him. 'Tis *my* case, sir, I assure you."

" And mine, Mr. George."

The trooper looks sideways at Allan's sun-burnt cheek and bright dark eye, rapidly measures his height and build, and seems to approve of him.

" Since you have been out, sir, I have been thinking that I unquestionably know the rooms in Lincoln's Inn Fields, where Bucket took the lad, according to his account. Though he is not acquainted with the name, I can help you to it. It's Tulkinghorn. That's what it is."

Allan looks at him inquiringly, repeating the name.

" Tulkinghorn. That's the name, sir. I know the man ; and know him to have been in communication with Bucket before, respecting a deceased person who had given him offence. *I* know the man, sir. To my sorrow."

Allan naturally asks what kind of man he is.

" What kind of man ! Do you mean to look at ? "

" I think I know that much of him. I mean to deal with. Generally, what kind of man ? "

" Why, then I'll tell you, sir," returns the trooper, stopping short, and folding his arms on his square chest, so angrily, that his face fires and flushes all over ; " he is a confoundedly bad kind of man. He is a slow-torturing kind of man. He is no more like flesh and blood, than a rusty old carbine is. He is a kind of man—by George !—that has caused me more restlessness, and more uneasiness, and more dissatisfaction with myself, than all other men put together. That's the kind of man Mr. Tulkinghorn is ! "

" I am sorry," says Allan, " to have touched so sore a place."

"Sore?" The trooper plants his legs wider apart, wets the palm of his broad right hand, and lays it on his imaginary moustache. "It's no fault of yours, sir; but you shall judge. He has got a power over me. He is the man I spoke of just now, as being able to tumble me out of this place neck and crop. He keeps me on a constant see-saw. He won't hold off, and he won't come on. If I have a payment to make him, or time to ask him for, or anything to go to him about, he don't see me, don't hear me—passes me on to Melchisedech's in Clifford's Inn, Melchisedech's in Clifford's Inn passes me back again to him—he keeps me prowling and dangling about him, as if I was made of the same stone as himself. Why, I spend half my life now, pretty well, loitering and dodging about his door. What does he care? Nothing. Just as much as the rusty old carbine I have compared him to. He chafes and goads me, till—Bah! nonsense—I am forgetting myself. Mr. Woodcourt;" the trooper resumes his march; "all I say is, he is an old man; but I am glad I shall never have the chance of setting spurs to my horse, and riding at him in a fair field. For if I had that chance, in one of the humours he drives me into—he'd go down, sir!"

Mr. George has been so excited, that he finds it necessary to wipe his forehead on his shirt-sleeve. Even while he whistles his impetuosity away with the National Anthem, some involuntary shakings of his head and heavings of his chest still linger behind; not to mention an occasional hasty adjustment with both hands of his open shirt-collar, as if it were scarcely open enough to prevent his being troubled by a choking sensation. In short, Allan Woodcourt has not much doubt about the going down of Mr. Tulkinghorn on the field referred to.

Jo and his conductor presently return, and Jo is assisted to his mattress by the careful Phil; to whom, after due administration of medicine by his own hands, Allan confides all needful means and instructions. The morning is by this time getting on apace. He repairs to his lodgings to dress and breakfast; and then, without seeking rest, goes away to Mr Jarndyce to communicate his discovery.

With him Mr. Jarndyce returns alone, confidentially telling him that there are reasons for keeping this matter very quiet indeed; and showing a serious interest in it. To Mr. Jarndyce, Jo repeats in substance what he said in the morning; without any material variation. Only, that cart of his is heavier to draw, and draws with a hollower sound.

"Let me lay here quiet, and not be chivied no more," falters Jo; "and be so kind any person as is a-passin' nigh where I used fur to sweep, as jist to say to Mr. Sangsby that Jo, wot he known once, is a-moving on right forards with his duty, and I'll be wery thankful. I'd be more thankful than I am aready, if it wos any ways possible for an unfortnet to be it."

He makes so many of these references to the law-stationer in the course of a day or two, that Allan, after conferring with Mr. Jarndyce, good-naturedly resolves to call in Cook's Court; the rather, as the cart seems to be breaking down.

To Cook's Court, therefore, he repairs. Mr. Snagsby is behind his counter in his grey coat and sleeves, inspecting an Indenture of several skins which has just come in from the engrosser's; an immense desert of law-hand and parchment, with here and there a resting-place of a few large letters, to break the awful monotony, and save the traveller from despair. Mr. Snagsby puts up at one of these inky wells, and greets the stranger with his cough of general preparation for business.

"You don't remember me, Mr. Snagsby?"

The stationer's heart begins to thump heavily, for his old apprehensions have never abated. It is as much as he can do to answer, "No, sir, I can't say I do. I should have considered—not to put too fine a point upon it—that I never saw you before, sir."

"Twice before," says Allan Woodcourt. "Once at a poor bedside, and once——"

"It's come at last!" thinks the afflicted stationer, as recollection breaks upon him. "It's got to a head now, and is going to burst!" But, he has sufficient presence of mind to conduct his visitor into the little counting-house, and to shut the door.

"Are you a married man, sir?"

"No, I am not."

"Would you make the attempt, though single," says Mr. Snagsby, in a melancholy whisper, "to speak as low as you can? For my little woman is a-listening somewheres, or I'll forfeit the business and five hundred pound!"

In deep dejection Mr. Snagsby sits down on his stool, with his back against his desk, protesting:

"I never had a secret of my own, sir. I can't charge my memory with ever having once attempted to deceive my little woman on my own account, since she named the day. I wouldn't have done it, sir. Not to put too fine a point upon it, I couldn't have done it, I durstn't have done it. Whereas, and nevertheless, I find myself wrapped round with secrecy and mystery, till my life is a burden to me."

His visitor professes his regret to hear it, and asks him does he remember Jo? Mr. Snagsby answers with a suppressed groan, Oh don't he!

"You couldn't name an individual human being—except myself—that my little woman is more set and determined against than Jo," says Mr. Snagsby.

Allan asks why?

"Why?" repeats Mr. Snagsby, in his desperation clutching at the clump of hair at the back of his bald head. "How should *I* know why? But you are a single person, sir, and may you long be spared to ask a married person such a question!"

With this beneficent wish, Mr. Snagsby coughs a cough of dismal resignation, and submits himself to hear what the visitor has to communicate.

"There again!" says Mr. Snagsby, who, between the earnestness of his feelings, and the suppressed tones of his voice, is discoloured in the face. "At it again, in a new direction! A certain person charges me, in the solemnest way, not to talk of Jo to any one, even my little woman. Then comes another certain person, in the person of yourself, and charges me, in an equally solemn way, not to mention Jo to that other certain person above all other persons. Why, this is a private asylum! Why, not to put too fine a point upon it, this is Bedlam, sir!" says Mr. Snagsby.

But it is better than he expected, after all; being no explosion of the mine below him, or deepening of the pit into which he has fallen. And being tender-hearted, and affected by the account he hears of Jo's condition, he readily engages to "look round" as early in the evening as he can manage it quietly. He looks round very quietly, when the evening comes; but it may turn out that Mrs. Snagsby is as quiet a manager as he.

Jo is very glad to see his old friend; and says, when they are left alone, that he takes it uncommon kind as Mr. Sangsby should come so far out of his way on accounts of sich as him. Mr. Snagsby, touched by the spectacle before him, immediately lays upon the table half-a-crown: that magic balsam of his for all kinds of wounds.

"And how do you find yourself, my poor lad?" inquires the stationer, with his cough of sympathy.

"I am in luck, Mr. Sangsby, I am," returns Jo, "and don't want for nothink. I'm more cumfbler nor you can't think. Mr. Sangsby! I'm wery sorry that I done it, but I didn't go fur to do it, sir."

The stationer softly lays down another half-crown, and asks him what it is that he is sorry for having done?

"Mr. Sangsby," says Jo, "I went and giv a illness to the lady as wos and yit as warn't the t'other lady, and none of 'em never says nothink to me for having done it, on accounts of their being ser good and my having been s'unfortnet. The lady come herself and see me yesday, and she ses, 'Ah Jo!' she ses. 'We thought we'd lost you, Jo!' she ses. And she sits down a-smilin so quiet, and don't pass a word nor yit a look upon me for having done it, she don't, and I turns agin the wall, I doos, Mr. Sangsby. And Mr. Jarnders, I see him a-forced to turn away his own self. And Mr. Woodcot, he come fur to giv me somethink fur to ease me, wot he's allus a-doin on day and night, and wen he come a-bendin over me and a-speakin up so bold, I see his tears a-fallin, Mr. Sangsby."

The softened stationer deposits another half-crown on the table. Nothing less than a repetition of that infallible remedy will relieve his feelings.

"Wot I wos a-thinkin on, Mr. Sangsby," proceeds Jo, "wos, as you wos able to write wery large, p'raps?"

"Yes, Jo, please God," returns the stationer.

"Uncommon precious large, p'raps?" says Jo, with eagerness.

"Yes, my poor boy."

Jo laughs with pleasure. "Wot I wos a-thinkin on then, Mr. Sangsby, wos, that when I was moved on as fur as ever I could go and couldn't be moved no furder, whether you might be so good p'raps, as to write out, wery large so that any one could see it anywheres, as that I wos wery truly hearty sorry that I done it and that I never went fur to do it; and that though I didn't know nothink at all, I knowd as Mr. Woodcot once cried over it and wos allus grieved over it, and that I hoped as he'd be able to forgive me in his mind. If the writin could be made to say it wery large, he might."

"It shall say it, Jo. Very large."

Jo laughs again. "Thank'ee, Mr. Sangsby. It's wery kind of you, sir, and it makes me more cumfbler nor I was afore."

The meek little stationer, with a broken and unfinished cough, slips down his fourth half-crown—he has never been so close to a case requiring so many—and is fain to depart. And Jo and he, upon this little earth, shall meet no more. No more.

For the cart so hard to draw, is near its journey's end, and drags over stony ground. All round the clock it labours up the broken steeps, shattered and worn. Not many times can the sun rise, and behold it still upon its weary road.

Phil Squod, with his smoky gunpowder visage, at once acts as nurse and works as armourer at his little table in a corner; often looking round, and saying with a nod of his green baize cap, and an encouraging elevation of his one eyebrow, "Hold up, my boy! Hold up!" There, too, is Mr. Jarndyce many a time, and Allan Woodcourt almost always; both thinking, much, how strangely Fate has entangled this rough outcast in the web of very different lives. There, too, the trooper is a frequent visitor; filling the doorway with his athletic figure, and, from his superfluity of life and strength, seeming to shed down temporary vigour upon Jo, who never fails to speak more robustly in answer to his cheerful words.

Jo is in a sleep or in a stupor to-day, and Allan Woodcourt, newly arrived, stands by him, looking down upon his wasted form. After a while, he softly seats himself upon the bedside with his face towards him —just as he sat in the law-writer's room—and touches his chest and heart. The cart had very nearly given up, but labours on a little more.

The trooper stands in the doorway, still and silent. Phil has stopped in a low clinking noise, with his little hammer in his hand. Mr. Woodcourt looks round with that grave professional interest and attention on his face, and, glancing significantly at the trooper, signs to Phil to carry his table out. When the little hammer is next used, there will be a speck of rust upon it.

"Well, Jo! What is the matter? Don't be frightened."

"I thought," says Jo, who has started, and is looking round, "I thought I was in Tom-all-Alone's agin. Ain't there nobody here but you, Mr. Woodcot?"

"Nobody."

"And I ain't took back to Tom-all-Alone's. Am I, sir?"

"No." Jo closes his eyes, muttering, "I'm wery thankful."

After watching him closely a little while, Allan puts his mouth very near his ear, and says to him in a low, distinct voice:

"Jo! Did you ever know a prayer?"

"Never knowd nothink, sir."

"Not so much as one short prayer?"

"No, sir. Nothink at all. Mr. Chadbands he wos a-prayin wunst at Mr. Sangsby's and I heerd him, but he sounded as if he wos a-speakin' to hisself, and not to me. He prayed a lot, but *I* couldn't make out nothink on it. Different times, there was other genlmen come down Tom-all-Alone's a-prayin, but they all mostly sed as the t'other wuns prayed wrong, and all mostly sounded to be a-talking to theirselves, or a-passing blame on the t'others, and not a-talkin to us. *We* never knowd nothink. *I* never knowd what it wos all about."

It takes him a long time to say this; and few but an experienced and attentive listener could hear, or, hearing, understand him. After a short relapse into sleep or stupor, he makes, of a sudden, a strong effort to get out of bed.

"Stay, Jo! What now?"

"It's time for me to go to that there berryin ground, sir," he returns with a wild look.

"Lie down, and tell me. What burying ground, Jo?"

"Where they laid him as wos wery good to me, wery good to me indeed, he wos. It's time fur me to go down to that there berryin ground, sir, and ask to be put along with him. I wants to go there and be berried. He used fur to say to me, 'I am as poor as you to-day, Jo,' he ses. I wants to tell him that I am as poor as him now, and have come there to be laid along with him."

"By-and-by, Jo. By-and-by."

"Ah! P'raps they wouldn't do it if I wos to go myself. But will you promise to have me took there, sir, and laid along with him?"

"I will, indeed."

"Thank'ee, sir. Thank'ee, sir. They'll have to get the key of the gate afore they can take me in, for it's allus locked. And there's a step there, as I used fur to clean with my broom.—It's turned wery dark, sir. Is there any light a-comin?"

"It is coming fast, Jo."

Fast. The cart is shaken all to pieces, and the rugged road is very near its end.

"Jo, my poor fellow!"

"I hear you, sir, in the dark, but I'm a-gropin—a-gropin—let me catch hold of your hand."

"Jo, can you say what I say?"

"I'll say anythink as you say, sir, for I knows it's good."

"OUR FATHER."

"Our Father!"—yes, that's wery good, sir."

"WHICH ART IN HEAVEN."

"Art in Heaven—is the light a-comin, sir?"

"It is close at hand. HALLOWED BE THY NAME!"

"Hallowed be—thy—"

The light is come upon the dark benighted way. Dead!

Dead, your Majesty. Dead, my lords and gentlemen. Dead, Right Reverends and Wrong Reverends of every order. Dead, men and women, born with Heavenly compassion in your hearts. And dying thus around us every day.

CHAPTER XLVIII

CLOSING IN

THE place in Lincolnshire has shut its many eyes again, and the house in town is awake. In Lincolnshire, the Dedlocks of the past doze in their picture-frames, and the low wind murmurs through the long drawing-room as if they were breathing pretty regularly. In town, the Dedlocks of the present rattle in their fire-eyed carriages through the darkness of the night, and the Dedlock Mercuries, with ashes (or hair-powder) on their heads, symptomatic of their great humility, loll away the drowsy mornings in the little windows of the hall. The fashionable world—tremendous orb, nearly five miles round—is in full swing, and the solar system works respectfully at its appointed distances.

Where the throng is thickest, where the lights are brightest, where all the senses are ministered to with the greatest delicacy and refinement, Lady Dedlock is. From the shining heights she has scaled and taken, she is never absent. Though the belief she of old reposed in herself, as one able to reserve whatsoever she would under her mantle of pride, is beaten down; though she has no assurance that what she is to those around her, she will remain another day; it is not in her nature, when envious eyes are looking on, to yield or to droop. They say of her, that she has lately grown more handsome and more haughty. The debilitated cousin says of her that she's beauty nough—tsetup Shopof-women—but rather larming kind—remindingmanfact—inconvenient woman—who *will* getoutofbedandbawthstablishment—Shakespeare.

Mr. Tulkinghorn says nothing; looks nothing. Now, as heretofore, he is to be found in doorways of rooms, with his limp white cravat loosely twisted into its old-fashioned tie, receiving patronage from the Peerage, and making no sign. Of all men he is still the last who might be supposed to have any influence upon my Lady. Of all women she is still the last who might be supposed to have any dread of him.

One thing has been much on her mind since their late interview in his turret-room at Chesney Wold. She is now decided, and prepared to throw it off.

It is morning in the great world; afternoon according to the little sun. The Mercuries, exhausted by looking out of window, are reposing in the hall; and hang their heavy heads, the gorgeous creatures, like overblown sunflowers. Like them, too, they seem to run to a deal of seed in their tags and trimmings. Sir Leicester, in the library, has fallen asleep for the good of the country, over the report of a Parliamentary committee. My Lady sits in the room in which she gave audience to the young man of the name of Guppy. Rosa is with her, and has been writing for her and reading to her. Rosa is now at work upon embroidery, or some such pretty thing; and as she bends her head over it, my Lady watches her in silence. Not for the first time to-day.

" Rosa."

The pretty village face looks brightly up. Then, seeing how serious my Lady is, looks puzzled and surprised.

" See to the door. Is it shut ? "

Yes. She goes to it and returns, and looks yet more surprised.

" I am about to place confidence in you, child, for I know I may trust your attachment, if not your judgment. In what I am going to do, I will not disguise myself to you at least. But I confide in you. Say nothing to any one of what passes between us."

The timid little beauty promises in all earnestness to be trustworthy.

" Do you know," Lady Dedlock asks her, signing to her to bring her chair nearer ; "do you know, Rosa, that I am different to you from what I am to any one ? "

" Yes, my Lady. Much kinder. But then I often think I know you as you really are."

" You often think you know me as I really am ? Poor child, poor child ! "

She says it with a kind of scorn—though not of Rosa—and sits brooding, looking dreamily at her.

" Do you think, Rosa, you are any relief or comfort to me ? Do you suppose your being young and natural, and fond of me and grateful to me, makes it any pleasure to me to have you near me ? "

" I don't know, my Lady ; I can scarcely hope so. But, with all my heart, I wish it was so."

" It is so, little one."

The pretty face is checked in its flush of pleasure, by the dark expression on the handsome face before it. It looks timidly for an explanation.

" And if I were to say to-day, Go ! Leave me ! I should say what would give me great pain and disquiet, child, and what would leave me very solitary."

" My Lady ! Have I offended you ? "

" In nothing. Come here."

Rosa bends down on the footstool at my Lady's feet. My Lady, with that motherly touch of the famous Ironmaster night, lays her hand upon her dark hair, and gently keeps it there.

" I told you, Rosa, that I wished you to be happy, and that I would make you so if I could make anybody happy on this earth. I can not There are reasons now known to me, reasons in which you have no part,

2 ɪ

rendering it far better for you that you should not remain here. You must not remain here. I have determined that you shall not. I have written to the father of your lover, and he will be here to-day. All this I have done for your sake."

The weeping girl covers her hand with kisses, and says what shall she do, what shall she do, when they are separated. Her mistress kisses her on the cheek, and makes no other answer.

"Now, be happy, child, under better circumstances. Be beloved and happy!"

"Ah, my Lady, I have sometimes thought—forgive my being so free —that *you* are not happy."

"I!"

"Will you be more so, when you have sent me away? Pray, pray, think again. Let me stay a little while!"

"I have said, my child, that what I do, I do for your sake, not my own. It is done. What I am towards you, Rosa, is what I am now— not what I shall be a little while hence. Remember this, and keep my confidence. Do so much for my sake, and thus all ends between us!"

She detaches herself from her simple-hearted companion, and leaves the room. Late in the afternoon, when she next appears upon the staircase, she is in her haughtiest and coldest state. As indifferent as if all passion, feeling, and interest had been worn out in the earlier ages of the world, and had perished from its surface with its other departed monsters.

Mercury has announced Mr. Rouncewell, which is the cause of her appearance. Mr. Rouncewell is not in the library; but she repairs to the library. Sir Leicester is there, and she wishes to speak to him first.

"Sir Leicester, I am desirous—but you are engaged."

Oh dear no! Not at all. Only Mr. Tulkinghorn.

Always at hand. Haunting every place. No relief or security from him for a moment.

"I beg your pardon, Lady Dedlock. Will you allow me to retire?"

With a look that plainly says, "You know you have the power to remain if you will," she tells him it is not necessary, and moves towards a chair. Mr. Tulkinghorn brings it a little forward for her with his clumsy bow, and retires into a window opposite. Interposed between her and the fading light of day in the now quiet street, his shadow falls upon her, and he darkens all before her. Even so does he darken her life.

It is a dull street under the best conditions; where the two long rows of houses stare at each other with that severity, that half-a-dozen of its greatest mansions seem to have been slowly stared into stone, rather than originally built in that material. It is a street of such dismal grandeur, so determined not to condescend to liveliness, that the doors and windows hold a gloomy state of their own in black paint and dust, and the echoing mews behind have a dry and massive appearance, as if they were reserved to stable the stone chargers of noble statues. Complicated garnish of iron-work entwines itself over the flights of steps in this awful street; and, from these petrified bowers, extinguishers for obsolete flambeaux gasp at the upstart gas. Here and there a weak little iron hoop, through which bold boys aspire to throw their friends' caps (its only present use), retains its place among the rusty foliage, sacred to the memory of departed oil. Nay, even oil itself, yet lingering at long intervals in a little absurd glass pot, with a knob in the bottom like an oyster, blinks and sulks at newer lights every night, like its high and dry master in the House of Lords.

Therefore there is not much that Lady Dedlock, seated in her chair, could wish to see through the window in which Mr. Tulkinghorn stands. And yet—and yet—she sends a look in that direction, as if it were her heart's desire to have that figure moved out of the way.

Sir Leicester begs his Lady's pardon. She was about to say?

"Only that Mr. Rouncewell is here (he has called by my appointment), and that we had better make an end of the question of that girl. I am tired to death of the matter."

"What can I do—to—assist?" demands Sir Leicester, in some considerable doubt.

"Let us see him here, and have done with it. Will you tell them to send him up?"

"Mr. Tulkinghorn, be so good as to ring. Thank you. Request," says Sir Leicester, to Mercury, not immediately remembering the business term, "request the iron gentleman to walk this way."

Mercury departs in search of the iron gentleman, finds, and produces him. Sir Leicester receives that ferruginous person graciously.

"I hope you are well, Mr. Rouncewell. Be seated. (My solicitor, Mr. Tulkinghorn.) My Lady was desirous, Mr. Rouncewell," Sir Leicester skilfully transfers him with a solemn wave of his hand, "was desirous to speak with you. Hem!"

"I shall be very happy," returns the iron gentleman, "to give my best attention to anything Lady Dedlock does me the honour to say."

As he turns towards her, he finds that the impression she makes upon him is less agreeable than on the former occasion. A distant supercilious air makes a cold atmosphere about her; and there is nothing in her bearing, as there was before, to encourage openness.

"Pray, sir," says Lady Dedlock listlessly, "may I be allowed to inquire whether anything has passed between you and your son, respecting your son's fancy?"

It is almost too troublesome to her languid eyes to bestow a look upon him, as she asks this question.

"If my memory serves me, Lady Dedlock, I said, when I had the pleasure of seeing you before, that I should seriously advise my son to conquer that—fancy." The ironmaster repeats her expression with a little emphasis.

"And did you?"

"Oh! of course I did."

Sir Leicester gives a nod, approving and confirmatory. Very proper.

The iron gentleman having said that he would do it, was bound to do it. No difference in this respect between the base metals and the precious. Highly proper.

"And pray has he done so?"

"Really, Lady Dedlock, I cannot make you a definite reply. I fear not. Probably not yet. In our condition of life, we sometimes couple an intention with our—our fancies, which renders them not altogether easy to throw off. I think it is rather our way to be in earnest."

Sir Leicester has a misgiving that there may be a hidden Wat Tylerish meaning in this expression, and fumes a little. Mr. Rouncewell is perfectly good-humoured and polite; but, within such limits, evidently adapts his tone to his reception.

"Because," proceeds my Lady, "I have been thinking of the subject —which is tiresome to me."

"I am very sorry, I am sure."

"And also of what Sir Leicester said upon it, in which I quite concur;" Sir Leicester flattered: "and if you cannot give us the assurance that this fancy is at an end, I have come to the conclusion that the girl had better leave me."

"I can give no such assurance, Lady Dedlock. Nothing of the kind."

"Then she had better go."

"Excuse me, my Lady," Sir Leicester considerately interposes, "but perhaps this may be doing an injury to the young woman, which she has not merited. Here is a young woman," says Sir Leicester, magnificently laying out the matter with his right hand, like a service of plate, "whose good fortune it is to have attracted the notice and favour of an eminent lady, and to live under the protection of that eminent lady, surrounded by the various advantages which such a position confers, and which are unquestionably very great—I believe unquestionably very great, sir—for a young woman in that station of life. The question then arises, should that young woman be deprived of these many advantages and that good fortune, simply because she has;" Sir Leicester, with an apologetic but dignified inclination of his head towards the ironmaster, winds up his sentence: "has attracted the notice of Mr. Rouncewell's son? Now, has she deserved this punishment? Is this just towards her? Is this our previous understanding?"

"I beg your pardon," interposes Mr. Rouncewell's son's father. "Sir Leicester, will you allow me? I think I may shorten the subject. Pray dismiss that from your consideration. If you remember anything so unimportant—which is not to be expected—you would recollect that my first thought in the affair was directly opposed to her remaining here."

Dismiss the Dedlock patronage from consideration? Oh! Sir Leicester is bound to believe a pair of ears that have been handed down to him through such a family, or he really might have mistrusted their report of the iron gentleman's observations.

"It is not necessary," observes my Lady, in her coldest manner, before he can do anything but breathe amazedly, "to enter into these matters on either side. The girl is a very good girl; I have nothing whatever to say against her; but she is so far insensible to her many advantages and her good fortune, that she is in love—or supposes she is, poor little fool—and unable to appreciate them."

Sir Leicester begs to observe, that wholly alters the case. He might have been sure that my Lady had the best grounds and reasons in support of her view. He entirely agrees with my Lady. The young woman had better go.

"As Sir Leicester observed, Mr. Rouncewell, on the last occasion, when we were fatigued by this business," Lady Dedlock languidly proceeds, "we cannot make conditions with you. Without conditions, and under present circumstances, the girl is quite misplaced here, and had better go. I have told her so. Would you wish to have her sent back to the village, or would you like to take her with you, or what would you prefer?"

"Lady Dedlock, if I may speak plainly——"

"By all means."

"——I should prefer the course which will the soonest relieve you of the incumbrance, and remove her from her present position."

"And to speak as plainly," she returns, with the same studied carelessness, "so should I. Do I understand that you will take her with you?"

The iron gentleman makes an iron bow.

"Sir Leicester, will you ring?" Mr. Tulkinghorn steps forward from his window and pulls the bell. "I had forgotten you. Thank you." He makes his usual bow, and goes quietly back again. Mercury, swift-responsive, appears, receives instructions whom to produce, skims away, produces the aforesaid, and departs.

Rosa has been crying, and is yet in distress. On her coming in, the ironmaster leaves his chair, takes her arm in his, and remains with her near the door ready to depart.

"You are taken charge of, you see," says my Lady, in her weary manner, "and are going away well protected. I have mentioned that you are a very good girl, and you have nothing to cry for."

"She seems after all," observes Mr. Tulkinghorn, loitering a little forward with his hands behind him, "as if she were crying at going away."

"Why, she is not well bred, you see," returns Mr. Rouncewell with some quickness in his manner, as if he were glad to have the lawyer to retort upon; "and she is an inexperienced little thing, and knows no better. If she had remained here, sir, she would have improved, no doubt."

"No doubt," is Mr. Tulkinghorn's composed reply.

Rosa sobs out that she is very sorry to leave my Lady, and that she was happy at Chesney Wold, and has been happy with my Lady, and that she thanks my Lady over and over again. "Out, you silly little puss!" says the ironmaster, checking her in a low voice, though not angrily; "have a spirit, if you're fond of Wat!" My Lady merely waves her off with indifference, saying, "There, there, child! You are a good girl. Go away!" Sir Leicester has magnificently disengaged himself from the subject, and retired into the sanctuary of his blue coat

Mr. Tulkinghorn, an indistinct form against the dark street now dotted with lamps, looms in my Lady's view, bigger and blacker than before.

"Sir Leicester and Lady Dedlock," says Mr. Rouncewell, after a pause of a few moments, "I beg to take my leave, with an apology for having again troubled you, though not of my own act, on this tiresome subject. I can very well understand, I assure you, how tiresome so small a matter must have become to Lady Dedlock. If I am doubtful of my dealing with it, it is only because I did not at first quietly exert my influence to take my young friend here away, without troubling you at all. But it appeared to me—I dare say magnifying the importance of the thing—that it was respectful to explain to you how the matter stood, and candid to consult your wishes and convenience. I hope you will excuse my want of acquaintance with the polite world."

Sir Leicester considers himself evoked out of the sanctuary by these remarks. "Mr. Rouncewell," he returns, "do not mention it. Justifications are unnecessary, I hope, on either side."

"I am glad to hear it, Sir Leicester; and if I may, by way of a last word, revert to what I said before of my mother's long connection with the family, and the worth it bespeaks on both sides, I would point out this little instance here on my arm, who shows herself so affectionate and faithful in parting, and in whom my mother, I dare say, has done something to awaken such feelings—though of course Lady Dedlock, by her heartfelt interest and her genial condescension, has done much more."

If he means this ironically, it may be truer than he thinks. He points it, however, by no deviation from his straightforward manner of speech, though in saying it he turns towards that part of the dim room where my Lady sits. Sir Leicester stands to return his parting salutation, Mr. Tulkinghorn again rings, Mercury takes another flight, and Mr. Rouncewell and Rosa leave the house.

Then lights are brought in, discovering Mr. Tulkinghorn still standing in his window with his hands behind him, and my Lady still sitting with his figure before her, closing up her view of the night as well as of the day. She is very pale. Mr. Tulkinghorn observing it as she rises to retire, thinks, "Well she may be! The power of this woman is astonishing. She has been acting a part the whole time." But he can act a part too—his one unchanging character—and as he holds the door open for this woman, fifty pairs of eyes, each fifty times sharper than Sir Leicester's pair, should find no flaw in him.

Lady Dedlock dines alone in her own room to-day. Sir Leicester is whipped in to the rescue of the Doodle Party, and the discomfiture of the Coodle Faction. Lady Dedlock asks, on sitting down to dinner, still deadly pale (and quite an illustration of the debilitated cousin's text), whether he is gone out? Yes. Whether Mr. Tulkinghorn is gone yet? No. Presently she asks again, is he gone *yet*? No. What is he doing? Mercury thinks he is writing letters in the library. Would my Lady wish to see him? Anything but that.

But he wishes to see my Lady. Within a few more minutes he is reported as sending his respects, and could my Lady please to receive him for a word or two after her dinner? My Lady will receive him now. He comes now, apologising for intruding, even by her permission, while she is at table. When they are alone, my Lady waves her hand to dispense with such mockeries.

"What do you want, sir?"

"Why, Lady Dedlock," says the lawyer, taking a chair at a little distance from her, and slowly rubbing his rusty legs up and down, up and down, up and down; "I am rather surprised by the course you have taken."

"Indeed?"

"Yes, decidedly. I was not prepared for it. I consider it a departure from our agreement and your promise. It puts us in a new position, Lady Dedlock. I feel myself under the necessity of saying that I don't approve of it."

He stops in his rubbing, and looks at her, with his hands on his knees. Imperturbable and unchangeable as he is, there is still an undefinable freedom in his manner, which is new, and which does not escape this woman's observation.

"I do not quite understand you."

"Oh yes you do, I think. I think you do. Come, come, Lady Dedlock, we must not fence and parry now. You know you like this girl."

"Well, sir?"

"And you know—and I know—that you have not sent her away for the reasons you have assigned, but for the purpose of separating her as much as possible from—excuse my mentioning it as a matter of business—any reproach and exposure that impend over yourself."

"Well, sir?"

"Well, Lady Dedlock," returns the lawyer, crossing his legs, and nursing the uppermost knee, "I object to that. I consider that a dangerous proceeding. I know it to be unnecessary, and calculated to awaken speculation, doubt, rumour, I don't know what, in the house. Besides, it is a violation of our agreement. You were to be exactly what you were before. Whereas, it must be evident to yourself, as it is to me, that you have been this evening very different from what you were before. Why, bless my soul, Lady Dedlock, transparently so!"

"If, sir," she begins, "in my knowledge of my secret—" But he interrupts her.

"Now, Lady Dedlock, this is a matter of business, and in a matter of business the ground cannot be kept too clear. It is no longer your secret. Excuse me. That is just the mistake. It is my secret, in trust for Sir Leicester and the family. If it were your secret, Lady Dedlock, we should not be here, holding this conversation."

"That is very true. If, in my knowledge of *the* secret, I do what I can to spare an innocent girl (especially, remembering your own reference to her when you told my story to the assembled guests at Chesney Wold) from the taint of my impending shame, I act upon a resolution I have taken. Nothing in the world, and no one in the world, could shake it, or could move me." This she says with great deliberation and distinctness, and with no more outward passion than himself. As for him, he methodically discusses his matter of business, as if she were any insensible instrument used in business.

"Really? Then you see, Lady Dedlock," he returns, "you are not to be trusted. You have put the case in a perfectly plain way, and according to the literal fact; and, that being the case, you are not to be trusted."

"Perhaps you may remember that I expressed some anxiety on this same point, when we spoke at night at Chesney Wold?"

"Yes," says Mr. Tulkinghorn, coolly getting up and standing on the hearth. "Yes. I recollect, Lady Dedlock, that you certainly referred to the girl; but that was before we came to our arrangement, and both the letter and the spirit of our arrangement altogether precluded any action on your part, founded upon my discovery. There can be no doubt about that. As to sparing the girl, of what importance or value is she? Spare! Lady Dedlock, here is a family name compromised. One might have supposed that the course was straight on—over everything, neither to the right nor to the left, regardless of all considerations in the way, sparing nothing, treading everything under foot."

She has been looking at the table. She lifts up her eyes, and looks at him. There is a stern expression on her face, and a part of her lower lip is compressed under her teeth. "This woman understands me," Mr. Tulkinghorn thinks, as she lets her glance fall again. "*She* cannot be spared. Why should she spare others?"

For a little while they are silent. Lady Dedlock has eaten no dinner, but has twice or thrice poured out water with a steady hand and drunk it. She rises from table, takes a lounging-chair, and reclines in it, shading her face. There is nothing in her manner to express weakness or excite compassion. It is thoughtful, gloomy, concentrated. "This woman," thinks Mr. Tulkinghorn, standing on the hearth, again a dark object closing up her view, "is a study."

He studies her at his leisure, not speaking for a time. She, too, studies something at her leisure. She is not the first to speak; appearing indeed so unlikely to be so, though he stood there until midnight, that even he is driven upon breaking silence.

"Lady Dedlock, the most disagreeable part of this business interview remains; but it is business. Our agreement is broken. A lady of your sense and strength of character will be prepared for my now declaring it void, and taking my own course."

"I am quite prepared."

Mr. Tulkinghorn inclines his head. "That is all I have to trouble you with, Lady Dedlock."

She stops him as he is moving out of the room, by asking, "This is the notice I was to receive? I wish not to misapprehend you."

"Not exactly the notice you were to receive, Lady Dedlock, because the contemplated notice supposed the agreement to have been observed.

But virtually the same, virtually the same. The difference is merely in a lawyer's mind."

"You intend to give me no other notice?"

"You are right. No."

"Do you contemplate undeceiving Sir Leicester to-night?"

"A home question!" says Mr. Tulkinghorn, with a slight smile, and cautiously shaking his head at the shaded face. "No, not to-night."

"To-morrow?"

"All things considered, I had better decline answering that question, Lady Dedlock. If I were to say I don't know when, exactly, you would not believe me, and it would answer no purpose. It may be to-morrow. I would rather say no more. You are prepared, and I hold out no expectations which circumstances might fail to justify. I wish you good evening."

She removes her hand, turns her pale face towards him as he walks silently to the door, and stops him once again as he is about to open it.

"Do you intend to remain in the house any time? I heard you were writing in the library. Are you going to return there?"

"Only for my hat. I am going home."

She bows her eyes rather than her head, the movement is so slight and curious; and he withdraws. Clear of the room he looks at his watch, but is inclined to doubt it by a minute or thereabouts. There is a splendid clock upon the staircase, famous, as splendid clocks not often are, for its accuracy. "And what do *you* say?" Mr. Tulkinghorn inquires, referring to it. "What do you say?"

If it said now, "Don't go home!" What a famous clock, hereafter, if it said to-night of all the nights that it has counted off, to this old man of all the young and old men who have ever stood before it, "Don't go home!" With its sharp clear bell, it strikes three-quarters after seven, and ticks on again. "Why, you are worse than I thought you," says Mr. Tulkinghorn, muttering reproof to his watch. "Two minutes wrong? At this rate you won't last my time." What a watch to return good for evil, if it ticked in answer "Don't go home!"

He passes out into the streets, and walks on, with his hands behind him, under the shadow of the lofty houses, many of whose mysteries, difficulties, mortgages, delicate affairs of all kinds, are treasured up within his old black satin waistcoat. He is in the confidence of the very bricks and mortar. The high chimney-stacks telegraph family secrets to him. Yet there is not a voice in a mile of them to whisper "Don't go home!"

Through the stir and motion of the commoner streets; through the roar and jar of many vehicles, many feet, many voices; with the blazing shop-lights lighting him on, the west wind blowing him on, and the crowd pressing him on; he is pitilessly urged upon his way, and nothing meets him, murmuring "Don't go home!" Arrived at last in his dull room, to light his candles, and look round and up, and see the Roman pointing from the ceiling, there is no new significance in the Roman's hand to-night, or in the flutter of the attendant groups, to give him the late warning, "Don't come here!"

It is a moonlight night; but the moon, being past the full, is only now rising over the great wilderness of London. The stars are shining as they shone above the turret-leads at Chesney Wold. This woman, as he has of late been so accustomed to call her, looks out upon them. Her soul is turbulent within her; she is sick at heart, and restless. The large rooms are too cramped and close. She cannot endure their restraint, and will walk alone in a neighbouring garden.

Too capricious and imperious in all she does, to be the cause of much surprise in those about her as to anything she does, this woman, loosely muffled, goes out into the moonlight. Mercury attends with the key. Having opened the garden-gate, he delivers the key into his Lady's hand at her request, and is bidden to go back. She will walk there some time, to ease her aching head. She may be an hour; she may be more. She needs no further escort. The gate shuts upon its spring with a clash, and he leaves her, passing on into the dark shade of some trees.

A fine night, and a bright large moon, and multitudes of stars. Mr. Tulkinghorn, in repairing to his cellar, and in opening and shuting those resounding doors, has to cross a little prison-like yard. He looks up casually, thinking what a fine night, what a bright large moon, what multitudes of stars! A quiet night, too.

A very quiet night. When the moon shines very brilliantly, a solitude and stillness seem to proceed from her, that influence even crowded places full of life. Not only is it a still night on dusty high roads and on hill-summits, whence a wide expanse of country may be seen in repose, quieter and quieter as it spreads away into a fringe of trees against the sky, with the grey ghost of a bloom upon them; not only is it a still night in gardens and in woods, and on the river where the water-meadows are fresh and green, and the stream sparkles on among pleasant islands, murmuring weirs, and whispering rushes; not only does the stillness attend it as it flows where houses cluster thick, where many bridges are reflected in it, where wharves and shipping make it black and awful, where it winds from these disfigurements through marshes whose grim beacons stand like skeletons washed ashore, where it expands through the bolder region of rising grounds, rich in corn-field, wind-mill and steeple, and where it mingles with the ever-heaving sea; not only is it a still night on the deep, and on the shore where the watcher stands to see the ship with her spread wings cross the path of light that appears to be presented to only him; but even on this stranger's wilderness of London there is some rest. Its steeples and towers, and its one great dome, grow more ethereal; its smoky house-tops lose their grossness, in the pale effulgence; the noises that arise from the streets are fewer and are softened, and the footsteps on the pavements pass more tranquilly away. In these fields of Mr. Tulking-horn's inhabiting, where the shepherds play on Chancery pipes that

A NEW MEANING IN THE ROMAN.

have no stop, and keep their sheep in the fold by hook and by crook until they have shorn them exceeding close, every noise is merged, this moonlight night, into a distant ringing hum, as if the city were a vast glass, vibrating.

What's that? Who fired a gun or pistol? Where was it?

The few foot-passengers start, stop, and stare about them. Some windows and doors are opened, and people come out to look. It was a loud report, and echoed and rattled heavily. It shook one house, or so a man says who was passing. It has aroused all the dogs in the neighbourhood, who bark vehemently. Terrified cats scamper across the road. While the dogs are yet barking and howling—there is one dog howling like a demon—the church-clocks, as if they were startled too, begin to strike. The hum from the streets, likewise, seems to swell into a shout. But it is soon over. Before the last clock begins to strike ten, there is a lull. When it has ceased, the fine night, the bright large moon, and multitudes of stars, are left at peace again.

Has Mr. Tulkinghorn been disturbed? His windows are dark and quiet, and his door is shut. It must be something unusual indeed, to bring *him* out of his shell. Nothing is heard of him, nothing is seen of him. What power of cannon might it take to shake that rusty old man out of his immovable composure?

For many years, the persistent Roman has been pointing, with no particular meaning, from that ceiling. It is not likely that he has any new meaning in him to-night. Once pointing, always pointing—like any Roman, or even Briton, with a single idea. There he is, no doubt, in his impossible attitude, pointing, unavailingly, all night long. Moonlight, darkness, dawn, sunrise, day. There he is still, eagerly pointing, and no one minds him.

But, a little after the coming of the day, come people to clean the rooms. And either the Roman has some new meaning in him, not expressed before, or the foremost of them goes wild; for, looking up at his outstretched hand, and looking down at what is below it, that person shrieks and flies. The others, looking in as the first one looked, shriek and fly too, and there is an alarm in the street.

What does it mean? No light is admitted into the darkened chamber, and people unaccustomed to it, enter, and, treading softly, but heavily, carry a weight into the bedroom, and lay it down. There is whispering and wondering all day, strict search of every corner, careful tracing of steps, and careful noting of the disposition of every article of furniture. All eyes look up at the Roman, and all voices murmur, "If he could only tell what he saw!"

He is pointing at a table, with a bottle (nearly full of wine) and a glass upon it, and two candles that were blown out suddenly, soon after being lighted. He is pointing at an empty chair, and at a stain upon the ground before it that might be almost covered with a hand. These objects lie directly within his range. An excited imagination might suppose that there was something in them so terrific, as to drive the rest of the composition, not only the attendant big-legged boys, but the clouds and flowers and pillars too—in short, the very body and soul of Allegory, and all the brains it has—stark mad. It happens surely, that every one who comes into the darkened room and looks at these things, looks up at the Roman, and that he is invested in all eyes with mystery and awe, as if he were a paralysed dumb witness.

So, it shall happen surely, through many years to come, that ghostly stories shall be told of the stain upon the floor, so easily to be covered, so hard to be got out; and that the Roman, pointing from the ceiling, shall point, so long as dust and damp and spiders spare him, with far greater significance than he had ever had in Mr. Tulkinghorn's time, and with a deadly meaning. For, Mr. Tulkinghorn's time is over for evermore ; and the Roman pointed at the murderous hand uplifted against his life, and pointed helplessly at him, from night to morning, lying face downward on the floor, shot through the heart.

CHAPTER XLIX

DUTIFUL FRIENDSHIP

A GREAT annual occasion has come round in the establishment of Mr. Joseph Bagnet, otherwise Lignum Vitæ, ex-artilleryman and present bassoon-player. An occasion of feasting and festival. The celebration of a birthday in the family.

It is not Mr. Bagnet's birthday. Mr. Bagnet merely distinguishes that epoch in the musical instrument business, by kissing the children with an extra smack before breakfast, smoking an additional pipe after dinner, and wondering towards evening what his poor old mother is thinking about it,—a subject of infinite speculation, and rendered so by his mother having departed this life twenty years. Some men rarely revert to their father, but seem, in the bank-books of their remembrance, to have transferred all the stock of filial affection into their mother's name. Mr. Bagnet is one of these. Perhaps his exalted appreciation of the merits of the old girl, causes him usually to make the noun-substantive, Goodness, of the feminine gender.

It is not the birthday of one of the three children. Those occasions are kept with some marks of distinction, but they rarely overleap the bounds of happy returns and a pudding. On young Woolwich's last birthday, Mr. Bagnet certainly did, after observing upon his growth and general advancement, proceed, in a moment of profound reflection on the changes wrought by time, to examine him in the catechism ; accomplishing with extreme accuracy the questions number one and two. What is your name ? and Who gave you that name ? but there failing in the exact precision of his memory, and substituting for number three, the question And how do you like that name ? which he propounded with a sense of its importance, in itself so edifying and improving, as to give it quite an orthodox air. This, however, was a speciality on that particular birthday, and not a general solemnity.

It is the old girl's birthday; and that is the greatest holiday and reddest-letter day in Mr. Bagnet's calendar. The auspicious event is always commemorated according to certain forms, settled and prescribed by Mr. Bagnet some years since. Mr. Bagnet being deeply convinced that to have a pair of fowls for dinner is to attain the highest pitch of imperial luxury, invariably goes forth himself very early in the morning of this day to buy a pair; he is, as invariably, taken in by the vendor, and installed in the possession of the oldest inhabitants of any coop in Europe. Returning with these triumphs of toughness tied up in a clean blue and white cotton handkerchief (essential to the arrangements), he in a casual manner invites Mrs. Bagnet to declare at breakfast what she would like for dinner. Mrs. Bagnet, by a coincidence never known to fail, replying Fowls, Mr. Bagnet instantly produces his bundle from a place of concealment, amidst general amazement and rejoicing. He further requires that the old girl shall do nothing all day long, but sit in her very best gown, and be served by himself and the young people. As he is not illustrious for his cookery, this may be supposed to be a matter of state rather than enjoyment on the old girl's part; but she keeps her state with all imaginable cheerfulness.

On this present birthday, Mr. Bagnet has accomplished the usual preliminaries. He has bought two specimens of poultry, which, if there be any truth in adages, were certainly not caught with chaff, to be prepared for the spit; he has amazed and rejoiced the family by their unlooked-for production; he is himself directing the roasting of the poultry; and Mrs. Bagnet, with her wholesome brown fingers itching to prevent what she sees going wrong, sits in her gown of ceremony, an honoured guest.

Quebec and Malta lay the cloth for dinner, while Woolwich, serving, as beseems him, under his father, keeps the fowls revolving. To these young scullions Mrs. Bagnet occasionally imparts a wink, or a shake of the head, or a crooked face, as they made mistakes.

"At half-after one," says Mr. Bagnet. "To the minute. They'll be done."

Mrs. Bagnet, with anguish, beholds one of them at a stand-still before the fire, and beginning to burn.

"You shall have a dinner, old girl," says Mr. Bagnet. "Fit for a queen."

Mrs. Bagnet shows her white teeth cheerfully, but to the perception of her son betrays so much uneasiness of spirit, that he is impelled by the dictates of affection to ask her, with his eyes, what is the matter? —thus standing, with his eyes wide open, more oblivious of the fowls than before, and not affording the least hope of a return to consciousness. Fortunately, his elder sister perceives the cause of the agitation in Mrs. Bagnet's breast, and with an admonitory poke recalls him. The stopped fowls going round again, Mrs. Bagnet closes her eyes, in the intensity of her relief.

"George will look us up," says Mr. Bagnet. "At half-after four. To the moment. How many years, old girl. Has George looked us up. This afternoon?"

"Ah, Lignum, Lignum, as many as make an old woman of a young one, I begin to think. Just about that, and no less," returns Mrs. Bagnet, laughing, and shaking her head.

"Old girl," says Mr. Bagnet, "Never mind. You'd be as young as ever you was. If you wasn't younger. Which you are. As everybody knows."

Quebec and Malta here exclaim, with clapping of hands, that Bluffy is sure to bring mother something, and begin to speculate on what it will be.

"Do you know, Lignum," says Mrs. Bagnet, casting a glance on the table-cloth, and winking "salt!" at Malta with her right eye, and shaking the pepper away from Quebec with her head; "I begin to think George is in the roving way again."

"George," returns Mr. Bagnet, "will never desert. And leave his old comrade. In the lurch. Don't be afraid of it."

"No, Lignum. No. I don't say he will. I don't think he will. But if he could get over this money-trouble of his, I believe he would be off."

Mr. Bagnet asks why?

"Well," returns his wife, considering. "George seems to me to be getting not a little impatient and restless. I don't say but what he's as free as ever. Of course he must be free, or he wouldn't be George; but he smarts, and seems put out."

"He's extra-drilled," says Mr. Bagnet. "By a lawyer. Who would put the devil out."

"There's something in that," his wife assents; "but so it is, Lignum."

Further conversation is prevented, for the time, by the necessity under which Mr. Bagnet finds himself of directing the whole force of his mind to the dinner, which is a little endangered by the dry humour of the fowls in not yielding any gravy, and also by the made-gravy acquiring no flavour, and turning out of a flaxen complexion. With a similar perverseness, the potatoes crumble off forks in the process of peeling, upheaving from their centres in every direction, as if they were subject to earthquakes. The legs of the fowls, too, are longer than could be desired, and extremely scaly. Overcoming these disadvantages to the best of his ability, Mr. Bagnet at last dishes, and they sit down at table; Mrs. Bagnet occupying the guest's place at his right hand.

It is well for the old girl that she has but one birthday in a year, for two such indulgences in poultry might be injurious. Every kind of finer tendon and ligament that it is in the nature of poultry to possess, is developed in these specimens in the singular form of guitar-strings. Their limbs appear to have struck roots into their breasts and bodies, as aged trees strike roots into the earth. Their legs are so hard, as to encourage the idea that they must have devoted the greater part of their long and arduous lives to pedestrian exercises, and the walking of matches. But Mr. Bagnet, unconscious of these little defects, sets his heart on Mrs.

Bagnet eating a most severe quantity of the delicacies before her; and as that good old girl would not cause him a moment's disappointment on any day, least of all on such a day, for any consideration, she imperils her digestion fearfully. How young Woolwich cleans the drum-sticks without being of ostrich descent, his anxious mother is at a loss to understand.

The old girl has another trial to undergo after the conclusion of the repast, in sitting in state to see the room cleared, the hearth swept, and the dinner-service washed up and polished in the back yard. The great delight and energy with which the two young ladies apply themselves to these duties, turning up their skirts in imitation of their mother, and skating in and out on little scaffolds of pattens, inspire the highest hopes for the future, but some anxiety for the present. The same causes lead to a confusion of tongues, a clattering of crockery, a rattling of tin mugs, a whisking of brooms, and an expenditure of water, all in excess; while the saturation of the young ladies themselves is almost too moving a spectacle for Mrs. Bagnet to look upon, with the calmness proper to her position. At last the various cleansing processes are triumphantly completed; Quebec and Malta appear in fresh attire, smiling and dry; pipes, tobacco, and something to drink, are placed upon the table; and the old girl enjoys the first peace of mind she ever knows on the day of this delightful entertainment.

When Mr. Bagnet takes his usual seat, the hands of the clock are very near to half-past four; as they mark it accurately, Mr. Bagnet announces.

"George! Military time."

It is George; and he has hearty congratulations for the old girl (whom he kisses on the great occasion), and for the children, and for Mr. Bagnet. "Happy returns to all!" says Mr. George.

"But, George, old man!" cries Mrs. Bagnet, looking at him curiously. "What's come to you?"

"Come to me?"

"Ah! you are so white, George—for you—and look so shocked. Now don't he, Lignum?"

"George," says Mr. Bagnet, "tell the old girl. What's the matter."

"I didn't know I looked white," says the trooper, passing his hand over his brow, "and I didn't know I looked shocked, and I'm sorry I do. But the truth is, that boy who was taken in at my place died yesterday afternoon, and it has rather knocked me over."

"Poor creetur!" says Mrs. Bagnet, with a mother's pity. "Is he gone? Dear, dear!"

"I didn't mean to say anything about it, for it's not birthday talk, but you have got it out of me, you see, before I sit down. I should have roused up in a minute," says the trooper, making himself speak more gaily, "but you're so quick, Mrs. Bagnet."

"You're right. The old girl," says Mr. Bagnet, "is as quick. As powder."

"And what's more, she's the subject of the day, and we'll stick to her," cries Mr. George. "See here, I have brought a little brooch along with me. It's a poor thing, you know, but it's a keepsake. That's all the good it is, Mrs. Bagnet."

Mr. George produces his present, which is greeted with admiring leapings and clappings by the young family, and with a species of reverential admiration by Mr. Bagnet. "Old girl," says Mr. Bagnet, "tell him my opinion of it."

"Why, it's a wonder, George!" Mrs. Bagnet exclaims. "It's the beautifullest thing that ever was seen!"

"Good!" says Mr. Bagnet. "My opinion."

"It's so pretty, George," cries Mrs. Bagnet, turning it on all sides, and holding it out at arm's length, "that it seems too choice for me."

"Bad!" says Mr. Bagnet. "Not my opinion."

"But whatever it is, a hundred thousand thanks, old fellow," says Mrs. Bagnet, her eyes sparkling with pleasure, and her hand stretched out to him; "and though I have been a cross-grained soldier's wife to you sometimes, George, we are as strong friends, I am sure, in reality, as ever can be. Now you shall fasten it on yourself, for good luck, if you will, George."

The children close up to see it done, and Mr. Bagnet looks over young Woolwich's head to see it done, with an interest so maturely wooden, yet so pleasantly childish, that Mrs. Bagnet cannot help laughing in her airy way, and saying, "O Lignum, Lignum, what a precious old chap you are!" But the trooper fails to fasten the brooch. His hand shakes, he is nervous, and it falls off. "Would any one believe this?" says he, catching it as it drops, and looking round. "I am so out of sorts that I bungle at an easy job like this!"

Mrs. Bagnet concludes that for such a case there is no remedy like a pipe; and fastening the brooch herself in a twinkling, causes the trooper to be inducted into his usual snug place, and the pipes to be got into action. "If that don't bring you round, George," says she, "just throw your eye across here at your present now and then, and the two together *must* do it."

"You ought to do it of yourself," George answers; "I know that very well, Mrs. Bagnet. I'll tell you how, one way and another, the blues have got to be too many for me. Here was this poor lad. 'Twas dull work to see him dying as he did, and not be able to help him."

"What do you mean, George? You did help him. You took him under your roof."

"I helped him so far, but that's little. I mean, Mrs. Bagnet, there he was, dying without ever having been taught much more than to know his right hand from his left. And he was too far gone to be helped out of that."

"Ah, poor creetur!" says Mrs. Bagnet.

"Then," says the trooper, not yet lighting his pipe, and passing his heavy hand over his hair, "that brought up Gridley in a man's mind.

His was a bad case too, in a different way. Then the two got mixed up in a man's mind with a flinty old rascal who had to do with both. And to think of that rusty carbine, stock and barrel, standing up on end in his corner, hard, indifferent, taking everything so evenly—it made flesh and blood tingle, I do assure you."

"My advice to you," returns Mrs. Bagnet, "is to light your pipe, and tingle that way. It's wholesomer and comfortabler, and better for the health altogether."

"You're right," says the trooper, "and I'll do it."

So, he does it : though still with an indignant gravity that impresses the young Bagnets, and even causes Mr. Bagnet to defer the ceremony of drinking Mrs. Bagnet's health ; always given by himself, on these occasions, in a speech of exemplary terseness. But the young ladies having composed what Mr. Bagnet is in the habit of calling " the mixtur," and George's pipe being now in a glow, Mr. Bagnet considers it his duty to proceed to the toast of the evening. He addresses the assembled company in the following terms.

"George. Woolwich. Quebec. Malta. This is her birthday. Take a day's march. And you won't find such another. Here's towards her !"

The toast having been drunk with enthusiasm, Mrs. Bagnet returns thanks in a neat address of corresponding brevity. This model composition is limited to the three words "And wishing yours !" which the old girl follows up with a nod at everybody in succession, and a well-regulated swig of the mixture. This she again follows up, on the present occasion, by the wholly unexpected exclamation, "Here's a man !"

Here *is* a man, much to the astonishment of the little company, looking in at the parlour-door. He is a sharp-eyed man—a quick keen man— and he takes in everybody's look at him, all at once, individually and collectively, in a manner that stamps him a remarkable man.

"George," says the man, nodding, "how do you find yourself?"

"Why, it's Bucket !" cries Mr. George.

"Yes," says the man, coming in and closing the door. "I was going down the street here, when I happened to stop and look in at the musical instruments in the shop-window—a friend of mine is in wants of a second-hand wiolinceller, of a good tone—and I saw a party enjoying themselves, and I thought it was you in the corner ; I thought I couldn't be mistaken. How goes the world with you, George, at the present moment ? Pretty smooth ? And with you, ma'am ? And with you, governor ? And Lord !" says Mr. Bucket, opening his arms, "here's children too ! You may do anything with me, if you only show me children. Give us a kiss, my pets. No occasion to inquire who *your* father and mother is. Never saw such a likeness in my life !"

Mr. Bucket, not unwelcome, has sat himself down next to Mr. George, and taken Quebec and Malta on his knees. "You pretty dears," says Mr. Bucket, "give us another kiss ; it's the only thing I'm greedy in. Lord bless you, how healthy you look ! And what may be the ages of these two, ma'am? I should put 'em down at the figures of about eight and ten."

"You're very near, sir," says Mrs. Bagnet.

"I generally am near," returns Mr. Bucket, "being so fond of children. A friend of mine has had nineteen of 'em, ma'am, all by one mother, and she's still as fresh and rosy as the morning. Not so much so as yourself, but, upon my soul, she comes near you! And what do you call these, my darling?" pursues Mr. Bucket, pinching Malta's cheeks. "These are peaches, these are. Bless your heart! And what do you think about father? Do you think father could recommend a second-hand wiolinceller of a good tone for Mr. Bucket's friend, my dear? My name's Bucket. Ain't that a funny name?"

These blandishments have entirely won the family heart. Mrs. Bagnet forgets the day to the extent of filling a pipe and a glass for Mr. Bucket, and waiting upon him hospitably. She would be glad to receive so pleasant a character under any circumstances, but she tells him that as a friend of George's she is particularly glad to see him this evening, for George has not been in his usual spirits.

"Not in his usual spirits?" exclaims Mr. Bucket. "Why, I never heard of such a thing! What's the matter, George? You don't intend to tell me you've been out of spirits. What should you be out of spirits for? You haven't got anything on your mind, you know."

"Nothing particular," returns the trooper.

"*I* should think not," rejoins Mr. Bucket. "What could you have on your mind, you know! And have these pets got anything on *their* minds, eh? Not they; but they'll be upon the minds of some of the young fellows, some of these days, and make 'em precious low-spirited. I ain't much of a prophet, but I can tell you that, ma'am."

Mrs. Bagnet, quite charmed, hopes Mr. Bucket has a family of his own.

"There, ma'am!" says Mr. Bucket. "Would you believe it? No, I haven't. My wife, and a lodger, constitute my family. Mrs. Bucket is as fond of children as myself, and as wishful to have 'em; but no. So it is. Worldly goods are divided unequally, and man must not repine. What a very nice back yard, ma'am! Any way out of that yard, now?"

There is no way out of that yard.

"Ain't there really?" says Mr. Bucket. "I should have thought there might have been. Well, I don't know as I ever saw a back yard that took my fancy more. Would you allow me to look at it? Thank you. No, I see there's no way out. But what a very good-proportioned yard it is!"

Having cast his sharp eye all about it, Mr. Bucket returns to his chair next his friend Mr. George, and pats Mr. George affectionately on the shoulder.

"How are your spirits, now, George?"

"All right now," returns the trooper.

"That's your sort!" says Mr. Bucket. "Why should you ever have been otherwise? A man of your fine figure and constitution has no right to be out of spirits. That ain't a chest to be out of spirits, is it, ma'am? And you haven't got anything on your mind, you know, George; what could you have on your mind!"

Somewhat harping on this phrase, considering the extent and variety of his conversational powers, Mr. Bucket twice or thrice repeats it to the pipe he lights, and with a listening face that is particularly his own. But the sun of his sociality soon recovers from this brief eclipse, and shines again.

"And this is brother, is it, my dears?" says Mr. Bucket, referring to Quebec and Malta for information on the subject of young Woolwich. "And a nice brother he is—half brother I mean to say. For he's too old to be your boy, ma'am."

"I can certify, at all events, that he is not anybody else's," returns Mrs. Bagnet, laughing.

"Well, you do surprise me! Yet he's like you, there's no denying. Lord, he's wonderfully like you! But about what you may call the brow, you know, *there* his father comes out!" Mr. Bucket compares the faces with one eye shut up, while Mr. Bagnet smokes in stolid satisfaction.

This is an opportunity for Mrs. Bagnet to inform him that the boy is George's godson.

"George's godson, is he?" rejoins Mr. Bucket, with extreme cordiality. "I must shake hands over again with George's godson. Godfather and godson do credit to one another. And what do you intend to make of him, ma'am? Does he show any turn for any musical instrument?"

Mr. Bagnet suddenly interposes, "Plays the Fife. Beautiful."

"Would you believe it, governor," says Mr. Bucket, struck by the coincidence, "that when I was a boy I played the fife myself? Not in a scientific way, as I expect he does, but by ear. Lord bless you! British Grenadiers—there's a tune to warm an Englishman up! *Could* you give us British Grenadiers, my fine fellow?"

Nothing could be more acceptable to the little circle than this call upon young Woolwich, who immediately fetches his fife and performs the stirring melody; during which performance Mr. Bucket, much enlivened, beats time, and never fails to come in sharp with the burden, "Brit Ish Gra-a-anadeers!" In short, he shows so much musical taste, that Mr. Bagnet actually takes his pipe from his lips to express his conviction that he is a singer. Mr. Bucket receives the harmonious impeachment so modestly: confessing how that he did once chaunt a little, for the expression of the feelings of his own bosom, and with no presumptuous idea of entertaining his friends: that he is asked to sing. Not to be behindhand in the sociality of the evening, he complies, and gives them "Believe me if all those endearing young charms." This ballad, he informs Mrs. Bagnet, he considers to have been his most powerful ally in moving the heart of Mrs. Bucket when a maiden, and inducing her to approach the altar—Mr. Bucket's own words are, to come up to the scratch.

This sparkling stranger is such a new and agreeable feature in the evening, that Mr. George, who testified no great emotions of pleasure on his entrance, begins, in spite of himself, to be rather proud of him. He is so friendly, is a man of so many resources, and so easy to get on with, that it is something to have made him known there. Mr. Bagnet becomes, after another pipe, so sensible of the value of his acquaintance, that he solicits the honour of his company on the old girl's next birthday. If anything can more closely cement and consolidate the esteem which Mr. Bucket has formed for the family, it is the discovery of the nature of the occasion. He drinks to Mrs. Bagnet with a warmth approaching to rapture, engages himself for that day twelvemonth more than thankfully, makes a memorandum of the day in a large black pocket-book with a girdle to it, and breathes a hope that Mrs. Bucket and Mrs. Bagnet may before then become, in a manner, sisters. As he says himself, what is public life without private ties? He is in his humble way a public man, but it is not in that sphere that he finds happiness. No, it must be sought within the confines of domestic bliss.

It is natural, under these circumstances, that he, in his turn, should remember the friend to whom he is indebted for so promising an acquaintance. And he does. He keeps very close to him. Whatever the subject of the conversation, he keeps a tender eye upon him. He waits to walk home with him. He is interested in his very boots ; and observes even them attentively, as Mr. George sits smoking cross-legged in the chimney-corner.

At length, Mr. George rises to depart. At the same moment Mr. Bucket, with the secret sympathy of friendship, also rises. He dotes upon the children to the last, and remembers the commission he has undertaken for an absent friend.

"Respecting that second-hand wiolinceller, governor—could you recommend me such a thing?"

"Scores," says Mr. Bagnet.

"I am obliged to you," returns Mr. Bucket, squeezing his hand. "You're a friend in need. A good tone, mind you! My friend is a regular dab at it. Ecod, he saws away at Mo-zart and Handel, and the rest of the big-wigs, like a thorough workman. And you needn't," says Mr. Bucket, in a considerate and private voice, "you needn't commit yourself to too low a figure, governor. I don't want to pay too large a price for my friend ; but I want you to have your proper percentage, and be remunerated for your loss of time. That is but fair. Every man must live, and ought to it."

Mr. Bagnet shakes his head at the old girl, to the effect that they have found a jewel of price.

"Suppose I was to give you a look in, say at half-arter ten to-morrow morning. Perhaps you could name the figures of a few wiolincellers of a good tone?" says Mr. Bucket.

Nothing easier. Mr. and Mrs. Bagnet both engage to have the requisite information ready, and even hint to each other at the practicability of having a small stock collected there for approval.

FRIENDLY BEHAVIOUR OF MR. BUCKET.

"Thank you," says Mr. Bucket, "thank you. Good night, ma'am. Good night, governor. Good night, darlings. I am much obliged to you for one of the pleasantest evenings I ever spent in my life."

They, on the contrary, are much obliged to him for the pleasure he has given them in his company; and so they part with many expressions of goodwill on both sides. "Now, George, old boy," says Mr. Bucket, taking his arm at the shop-door, "come along!" As they go down the little street, and the Bagnets pause for a minute looking after them, Mrs. Bagnet remarks to the worthy Lignum that Mr. Bucket "almost clings to George like, and seems to be really fond of him."

The neighbouring streets being narrow and ill-paved, it is a little inconvenient to walk there two abreast and arm-in-arm. Mr. George therefore soon proposes to walk singly. But Mr. Bucket, who cannot make up his mind to relinquish his friendly hold, replies, "Wait half a minute, George. I should wish to speak to you first." Immediately afterwards, he twists him into a public-house and into a parlour, where he confronts him, and claps his own back against the door.

"Now, George," says Mr. Bucket. "Duty is duty, and friendship is friendship. I never want the two to clash, if I can help it. I have endeavoured to make things pleasant to-night, and I put it to you whether I have done it or not. You must consider yourself in custody, George."

"Custody? What for?" returns the trooper, thunderstruck.

"Now, George," says Mr. Bucket, urging a sensible view of the case upon him with his fat forefinger, "duty, as you know very well, is one thing, and conversation is another. It's my duty to inform you that any observations you may make will be liable to be used against you. Therefore, George, be careful what you say. You don't happen to have heard of a murder?"

"Murder!"

"Now, George," says Mr. Bucket, keeping his forefinger in an impressive state of action, "bear in mind what I've said to you. I ask you nothing. You've been in low spirits this afternoon. I say, you don't happen to have heard of a murder."

"No. Where has there been a murder?"

"Now, George," says Mr. Bucket, "don't you go and commit yourself. I'm a-going to tell you what I want you for. There has been a murder in Lincoln's Inn Fields—gentleman of the name of Tulkinghorn. He was shot last night. I want you for that."

The trooper sinks upon a seat behind him, and great drops start out upon his forehead, and a deadly pallor overspreads his face.

"Bucket! It's not possible that Mr. Tulkinghorn has been killed, and that you suspect *me*?"

"George," returns Mr. Bucket, keeping his forefinger going, "it is certainly possible, because it's the case. This deed was done last night at ten o'clock. Now, you know where you were last night at ten o'clock, and you'll be able to prove it, no doubt."

"Last night! Last night?" repeats the trooper, thoughtfully. Then it flashes upon him. "Why, great Heaven, I was there, last night!"

"So I have understood, George," returns Mr. Bucket, with great deliberation. "So I have understood. Likewise you've been very often there. You've been seen hanging about the place, and you've been heard more than once in a wrangle with him, and it's possible—I don't say it's certainly so, mind you, but it's possible—that he may have been heard to call you a threatening, murdering, dangerous fellow."

The trooper gasps as if he would admit it all, if he could speak.

"Now, George," continues Mr. Bucket, putting his hat upon the table, with an air of business rather in the upholstery way than otherwise, "My wish is, as it has been all the evening, to make things pleasant. I tell you plainly there's a reward out, of a hundred guineas, offered by Sir Leicester Dedlock, Baronet. You and me have always been pleasant together; but I have got a duty to discharge; and if that hundred guineas is to be made, it may as well be made by me as any other man. On all of which accounts, I should hope it was clear to you that I must have you, and that I'm damned if I don't have you. Am I to call in any assistance, or is the trick done?"

Mr. George has recovered himself, and stands up like a soldier. "Come," he says; "I am ready."

"George," continues Mr. Bucket, "wait a bit!" With his upholsterer manner, as if the trooper were a window to be fitted up, he takes from his pocket a pair of handcuffs. "This is a serious charge, George, and such is my duty."

The trooper flushes angrily, and hesitates a moment; but holds out his two hands, clasped together, and says, "There! Put them on!"

Mr. Bucket adjusts them in a moment. "How do you find them? Are they comfortable? If not, say so, for I wish to make things as pleasant as is consistent with my duty, and I've got another pair in my pocket." This remark he offers like a most respectable tradesman, anxious to execute an order neatly, and to the perfect satisfaction of his customer. "They'll do as they are? Very well! Now, you see, George;" he takes a cloak from a corner, and begins adjusting it about the trooper's neck; "I was mindful of your feelings when I come out, and brought this on purpose. There! Who's the wiser?"

"Only I," returns the trooper; "but, as I know it, do me one more good turn, and pull my hat over my eyes."

"Really, though! Do you mean it? Ain't it a pity? It looks so."

"I can't look chance men in the face with these things on," Mr. George hurriedly replies. "Do, for God's sake, pull my hat forward."

So strongly entreated, Mr. Bucket complies, puts his own hat on, and conducts his prize into the streets; the trooper marching on as steadily as usual, though with his head less erect; and Mr. Bucket steering him with his elbow over the crossings and up the turnings.

CHAPTER L

ESTHER'S NARRATIVE

IT happened that when I came home from Deal, I found a note from Caddy Jellyby (as we always continued to call her), informing me that her health, which had been for some time very delicate, was worse, and that she would be more glad than she could tell me if I would go to see her. It was a note of a few lines, written from the couch on which she lay, and enclosed to me in another from her husband, in which he seconded her entreaty with much solicitude. Caddy was now the mother, and I the godmother, of such a poor little baby—such a tiny old-faced mite, with a countenance that seemed to be scarcely anything but cap-border, and a little lean, long-fingered hand, always clenched under its chin. It would lie in this attitude all day, with its bright specks of eyes open, wondering (as I used to imagine) how it came to be so small and weak. Whenever it was moved it cried; but at all other times it was so patient, that the sole desire of its life appeared to be, to lie quiet, and think. It had curious little dark veins in its face, and curious little dark marks under its eyes, like faint remembrances of poor Caddy's inky days; and altogether, to those who were not used to it, it was quite a piteous little sight.

But it was enough for Caddy that *she* was used to it. The projects with which she beguiled her illness, for little Esther's education, and little Esther's marriage, and even for her own old age, as the grandmother of little Esther's little Esthers, was so prettily expressive of devotion to this pride of her life, that I should be tempted to recall some of them, but for the timely remembrance that I am getting on irregularly as it is.

To return to the letter. Caddy had a superstition about me, which had been strengthening in her mind ever since that night long ago, when she had lain asleep with her head in my lap. She almost—I think I must say quite—believed that I did her good whenever I was near her. Now, although this was such a fancy of the affectionate girl's that I am almost ashamed to mention it, still it might have all the force of a fact when she was really ill. Therefore I set off to Caddy, with my guardian's consent, post-haste; and she and Prince made so much of me, that there never was anything like it.

Next day I went again to sit with her, and next day I went again. It was a very easy journey; for I had only to rise a little earlier in the morning, and keep my accounts, and attend to housekeeping matters before leaving home. But when I had made these three visits, my guardian said to me, on my return at night:

"Now, little woman, little woman, this will never do. Constant dropping will wear away a stone, and constant coaching will wear out a Dame Durden. We will go to London for a while, and take possession of our old lodgings."

"Not for me, dear Guardian," said I, "for I never feel tired;" which was strictly true. I was only too happy to be in such request.

"For me then," returned my guardian; "or for Ada, or for both of us. It is somebody's birthday to-morrow, I think."

"Truly I think it is," said I, kissing my darling, who would be twenty-one to-morrow.

"Well," observed my guardian, half-pleasantly, half-seriously, "that's a great occasion, and will give my fair cousin some necessary business to transact in assortion of her independence, and will make London a more convenient place for all of us. So to London we will go. That being settled, there is another thing—how have you left Caddy?"

"Very unwell, Guardian. I fear it will be some time before she regains her health and strength."

"What do you call some time, now?" asked my guardian thoughtfully.

"Some weeks, I am afraid."

"Ah!" He began to walk about the room with his hands in his pockets, showing that he had been thinking as much. "Now what do you say about her doctor? Is he a good doctor, my love?"

I felt obliged to confess that I knew nothing to the contrary; but that Prince and I had agreed only that evening, that we would like his opinion to be confirmed by some one.

"Well, you know," returned my guardian quickly, "there's Woodcourt."

I had not meant that, and was rather taken by surprise. For a moment, all that I had had in my mind in connection with Mr. Woodcourt seemed to come back and confuse me.

"You don't object to him, little woman?"

"Object to him, Guardian? Oh no!"

"And you don't think the patient would object to him?"

So far from that, I had no doubt of her being prepared to have a great reliance on him, and to like him very much. I said that he was no stranger to her personally, for she had seen him often in his kind attendance on Miss Flite.

"Very good," said my guardian. ".He has been here to-day, my dear, and I will see him about it to-morrow."

I felt, in this short conversation—though I did not know how, for she was quiet, and we interchanged no look—that my dear girl well remembered how merrily she had clasped me round the waist, when no other hands than Caddy's had brought me the little parting token. This caused me to feel that I ought to tell her, and Caddy too, that I was going to be the mistress of Bleak House; and that if I avoided that disclosure any longer, I might become less worthy in my own eyes, of its master's love. Therefore, when we went upstairs, and had waited listening until the clock struck twelve, in order that only I might be the first to wish my darling all good wishes on her birthday, and to take her to my heart, I set before her, just as I had set before myself, the goodness and honour of her cousin John, and the happy life that was in store for me. If ever

my darling were fonder of me at one time than at another in all our intercourse, she was surely fondest of me that night. And I was so rejoiced
to know it, and so comforted by the sense of having done right, in casting
this last idle reservation away, that I was ten times happier than I had
been before. I had scarcely thought it a reservation a few hours ago;
but now that it was gone, I felt as if I understood its nature better.

Next day we went to London. We found our old lodging vacant, and
in half-an-hour were quietly established there, as if we had never gone
away. Mr. Woodcourt dined with us, to celebrate my darling's birthday;
and we were as pleasant as we could be with the great blank among us
that Richard's absence naturally made on such an occasion. After that
day I was for some weeks—eight or nine as I remember—very much
with Caddy; and thus it fell out that I saw less of Ada at this time than
any other since we had first come together, except the time of my own
illness. She often came to Caddy's; but our function there was to amuse
and cheer her, and we did not talk in our usual confidential manner.
Whenever I went home at night, we were together; but Caddy's rest
was broken by pain, and I often remained to nurse her.

With her husband and her poor little mite of a baby to love, and their
home to strive for, what a good creature Caddy was! So self-denying, so
uncomplaining, so anxious to get well on their account, so afraid of giving
trouble, and so thoughtful of the unassisted labours of her husband and
the comforts of old Mr. Turveydrop; I had never known the best of her
until now. And it seemed so curious that her pale face and helpless
figure should be lying there day after day, where dancing was the business
of life; where the kit and the apprentices began early every morning in
the ball-room, and where the untidy little boy waltzed by himself in the
kitchen all the afternoon.

At Caddy's request, I took the supreme direction of her apartment,
trimmed it up, and pushed her, couch and all, into a lighter and more
airy and more cheerful corner than she had yet occupied; then, every day,
when we were in our neatest array, I used to lay my small small namesake in her arms, and sit down to chat or work, or read to her. It was
at one of the first of these quiet times that I told Caddy about Bleak
House.

We had other visitors besides Ada. First of all, we had Prince, who in
his hurried intervals of teaching used to come softly in and sit softly down,
with a face of loving anxiety for Caddy and the very little child. Whatever Caddy's condition really was, she never failed to declare to Prince
that she was all but well—which I, Heaven forgive me, never failed to
confirm. This would put Prince in such good spirits, that he would sometimes take the kit from his pocket and play a chord or two to astonish
the baby—which I never knew it to do in the least degree, for my tiny
namesake never noticed it at all.

Then there was Mrs. Jellyby. She would come occasionally with her
usual distraught manner, and sit calmly looking miles beyond her grand-
child, as if her attention were absorbed by a young Borrioboolan on its

native shores. As bright-eyed as ever, as serene, and as untidy, she would say, "Well, Caddy, child, and how do you do to-day?" And then would sit amiably smiling, and taking no notice of the reply; or would sweetly glide off into a calculation of the number of letters she had lately received and answered, or of the coffee-bearing power of Borrioboola-Gha. This she would always do with a serene contempt for our limited sphere of action, not to be disguised.

Then there was old Mr. Turveydrop, who was from morning to night and from night to morning the subject of innumerable precautions. If the baby cried, it was nearly stifled lest the noise should make him uncomfortable. If the fire wanted stirring in the night, it was surreptitiously done lest his rest should be broken. If Caddy required any little comfort that the house contained, she first carefully discussed whether he was likely to require it too. In return for this consideration, he would come into the room once a day, all but blessing it—showing a condescension, and a patronage, and a grace of manner, in dispensing the light of his high-shouldered presence, from which I might have supposed him (if I had not known better) to have been the benefactor of Caddy's life.

"My Caroline," he would say, making the nearest approach that he could to bending over her. "Tell me that you are better to-day."

"Oh much better, thank you, Mr. Turveydrop," Caddy would reply.

"Delighted! Enchanted! And our dear Miss Summerson. She is not quite prostrated by fatigue?" Here he would crease up his eyelids, and kiss his fingers to me; though I am happy to say he had ceased to be particular in his attentions, since I had been so altered.

"Not at all," I would assure him.

"Charming! We must take care of our dear Caroline, Miss Summerson. We must spare nothing that will restore her. We must nourish her. My dear Caroline;" he would turn to his daughter-in-law with infinite generosity and protection; "want for nothing, my love. Frame a wish and gratify it, my daughter. Everything this house contains, everything my room contains, is at your service, my dear. Do not," he would sometimes add, in a burst of Deportment, "even allow my simple requirements to be considered, if they should at any time interfere with your own, my Caroline. Your necessities are greater than mine."

He had established such a long prescriptive right to this Deportment (his son's inheritance from his mother), that I several times knew both Caddy and her husband to be melted to tears by these affectionate self-sacrifices.

"Nay, my dears," he would remonstrate; and when I saw Caddy's thin arm about his fat neck as he said it, I would be melted too, though not by the same process; "Nay, nay! I have promised never to leave ye. Be dutiful and affectionate towards me, and I ask no other return. Now, bless ye! I am going to the Park."

He would take the air there, presently, and get an appetite for his hotel dinner. I hope I do old Mr. Turveydrop no wrong; but I never saw any better traits in him than these I faithfully record, except that he certainly conceived a liking for Peepy, and would take the child out walking with great pomp—always, on those occasions, sending him home before he went to dinner himself, and occasionally with a halfpenny in his pocket. But, even this disinterestedness was attended with no inconsiderable cost, to my knowledge; for before Peepy was sufficiently decorated to walk hand-in-hand with the professor of Deportment, he had to be newly dressed, at the expense of Caddy and her husband, from top to toe.

Last of our visitors, there was Mr. Jellyby. Really when he used to come in of an evening, and ask Caddy in his meek voice how she was, and then sit down with his head against the wall, and make no attempt to say anything more, I liked him very much. If he found me bustling about, doing any little thing, he sometimes half took his coat off, as if with an intention of helping by a great exertion; but he never got any further. His sole occupation was to sit with his head against the wall, looking hard at the thoughtful baby; and I could not quite divest my mind of a fancy that they understood one another.

I have not counted Mr. Woodcourt among our visitors, because he was now Caddy's regular attendant. She soon began to improve under his care; but he was so gentle, so skilful, so unwearying in the pains he took, that it is not to be wondered at, I am sure. I saw a good deal of Mr. Woodcourt during this time, though not so much as might be supposed; for, knowing Caddy to be safe in his hands, I often slipped home at about the hours when he was expected. We frequently met, notwithstanding. I was quite reconciled to myself now; but I still felt glad to think that he was sorry for me, and he still *was* sorry for me I believed. He helped Mr. Badger in his professional engagements, which were numerous; and had as yet no settled projects for the future.

It was when Caddy began to recover, that I began to notice a change in my dear girl. I cannot say how it first presented itself to me; because I observed it in many slight particulars, which were nothing in themselves, and only became something when they were pieced together. But I made it out, by putting them together, that Ada was not so frankly cheerful with me as she used to be. Her tenderness for me was as loving and true as ever; I did not for a moment doubt that; but there was a quiet sorrow about her which she did not confide to me, and in which I traced some hidden regret.

Now I could not understand this; and I was so anxious for the happiness of my own pet, that it caused me some uneasiness, and set me thinking often. At length, feeling sure that Ada suppressed this something from me, lest it should make me unhappy too, it came into my head that she was a little grieved—for me—by what I had told her about Bleak House.

How I persuaded myself that this was likely, I don't know. I had no idea that there was any selfish reference in my doing so. I was not grieved for myself: I was quite contented and quite happy. Still, that Ada might be thinking—for me, though I had abandoned all such thoughts

—of what once was, but was now all changed, seemed so easy to believe, that I believed it.

What could I do to reassure my darling (I considered then), and show her that I had no such feelings? Well! I could only be as brisk and busy as possible; and that, I had tried to be all along. However, as Caddy's illness had certainly interfered, more or less, with my home duties—though I had always been there in the morning to make my guardian's breakfast, and he had a hundred times laughed, and said there must be two little women, for his little woman was never missing—I resolved to be doubly diligent and gay. So I went about the house, humming all the tunes I knew; and I sat working and working in a desperate manner, and I talked and talked, morning, noon, and night.

And still there was the same shade between me and my darling.

"So, Dame Trot," observed my guardian, shutting up his book, one night when we were all three together; "so, Woodcourt has restored Caddy Jellyby to the full enjoyment of life again?"

"Yes," I said; "and to be repaid by such gratitude as hers, is to be made rich, Guardian."

"I wish it was," he returned, "with all my heart."

So did I too, for that matter. I said so.

"Ay! We would make him as rich as a Jew, if we knew how. Would we not, little woman?"

I laughed as I worked, and replied that I was not sure about that, for it might spoil him, and he might not be so useful, and there might be many who could ill spare him. As Miss Flite, and Caddy herself, and many others.

"True," said my guardian. "I had forgotten that. But we would agree to make him rich enough to live, I suppose? Rich enough to work with tolerable peace of mind? Rich enough to have his own happy home, and his own household gods—and household goddess too, perhaps?"

That was quite another thing, I said. We must all agree in that.

"To be sure," said my guardian. "All of us. I have a great regard for Woodcourt, a high esteem for him; and I have been sounding him delicately about his plans. It is difficult to offer aid to an independent man, with that just kind of pride which he possesses. And yet I would be glad to do it if I might, or if I knew how. He seems half inclined for another voyage. But that appears like casting such a man away."

"It might open a new world to him," said I.

"So it might, little woman," my guardian assented. "I doubt if he expects much of the old world. Do you know I have fancied that he sometimes feels some particular disappointment, or misfortune, encountered in it. You never heard of anything of that sort?"

I shook my head.

"Humph," said my guardian. "I am mistaken, I dare say."

As there was a little pause here, which I thought, for my dear girl's satisfaction, had better be filled up, I hummed an air as I worked which was a favourite with my guardian.

"And do you think Mr. Woodcourt will make another voyage?" I asked him, when I had hummed it quietly all through.

"I don't quite know what to think, my dear, but I should say it was likely at present that he will give a long trial to another country."

"I am sure he will take the best wishes of all our hearts with him wherever he goes," said I; "and though they are not riches, he will never be the poorer for them, Guardian, at least."

"Never, little woman," he replied.

I was sitting in my usual place, which was now beside my guardian's chair. That had not been my usual place before the letter, but it was now. I looked up at Ada, who was sitting opposite; and I saw, as she looked at me, that her eyes were filled with tears, and that tears were falling down her face. I felt that I had only to be placid and merry, once for all to undeceive my dear, and set her loving heart at rest. I really was so, and I had nothing to do but to be myself.

So I made my sweet girl lean upon my shoulder—how little thinking what was heavy on her mind!—and I said she was not quite well, and put my arm about her, and took her upstairs. When we were in our own room, and when she might perhaps have told me what I was so unprepared to hear, I gave her no encouragement to confide in me; I never thought she stood in need of it.

"Oh my dear good Esther," said Ada, "if I could only make up my mind to speak to you and my cousin John, when you are together!"

"Why, my love!" I remonstrated. "Ada? why should you not speak to us!"

Ada only drooped her head and pressed me closer to her heart.

"You surely don't forget, my beauty," said I, smiling, "what quiet, old-fashioned people we are, and how I have settled down to be the discreetest of dames? You don't forget how happily and peacefully my life is all marked out for me, and by whom? I am certain that you don't forget by what a noble character, Ada. That can never be."

"No, never, Esther."

"Why, then, my dear," said I, "there can be nothing amiss—and why should you not speak to us?"

"Nothing amiss, Esther?" returned Ada. "Oh when I think of all these years, and of his fatherly care and kindness, and of the old relations among us, and of you, what shall I do, what shall I do!"

I looked at my child in some wonder, but I thought it better not to answer, otherwise than by cheering her; and so I turned off into many little recollections of our life together, and prevented her from saying more. When she lay down to sleep, and not before, I returned to my guardian to say good night; and then I came back to Ada, and sat near her for a little while.

She was asleep, and I thought as I looked at her that she was a little changed. I had thought so, more than once lately. I could not decide, even looking at her while she was unconscious, how she was changed; but something in the familiar beauty of her face looked different to me.

My guardian's old hopes of her and Richard arose sorrowfully in my mind, and I said to myself, "she has been anxious about him," and I wondered how that love would end.

When I had come home from Caddy's while she was ill, I had often found Ada at work, and she had always put her work away, and I had never known what it was. Some of it now lay in a drawer near her, which was not quite closed. I did not open the drawer; but I still rather wondered what the work could be, for it was evidently nothing for herself.

And I noticed as I kissed my dear, that she lay with one hand under her pillow so that it was hidden.

How much less amiable I must have been than they thought me, how much less amiable than I thought myself, to be so pre-occupied with my own cheerfulness and contentment, as to think that it only rested with me to put my dear girl right, and set her mind at peace!

But I lay down, self-deceived, in that belief. And I awoke in it next day, to find that there was still the same shade between me and my darling.

CHAPTER LI

ENLIGHTENED

WHEN Mr. Woodcourt arrived in London, he went, that very same day, to Mr. Vholes's in Symond's Inn. For he never once, from the moment when I entreated him to be a friend to Richard, neglected or forgot his -promise. He had told me that he accepted the charge as a sacred trust, and he was ever true to it in that spirit.

He found Mr. Vholes in his office, and informed Mr. Vholes of his agreement with Richard, that he should call there to learn his address.

"Just so, sir," said Mr. Vholes. "Mr. C.'s address is not a hundred miles from here, sir, Mr. C.'s 'address is not a hundred miles from here. Would you take a seat, sir?"

Mr. Woodcourt thanked Mr. Vholes, but he had no business with him beyond what he had mentioned.

"Just so, sir. I believe, sir," said Mr. Vholes, still quietly insisting on the seat by not giving the address, "that you have influence with Mr. C. Indeed I am aware that you have."

"I was not aware of it myself," returned Mr. Woodcourt; "but I suppose you know best."

"Sir," rejoined Mr. Vholes, self-contained, as usual, voice and all, "it is a part of my professional duty to know best. It is a part of my professional duty to study and to understand a gentleman who confides his interests to me. In my professional duty I shall not be wanting, sir, if I know it. I may, with the best intentions, be wanting in it without knowing it; but not if I know it, sir."

Mr. Woodcourt again mentioned the address.

"Give me leave, sir," said Mr. Vholes. "Bear with me for a moment. Sir, Mr. C. is playing for a considerable stake, and cannot play without —need I say what?"

"Money, I presume?"

"Sir," said Mr. Vholes, "to be honest with you (honesty being my golden rule, whether I gain by it or lose, and I find that I generally lose), money is the word. Now, sir, upon the chances of Mr. C.'s game I express to you no opinion, *no* opinion. It might be highly impolitic in Mr. C., after playing so long and so high, to leave it off; it might be the reverse, I say nothing. No, sir," said Mr. Vholes, bringing his hand flat down upon his desk, in a positive manner, "nothing."

"You seem to forget," returned Mr. Woodcourt, "that I ask you to say nothing, and have no interest in anything you say."

"Pardon me, sir!" retorted Mr. Vholes, "you do yourself an injustice. No, sir! Pardon me! You shall not—shall not in my office, if I know it—do yourself an injustice. You are interested in anything, and in everything, that relates to your friend. I know human nature much better, sir, than to admit for an instant that a gentleman of your appearance is not interested in whatever concerns his friend."

"Well," replied Mr. Woodcourt, "that may be. I am particularly interested in his address."

("The number, sir,") said Mr. Vholes, parenthetically, ("I believe I have already mentioned.) If Mr. C. is to continue to play for this considerable stake, sir, he must have funds. Understand me! There are funds in hand at present. I ask for nothing; there are funds in hand. But, for the onward play, more funds must be provided; unless Mr. C. is to throw away what he has already ventured—which is wholly and solely a point for his consideration. This, sir, I take the opportunity of stating openly to you, as the friend of Mr. C. Without funds, I shall always be happy to appear and act for Mr. C., to the extent of all such costs as are safe to be allowed out of the estate: not beyond that. I could not go beyond that, sir, without wronging some one. I must either wrong my three dear girls; or my venerable father, who is entirely dependent on me—in the Vale of Taunton; or some one. Whereas, sir, my resolution is (call it weakness or folly if you please) to wrong no one."

Mr. Woodcourt rather sternly rejoined that he was glad to hear it.

"I wish, sir," said Mr. Vholes, "to leave a good name behind me. Therefore, I take every opportunity of openly stating to a friend of Mr. C., how Mr. C. is situated. As to myself, sir, the labourer is worthy of his hire. If I undertake to put my shoulder to the wheel, I do it, and I earn what I get. I am here for that purpose. My name is painted on the door outside, with that object."

"And Mr. Carstone's address, Mr. Vholes?"

"Sir," returned Mr. Vholes, "as I believe I have already mentioned, it is next door. On the second storey you will find Mr. C.'s apartments.

Mr. C. desires to be near his professional adviser; and I am far from objecting, for I court inquiry."

Upon this, Mr. Woodcourt wished Mr. Vholes good day, and went in search of Richard, the change in whose appearance he began to understand now but too well.

He found him in a dull room, fadedly furnished; much as I had found him in his barrack-room but a little while before, except that he was not writing, but was sitting with a book before him, from which his eyes and thoughts were far astray. As the door chanced to be standing open, Mr. Woodcourt was in his presence for some moments without being perceived; and he told me that he never could forget the haggardness of his face, and the dejection of his manner, before he was aroused from his dream.

"Woodcourt, my dear fellow!" cried Richard, starting up with extended hands, "you come upon my vision like a ghost."

"A friendly one," he replied, "and only waiting, as they say ghosts do, to be addressed. How does the mortal world go?" They were seated now, near together.

"Badly enough, and slowly enough," said Richard; "speaking at least for my part of it."

"What part is that?"

"The Chancery part."

"I never heard," returned Mr. Woodcourt, shaking his head, "of its going well yet."

"Nor I," said Richard moodily. "Who ever did?"

He brightened again in a moment, and said, with his natural openness:

"Woodcourt, I should be sorry to be misunderstood by you, even if I gained by it in your estimation. You must know that I have done no good this long time. I have not intended to do much harm, but I seem to have been capable of nothing else. It may be that I should have done better by keeping out of the net into which my destiny has worked me; but I think not, though I dare say you will soon hear, if you have not already heard, a very different opinion. To make short of a long story, I am afraid I have wanted an object; but I have an object now— or it has me—and it is too late to discuss it. Take me as I am, and make the best of me."

"A bargain," said Mr. Woodcourt. "Do as much by me in return."

"Oh! You," returned Richard, "you can pursue your art for its own sake; and can put your hand upon the plough, and never turn; and can strike a purpose out of anything. You, and I, are very different creatures."

He spoke regretfully, and lapsed for a moment into his weary condition.

"Well, well!" he cried, shaking it off, "everything has an end. We shall see! So you will take me as I am, and make the best of me?"

"Ay! indeed I will." They shook hands upon it laughingly, but in deep earnestness. I can answer, for one of them, with my heart of hearts.

"You come as a godsend," said Richard, "for I have seen nobody here yet but Vholes. Woodcourt, there is one subject I should like to mention, for once and for all, in the beginning of our treaty. You can hardly make the best of me if I don't. You know, I dare say, that I have an attachment to my cousin Ada?"

Mr. Woodcourt replied that I had hinted as much to him.

"Now, pray," returned Richard, "don't think me a heap of selfishness. Don't suppose that I am splitting my head and half breaking my heart over this miserable Chancery suit, for my own rights and interests alone. Ada's are bound up with mine; they can't be separated; Vholes works for both of us. Do think of that!"

He was so very solicitous on this head, that Mr. Woodcourt gave him the strongest assurances that he did him no injustice.

"You see," said Richard, with something pathetic in his manner of lingering on the point, though it was off-hand and unstudied, "to an upright fellow like you, bringing a friendly face like yours here, I cannot bear the thought of appearing selfish and mean. I want to see Ada righted, Woodcourt, as well as myself; I want to do my utmost to right her, as well as myself; I venture what I can scrape together to extricate her, as well as myself. Do, I beseech you, think of that!"

Afterwards, when Mr. Woodcourt came to reflect on what had passed, he was so very much impressed by the strength of Richard's anxiety on this point, that in telling me generally of his first visit to Symond's Inn, he particularly dwelt upon it. It revived a fear I had had before, that my dear girl's little property would be absorbed by Mr. Vholes, and that Richard's justification to himself would be sincerely this. It was just as I began to take care of Caddy, that the interview took place; and I now return to the time when Caddy had recovered, and the shade was still between me and my darling.

I proposed to Ada, that morning, that we should go and see Richard. It a little surprised me to find that she hesitated, and was not so radiantly willing as I had expected.

"My dear," said I, "you have not had any difference with Richard since I have been so much away?"

"No, Esther."

"Not heard of him, perhaps?" said I.

"Yes, I have heard of him," said Ada.

Such tears in her eyes, and such love in her face. I could not make my darling out. Should I go to Richard's by myself? I said. No, Ada thought I had better not go by myself. Would she go with me? Yes, Ada thought she had better go with me. Should we go now? Yes, let us go now. Well, I could not understand my darling, with the tears in her eyes and the love in her face!

We were soon equipped, and went out. It was a sombre day, and drops of chill rain fell at intervals. It was one of those colourless days when everything looks heavy and harsh. The houses frowned at us, the dust rose at us, the smoke swooped at us, nothing made any compromise about itself, or wore a softened aspect. I fancied my beautiful girl quite out of place in the rugged streets; and I thought there were more funerals passing along the dismal pavements, than I had ever seen before.

We had first to find out Symond's Inn. We were going to inquire in a shop, when Ada said she thought it was near Chancery Lane. "We are not likely to be far out, my love, if we go in that direction," said I. So to Chancery Lane we went; and there, sure enough, we saw it written up. Symond's Inn.

We had next to find out the number. "Or Mr. Vholes's office will do," I recollected, "for Mr. Vholes's office is next door." Upon which Ada said, perhaps that was Mr. Vholes's office in the corner there. And it really was.

Then came the question, which of the two next doors? I was for going to the one, and my darling was for going to the other; and my darling was right again. So, up we went to the second storey, when we came to Richard's name in great white letters on a hearse-like panel.

I should have knocked, but Ada said perhaps we had better turn the handle and go in. Thus we came to Richard, poring over a table covered with dusty bundles of papers which seemed to me like dusty mirrors reflecting his own mind. Wherever I looked, I saw the ominous words that ran in it, repeated. Jarndyce and Jarndyce.

He received us very affectionately, and we sat down. "If you had come a little earlier," he said, "you would have found Woodcourt here. There never was such a good fellow as Woodcourt is. He finds time to look in between whiles, when anybody else with half his work to do would be thinking about not being able to come. And he is so cheery, so fresh, so sensible, so earnest, so—everything that I am not, that the place brightens whenever he comes, and darkens whenever he goes again."

"God bless him," I thought, "for his truth to me!"

"He is not so sanguine, Ada," continued Richard, casting his dejected look over the bundles of papers, "as Vholes and I are usually; but he is only an outsider, and is not in the mysteries. We have gone into them, and he has not. He can't be expected to know much of such a labyrinth."

As his look wandered over the papers again, and he passed his two hands over his head, I noticed how sunken and how large his eyes appeared, how dry his lips were, and how his finger-nails were all bitten away.

"Is this a healthy place to live in, Richard, do you think?" said I.

"Why, my dear Minerva," answered Richard, with his old gay laugh, "it is neither a rural nor a cheerful place; and when the sun shines here, you may lay a pretty heavy wager that it is shining brightly in an open spot. But it's well enough for the time. It's near the offices, and near Vholes."

"Perhaps," I hinted, "a change from both——"

"—Might do me good?" said Richard, forcing a laugh as he finished the sentence. "I shouldn't wonder! But it can only come in one way now—in one of two ways, I should rather say. Either the suit must be ended, Esther, or the suitor. But it shall be the suit, my dear girl, the suit, my dear girl!"

These latter words were addressed to Ada, who was sitting nearest to him. Her face being turned away from me and towards him, I could not see it.

"We are doing very well," pursued Richard. "Vholes will tell you so. We are really spinning along. Ask Vholes. We are giving them no rest. Vholes knows all their windings and turnings, and we are upon them everywhere. We have astonished them already. We shall rouse up that nest of sleepers, mark my words!"

His hopefulness had long been more painful to me than his despondency; it was so unlike hopefulness, had something so fierce in its determination to be it, was so hungry and eager, and yet so conscious of being forced and unsustainable, that it had long touched me to the heart. But the commentary upon it now indelibly written in his handsome face, made it far more distressing than it used to be. I say indelibly; for I felt persuaded that if the fatal cause could have been for ever terminated, according to his brightest visions, in that same hour, the traces of the premature anxiety, self-reproach, and disappointment it had occasioned him, would have remained upon his features to the hour of his death.

"The sight of our dear little woman," said Richard: Ada still remaining silent and quiet: "is so natural to me, and her compassionate face is so like the face of old days——"

Ah! No, no. I smiled and shook my head.

"—So exactly like the face of old days," said Richard in his cordial voice, and taking my hand with the brotherly regard which nothing ever changed, "that I can't make pretences with her. I fluctuate a little; that's the truth. Sometimes I hope, my dear, and sometimes I—don't quite despair, but nearly. I get," said Richard, relinquishing my hand gently, and walking across the room, "so tired!"

He took a few turns up and down, and sunk upon the sofa. "I get," he repeated gloomily, "so tired. It is such weary, weary work!"

He was leaning on his arm, saying these words in a meditative voice, and looking at the ground, when my darling rose, put off her bonnet, kneeled down beside him with her golden hair falling like sunlight on his head, clasped her two arms round his neck, and turned her face to me. Oh, what a loving and devoted face I saw!

"Esther, dear," she said very quietly, "I am not going home again."

A light shone in upon me all at once.

"Never any more. I am going to stay with my dear husband. We have been married above two months. Go home without me, my own Esther; I shall never go home any more!" With those words my darling drew his head down on her breast, and held it there. And if ever in my life I saw a love that nothing but death could change, I saw it then before me.

"Speak to Esther, my dearest," said Richard, breaking the silence presently. "Tell her how it was."

I met her before she could come to me, and folded her in my arms. We neither of us spoke; but with her cheek against my own, I wanted to hear nothing. "My pet," said I. "My love. My poor, poor girl!" I pitied her so much. I was very fond of Richard, but the impulse that I had upon me was to pity her so much.

"Esther, will you forgive me? Will my cousin John forgive me?"

"My dear," said I, "to doubt it for a moment, is to do him a great wrong. And as to me!"—why, as to me, what had I to forgive!

I dried my sobbing darling's eyes, and sat beside her on the sofa, and Richard sat on my other side; and while I was reminded of that so different night when they had first taken me into their confidence, and had gone on in their own wild happy way, they told me between them how it was.

"All I had, was Richard's," Ada said; "and Richard would not take it, Esther, and what could I do but be his wife when I loved him dearly!"

"And you were so fully and so kindly occupied, excellent Dame Durden," said Richard, "that how could we speak to you at such a time! And besides, it was not a long-considered step. We went out one morning, and were married."

"And when it was done, Esther," said my darling, "I was always thinking how to tell you, and what to do for the best. And sometimes I thought you ought to know it directly; and sometimes I thought you ought not to know it, and keep it from my cousin John; and I could not tell what to do, and I fretted very much."

How selfish I must have been, not to have thought of this before! I don't know what I said now. I was so sorry, and yet I was so fond of them, and so glad that they were fond of me; I pitied them so much, and yet I felt a kind of pride in their loving one another. I never had experienced such painful and pleasurable emotion at one time; and in my own heart I did not know which predominated. But I was not there to darken their way; I did not do that.

When I was less foolish and more composed, my darling took her wedding-ring from her bosom, and kissed it, and put it on. Then I remembered last night, and told Richard that ever since her marriage she had worn it at night when there was no one to see. Then Ada blushingly asked me how did I know that, my dear? Then I told Ada how I had seen her hand concealed under her pillow, and had little thought why, my dear. Then they began telling me how it was, all over again; and I began to be sorry and glad again, and foolish again, and to hide my plain old face as much as I could, lest I should put them out of heart.

Thus the time went on, until it became necessary for me to think of returning. When that time arrived it was the worst of all, for then my darling completely broke down. She clung round my neck, calling me by every dear name she could think of, and saying what should she do without me! Nor was Richard much better; and as for me, I should

LIGHT.

have been the worst of the three, if I had not severely said to myself, "Now, Esther, if you do, I'll never speak to you again!"

"Why, I declare," said I, "I never saw such a wife. I don't think she loves her husband at all. Here, Richard, take my child, for goodness' sake." But I held her tight all the while, and could have wept over her I don't know how long.

"I give this dear young couple notice," said I, "that I am only going away to come back to-morrow; and that I shall be always coming backwards and forwards, until Symond's Inn is tired of the sight of me. So I shall not say good-bye, Richard. For what would be the use of that, you know, when I am coming back so soon!"

I had given my darling to him now, and I meant to go; but I lingered for one more look of the precious face, which it seemed to rive my heart to turn from.

So I said (in a merry bustling manner) that unless they gave me some encouragement to come back, I was not sure that I could take that liberty; upon which my dear girl looked up, faintly smiling through her tears, and I folded her lovely face between my hands, and gave it one last kiss, and laughed, and ran away.

And when I got downstairs, oh how I cried! It almost seemed to me that I had lost my Ada for ever. I was so lonely, and so blank without her, and it was so desolate to be going home with no hope of seeing her there, that I could get no comfort for a little while, as I walked up and down in a dim corner, sobbing and crying.

I came to myself by-and-by, after a little scolding, and took a coach home. The poor boy whom I had found at St. Albans had reappeared a short time before, and was lying at the point of death: indeed, was then dead, though I did not know it. My guardian had gone out to inquire about him, and did not return to dinner. Being quite alone, I cried a little again; though, on the whole, I don't think I behaved so very, very ill.

It was only natural that I should not be quite accustomed to the loss of my darling yet. Three or four hours were not a long time, after years. But my mind dwelt so much upon the uncongenial scene in which I had left her, and I pictured it as such an overshadowed stony-hearted one, and I so longed to be near her, and taking some sort of care of her, that I determined to go back in the evening, only to look up at her windows.

It was foolish, I dare say; but it did not then seem at all so to me, and it does not seem quite so even now. I took Charley into my confidence, and we went out at dusk. It was dark when we came to the new strange home of my dear girl, and there was a light behind the yellow blinds. We walked past cautiously three or four times, looking up; and narrowly missed encountering Mr. Vholes, who came out of his office while we were there, and turned his head to look up too, before going home. The sight of his lank black figure, and the lonesome air of that nook in the dark, were favourable to the state of my mind. I thought of the youth and love and beauty of my dear girl, shut up in such an ill-assorted refuge, almost as if it were a cruel place.

It was very solitary and very dull, and I did not doubt that I might safely steal upstairs. I left Charley below, and went up with a light foot, not distressed by any glare from the feeble oil lanterns on the way. I listened for a few moments; and in the musty rotting silence of the house, believed that I could hear the murmur of their young voices. I put my lips to the hearse-like panel of the door, as a kiss for my dear, and came quietly down again, thinking that one of these days I would confess to the visit.

And it really did me good; for, though nobody but Charley and I knew anything about it, I somehow felt as if it had diminished the separation between Ada and me, and had brought us together again for those moments. I went back, not quite accustomed yet to the change, but all the better for that hovering about my darling.

My guardian had come home, and was standing thoughtfully by the dark window. When I went in, his face cleared, and he came to his seat; but he caught the light upon my face, as I took mine.

"Little woman," said he. "You have been crying."

"Why, yes, Guardian," said I, "I am afraid I have been, a little. Ada has been in such distress, and is so very sorry, Guardian."

I put my arm on the back of his chair; and I saw in his glance that my words, and my look at her empty place, had prepared him.

"Is she married, my dear?"

I told him all about it, and how her first entreaties had referred to his forgiveness.

"She has no need of it," said he. "Heaven bless her, and her husband!" But just as my first impulse had been to pity her, so was his. "Poor girl, poor girl! Poor Rick! Poor Ada!"

Neither of us spoke after that; until he said with a sigh, "Well, well, my dear! Bleak House is thinning fast."

"But its mistress remains, Guardian." Though I was timid about saying it, I ventured because of the sorrowful tone in which he had spoken. "She will do all she can to make it happy," said I.

"She will succeed, my love!"

The letter had made no difference between us, except that the seat by his side had come to be mine; it made none now. He turned his old bright fatherly look upon me, laid his hand on my hand in his old way, and said again, "She will succeed, my dear. Nevertheless, Bleak House is thinning fast, O little woman!"

I was sorry presently that this was all we said about that. I was rather disappointed. I feared I might not quite have been all I had meant to be, since the letter and the answer.

CHAPTER LII

OBSTINACY

BUT one other day had intervened, when, early in the morning as we were going to breakfast, Mr. Woodcourt came in haste with the astounding news that a terrible murder had been committed, for which Mr. George had been apprehended and was in custody. When he told us that a large reward was offered by Sir Leicester Dedlock for the murderer's apprehension, I did not in my first consternation understand why; but a few more words explained to me that the murdered person was Sir Leicester's lawyer, and immediately my mother's dread of him rushed into my remembrance.

This unforeseen and violent removal of one whom she had long watched and distrusted, and who had long watched and distrusted her; one for whom she could have had few intervals of kindness, always dreading in him a dangerous and secret enemy, appeared so awful, that my first thoughts were of her. How appalling to hear of such a death, and be able to feel no pity! How dreadful to remember, perhaps, that she had sometimes even wished the old man away, who was so swiftly hurried out of life!

Such crowding reflections, increasing the distress and fear I always felt when the name was mentioned, made me so agitated that I could scarcely hold my place at the table. I was quite unable to follow the conversation, until I had had a little time to recover. But when I came to myself, and saw how shocked my guardian was; and found that they were earnestly speaking of the suspected man, and recalling every favourable impression we had formed of him, out of the good we had known of him; my interest and my fears were so strongly aroused in his behalf that I was quite set up again.

"Guardian, you don't think it possible that he is justly accused?"

"My dear, I *can't* think so. This man whom we have seen so openhearted and compassionate; who, with the might of a giant, has the gentleness of a child; who looks as brave a fellow as ever lived, and is so simple and quiet with it; this man justly accused of such a crime? I can't believe it. It's not that I don't or I won't. I can't!"

"And I can't," said Mr. Woodcourt. "Still, whatever we believe or know of him, we had better not forget that some appearances are against him. He bore an animosity towards the deceased gentleman. He has openly mentioned it in many places. He is said to have expressed himself violently towards him, and he certainly did about him, to my knowledge. He admits that he was alone, on the scene of the murder, within a few minutes of its commission. I sincerely believe him to be as innocent of any participation in it, as I am; but these are all reasons for suspicion falling upon him."

"True," said my guardian; and he added, turning to me, "it would be doing him a very bad service, my dear, to shut our eyes to the truth in any of these respects."

I felt, of course, that we must admit, not only to ourselves but to others, the full force of the circumstances against him. Yet I knew withal (I could not help saying) that their weight would not induce us to desert him in his need.

"Heaven forbid!" returned my guardian. "We will stand by him, as he himself stood by the two poor creatures who are gone." He meant Mr. Gridley and the boy, to both of whom Mr. George had given shelter.

Mr. Woodcourt then told us that the trooper's man had been with him before day, after wandering about the streets all night like a distracted creature. That one of the trooper's first anxieties was that we should not suppose him guilty. That he had charged his messenger to represent his perfect innocence, with every solemn assurance he could send us. That Mr. Woodcourt had only quieted the man by undertaking to come to our house very early in the morning, with these representations. He added that he was now upon his way to see the prisoner himself.

My guardian said, directly, he would go too. Now, besides that I liked the retired soldier very much, and that he liked me, I had that secret interest in what had happened, which was only known to my guardian. I felt as if it came close and near to me. It seemed to become personally important to myself that the truth should be discovered, and that no innocent people should be suspected; for suspicion, once run wild, might run wilder.

In a word, I felt as if it were my duty and obligation to go with them. My guardian did not seek to dissuade me, and I went.

It was a large prison, with many courts and passages so like one another, and so uniformly paved, that I seemed to gain a new comprehension, as I passed along, of the fondness that solitary prisoners, shut up among the same staring walls from year to year, have had—as I have read—for a weed, or a stray blade of grass. In an arched room by himself, like a cellar upstairs; with walls so glaringly white, that they made the massive iron window-bars and iron-bound door even more profoundly black than they were: we found the trooper standing in a corner. He had been sitting on a bench there, and had risen when he heard the locks and bolts turn.

When he saw us, he came forward a step with his usual heavy tread, and there stopped and made a slight bow. But as I still advanced, putting out my hand to him, he understood us in a moment.

"This is a load off my mind, I do assure you, miss and gentlemen," said he, saluting us with great heartiness and drawing a long breath. "And now I don't so much care how it ends."

He scarcely seemed to be the prisoner. What with his coolness and his soldierly bearing, he looked far more like the prison guard.

"This is even a rougher place than my gallery to receive a lady in," said Mr. George, "but I know Miss Summerson will make the best of it." As he handed me to the bench on which he had been sitting, I sat down; which seemed to give him great satisfaction.

"I thank you, miss," said he.

"Now, George," observed my guardian, "as we require no new assurances on your part, so I believe we need give you none on ours."

"Not at all, sir. I thank you with all my heart. If I was not innocent of this crime, I couldn't look at you and keep my secret to myself, under the condescension of the present visit. I feel the present visit very much. I am not one of the eloquent sort, but I feel it, Miss Summerson and gentlemen, deeply."

He laid his hand for a moment on his broad chest, and bent his head to us. Although he squared himself again directly, he expressed a great amount of natural emotion by these simple means.

"First," said my guardian, "can we do anything for your personal comfort, George?"

"For which, sir?" he inquired, clearing his throat.

"For your personal comfort. Is there anything you want, that would lessen the hardship of this confinement?"

"Well, sir," replied Mr. George, after a little cogitation, "I am equally obliged to you; but tobacco being against the rules, I can't say that there is."

"You will think of many little things perhaps, by-and-by. Whenever you do, George, let us know."

"Thank you, sir. Howsoever," observed Mr. George, with one of his sunburnt smiles, "a man who has been knocking about the world in a vagabond kind of way as long as I have, gets on well enough in a place like the present, so far as that goes."

"Next, as to your case," observed my guardian.

"Exactly so, sir," returned Mr. George, folding his arms upon his breast with perfect self-possession and a little curiosity.

"How does it stand now?"

"Why, sir, it is under remand at present. Bucket gives me to understand that he will probably apply for a series of remands from time to time, until the case is more complete. How it is to be made more complete I don't myself see; but I dare say Bucket will manage it somehow."

"Why, Heaven save us, man!" exclaimed my guardian, surprised into his old oddity and vehemence, "you talk of yourself as if you were somebody else."

"No offence, sir," said Mr. George. "I am very sensible of your kindness. But I don't see how an innocent man is to make up his mind to this kind of thing without knocking his head against the walls, unless he takes it in that point of view."

"That is true enough, to a certain extent," returned my guardian, softened. "But, my good fellow, even an innocent man must take ordinary precautions to defend himself."

"Certainly, sir. And I have done so. I have stated to the magistrates,

'Gentlemen, I am as innocent of this charge as yourselves; what has been stated against me in the way of facts, is perfectly true; I know no more about it.' I intend to continue stating that, sir. What more can I do? It's the truth."

"But the mere truth won't do," rejoined my guardian.

"Won't it, indeed, sir? Rather a bad look-out for me!" Mr. George good-humouredly observed.

"You must have a lawyer," pursued my guardian. "We must engage a good one for you."

"I ask your pardon, sir," said Mr. George, with a step backward. "I am equally obliged. But I must decidedly beg to be excused from anything of that sort."

"You won't have a lawyer?"

"No, sir." Mr. George shook his head in the most emphatic manner. "I thank you all the same, sir, but—no lawyer!"

"Why not?"

"I don't take kindly to the breed," said Mr. George. "Gridley didn't. And—if you'll excuse my saying so much—I should hardly have thought you did yourself, sir."

"That's Equity," my guardian explained, a little at a loss; "that's Equity, George."

"Is it, indeed, sir?" returned the trooper, in his off-hand manner. "I am not acquainted with those shades of names myself, but in a general way I object to the breed."

Unfolding his arms, and changing his position, he stood with one massive hand upon the table, and the other on his hip, as complete a picture of a man who was not to be moved from a fixed purpose as ever I saw. It was in vain that we all three talked to him, and endeavoured to persuade him; he listened with that gentleness which went so well with his bluff bearing, but was evidently no more shaken by our representations than his place of confinement was.

"Pray think, once more, Mr. George," said I. "Have you no wish, in reference to your case?"

"I certainly could wish it to be tried, miss," he returned, "by court-martial; but that is out of the question, as I am well aware. If you will be so good as to favour me with your attention for a couple of minutes, miss, not more, I'll endeavour to explain myself as clearly as I can."

He looked at us all three in turn, shook his head a little as if he were adjusting it in the stock and collar of a tight uniform, and after a moment's reflection went on.

"You see, miss, I have been handcuffed and taken into custody, and brought here. I am a marked and disgraced man, and here I am. My shooting-gallery is rummaged, high and low, by Bucket; such property as I have—'tis small—is turned this way and that, till it don't know itself; and (as aforesaid) here I am! I don't particular complain of that. Though I am in these present quarters through no immediately preceding fault of mine, I can very well understand that if I hadn't gone into the vagabond way in my youth, this wouldn't have happened. It *has* happened. Then comes the question, how to meet it."

He rubbed his swarthy forehead for a moment, with a good-humoured look, and said apologetically, "I am such a short-winded talker that I must think a bit." Having thought a bit, he looked up again, and resumed.

"How to meet it. Now, the unfortunate deceased was himself a lawyer, and had a pretty tight hold of me. I don't wish to rake up his ashes, but he had, what I should call if he was living, a Devil of a tight hold of me. I don't like his trade the better for that. If I had kept clear of his trade, I should have kept outside this place. But that's not what I mean. Now, suppose I had killed him. Suppose I really had discharged into his body any one of those pistols recently fired off, that Bucket has found at my place, and, dear me! might have found there any day since it has been my place. What should I have done as soon as I was hard and fast here? Got a lawyer."

He stopped on hearing some one at the locks and bolts, and did not resume until the door had been opened and was shut again. For what purpose opened, I will mention presently.

"I should have got a lawyer, and he would have said (as I have often read in the newspapers), 'my client says nothing, my client reserves his defence—my client this, that, and t'other.' Well; 'tis not the custom of that breed to go straight, according to my opinion, or to think that other men do. Say, I am innocent, and I get a lawyer. He would be as likely to believe me guilty as not; perhaps more. What would he do, whether or not? Act as if I was;—shut my mouth up, tell me not to commit myself, keep circumstances back, chop the evidence small, quibble, and get me off perhaps! But, Miss Summerson, do I care for getting off in that way; or would I rather be hanged in my own way—if you'll excuse my mentioning anything so disagreeable to a lady?"

He had warmed into his subject now, and was under no further necessity to wait a bit.

"I would rather be hanged in my own way. And I mean to be! I don't intend to say," looking round upon us, with his powerful arms akimbo and his dark eyebrows raised, "that I am more partial to being hanged than another man. What I say is, I must come off clear and full or not at all. Therefore, when I hear stated against me what is true, I say it's true; and when they tell me, 'whatever you say will be used,' I tell them I don't mind that; I mean it to be used. If they can't make me innocent out of the whole truth, they are not likely to do it out of anything less, or anything else. And if they are, it's worth nothing to me."

Taking a pace or two over the stone floor, he came back to the table, and finished what he had to say.

"I thank you, miss, and gentlemen both, many times for your attention, and many times more for your interest. That's the plain state of the matter, as it points itself out to a mere trooper with a blunt broadsword kind of a mind. I have never done well in life, beyond my duty as a soldier; and if the worst comes after all, I shall reap pretty much as I have sown. When I got over the first crash of being seized as a murderer—it don't take a rover, who has knocked about so much as myself, so very long to recover from a crash—I worked my way round to what you find me now. As such, I shall remain. No relations will be disgraced by me, or made unhappy for me, and—and that's all I've got to say."

The door had been opened to admit another soldier-looking man of less prepossessing appearance at first sight, and a weather-tanned, bright-eyed wholesome woman with a basket, who, from her entrance, had been exceedingly attentive to all Mr. George had said. Mr. George had received them with a familiar nod and a friendly look, but without any more particular greeting in the midst of his address. He now shook them cordially by the hand, and said, "Miss Summerson and gentlemen, this is an old comrade of mine, Joseph Bagnet. And this is his wife, Mrs. Bagnet."

Mr. Bagnet made us a stiff military bow, and Mrs. Bagnet dropped us a curtsey.

"Real good friends of mine, they are," said Mr. George. "It was at their house I was taken."

"With a second-hand wiolinceller," Mr. Bagnet put in, twitching his head angrily. "Of a good tone. For a friend. That money was no object to."

"Mat," said Mr. George, "you have heard pretty well all I have been saying to this lady and these two gentlemen. I know it meets your approval?"

Mr. Bagnet, after considering, referred the point to his wife. "Old girl," said he. "Tell him. Whether or not. It meets my approval."

"Why, George," exclaimed Mrs. Bagnet, who had been unpacking her basket, in which there was a piece of cold pickled pork, a little tea and sugar, and a brown loaf, "you ought to know it don't. You ought to know it's enough to drive a person wild to hear you. You won't be got off this way, and you won't be got off that way—what do you mean by such picking and choosing? It's stuff and nonsense, George."

"Don't be severe upon me in my misfortunes, Mrs. Bagnet," said the trooper lightly.

"Oh! Bother your misfortunes!" cried Mrs. Bagnet, "if they don't make you more reasonable than that comes to. I never was so ashamed in my life to hear a man talk folly, as I have been to hear you talk this day to the present company. Lawyers? Why, what but too many cooks should hinder you from having a dozen lawyers, if the gentleman recommended them to you?"

"This is a very sensible woman," said my guardian. "I hope you will persuade him, Mrs. Bagnet."

"Persuade him, sir?" she returned. "Lord bless you, no. You don't know George Now, there!" Mrs. Bagnet left her basket to point him out with both her bare brown hands. "There he stands! As self-willed and as determined a man, in the wrong way, as ever put a human creature under Heaven, out of patience! You could as soon take up and shoulder an eight-and-forty pounder by your own strength, as turn that man, when he has got a thing into his head, and fixed it there. Why, don't I know him!" cried Mrs. Bagnet. "Don't I know you, George! You don't mean to set up for a new character with *me*, after all these years, I hope?"

Her friendly indignation had an exemplary effect upon her husband, who shook his head at the trooper several times, as a silent recommendation to him to yield. Between whiles, Mrs. Bagnet looked at me; and I understood, from the play of her eyes, that she wished me to do something, though I did not comprehend what.

"But I have given up talking to you, old fellow, years and years," said Mrs. Bagnet, as she blew a little dust off the pickled pork, looking at me again; "and when ladies and gentlemen know you as well as I do, they'll give up talking to you too. If you are not too headstrong to accept of a bit of dinner, here it is."

"I accept it with many thanks," returned the trooper.

"Do you though, indeed?" said Mrs. Bagnet, continuing to grumble on good-humouredly. "I'm sure I'm surprised at that. I wonder you don't starve in your own way also. It would only be like you. Perhaps you'll set your mind upon *that*, next." Here she again looked at me; and I now perceived, from her glances at the door and at me, by turns, that she wished us to retire, and to await her following us, outside the prison. Communicating this by similar means to my guardian, and Mr. Woodcourt, I rose.

"We hope you will think better of it, Mr. George," said I; "and we shall come to see you again, trusting to find you more reasonable."

"More grateful, Miss Summerson, you can't find me," he returned.

"But more persuadable we can, I hope," said I. "And let me entreat you to consider that the clearing up of this mystery, and the discovery of the real perpetrator of this deed, may be of the last importance to others besides yourself."

He heard me respectfully, but without much heeding these words, which I spoke, a little turned from him, already on my way to the door; he was observing (this they afterwards told me) my height and figure, which seemed to catch his attention all at once.

"'Tis curious," said he. "And yet I thought so at the time!"

My guardian asked him what he meant.

"Why, sir," he answered, "when my ill-fortune took me to the dead man's staircase on the night of his murder, I saw a shape so like Miss Summerson's go by me in the dark, that I had half a mind to speak to it."

For an instant, I felt such a shudder as I never felt before or since, and hope I shall never feel again.

"It came downstairs as I went up," said the trooper, "and crossed the moon-lighted window with a loose black mantle on; I noticed a deep fringe to it. However, it has nothing to do with the present subject, excepting that Miss Summerson looked so like it at the moment, that it came into my head."

I cannot separate and define the feelings that arose in me after this: it is enough that the vague duty and obligation I had felt upon me from the first of following the investigation, was, without my distinctly daring to ask myself any question, increased; and that I was indignantly sure of there being no possibility of a reason for my being afraid.

We three went out of the prison, and walked up and down at some short distance from the gate, which was in a retired place. We had not waited long, when Mr. and Mrs. Bagnet came out too, and quickly joined us.

There was a tear in each of Mrs. Bagnet's eyes, and her face was flushed and hurried. "I didn't let George see what I thought about it, you know, miss," was her first remark when she came up; "but he's in a bad way, poor old fellow!"

"Not with care and prudence, and good help," said my guardian.

"A gentleman like you ought to know best, sir," returned Mrs. Bagnet, hurriedly drying her eyes on the hem of her grey cloak; "but I am uneasy for him. He has been so careless, and said so much that he never meant. The gentlemen of the juries might not understand him as Lignum and me do. And then such a number of circumstances have happened bad for him, and such a number of people will be brought forward to speak against him, and Bucket is so deep."

"With a second-hand wiolinceller. And said he played the fife. When a boy." Mr. Bagnet added, with great solemnity.

"Now, I tell you, miss," said Mrs. Bagnet; "and when I say miss, I mean all! Just come into the corner of the wall, and I'll tell you!"

Mrs. Bagnet hurried us into a more secluded place, and was at first too breathless to proceed; occasioning Mr. Bagnet to say, "Old girl! Tell 'em!"

"Why, then, miss," the old girl proceeded, untying the strings of her bonnet for more air, "you could as soon move Dover Castle as move George on this point, unless you had got a new power to move him with. And I have got it!"

"You are a jewel of a woman," said my guardian. "Go on!"

"Now, I tell you, miss," she proceeded, clapping her hands in her hurry and agitation a dozen times in every sentence, "that what he says concerning no relations is all bosh. They don't know of him, but he does know of them. He has said more to me at odd times than to anybody else, and it warn't for nothing that he once spoke to my Woolwich about whitening and wrinkling mothers' heads. For fifty pounds he had seen his mother that day. She's alive, and must be brought here straight!"

Instantly Mrs. Bagnet put some pins into her mouth, and began pinning up her skirts all round, a little higher than the level of her grey cloak; which she accomplished with surpassing despatch and dexterity.

"Lignum," said Mrs. Bagnet, "you take care of the children, old man, and give me the umbrella! I'm away to Lincolnshire, to bring that old lady here."

"But, bless the woman!" cried my guardian with his hand in his pocket, "how is she going? What money has she got?"

Mrs. Bagnet made another application to her skirts, and brought forth a leathern purse in which she hastily counted over a few shillings, and which she then shut up with perfect satisfaction.

"Never you mind for me, miss; I'm a soldier's wife, and accustomed to travelling in my own way. Lignum, old boy," kissing him, "one for yourself; three for the children. Now, I'm away into Lincolnshire after George's mother!"

And she actually set off while we three stood looking at one another lost in amazement. She actually trudged away in her grey cloak at a sturdy pace, and turned the corner, and was gone.

"Mr. Bagnet," said my guardian. "Do you mean to let her go in that way?"

"Can't help it," he returned. "Made her way home once. From another quarter of the world. With the same grey cloak. And same umbrella. Whatever the old girl says, do. Do it! Whenever the old girl says, *I'll* do it. She does it."

"Then she is as honest and genuine as she looks," rejoined my guardian, "and it is impossible to say more for her."

"She's Colour-Serjeant of the Nonpareil battalion," said Mr. Bagnet, looking at us over his shoulder, as he went his way also. "And there's not such another. But I never own to it before her. Discipline must be maintained."

CHAPTER LIII

THE TRACK

MR. BUCKET and his fat forefinger are much in consultation together under existing circumstances. When Mr. Bucket has a matter of this pressing interest under his consideration, the fat forefinger seems to rise to the dignity of a familiar demon. He puts it to his ears, and it whispers information; he puts it to his lips, and it enjoins him to secrecy; he rubs it over his nose, and it sharpens his scent; he shakes it before a guilty man, and it charms him to his destruction. The Augurs of the Detective Temple invariably predict, that when Mr. Bucket and that finger are much in conference, a terrible avenger will be heard of before long.

Otherwise mildly studious in his observation of human nature, on the whole a benignant philosopher not disposed to be severe upon the follies of mankind, Mr. Bucket pervades a vast number of houses, and strolls about an infinity of streets: to outward appearance rather languishing for want of an object. He is in the friendliest condition towards his species, and will drink with most of them. He is free with his money, affable in his manners, innocent in his conversation—but, through the placid stream of his life, there glides an under-current of forefinger.

Time and place cannot bind Mr. Bucket. Like man in the abstract, he is here to-day and gone to-morrow—but, very unlike man indeed, he is here again the next day. This evening he will be casually looking into the iron extinguishers at the door of Sir Leicester Dedlock's house in town; and to-morrow morning he will be walking on the leads at Chesney Wold, where erst the old man walked whose ghost is propitiated with a hundred guineas. Drawers, desks, pockets, all things belonging to him, Mr. Bucket examines. A few hours afterwards, he and the Roman will be alone together, comparing forefingers.

It is likely that these occupations are irreconcilable with home enjoyment, but it is certain that Mr. Bucket at present does not go home. Though in general he highly appreciates the society of Mrs. Bucket—a lady of a natural detective genius, which if it had been improved by professional exercise, might have done great things, but which has paused at the level of a clever amateur—he holds himself aloof from that dear solace. Mrs. Bucket is dependent on their lodger (fortunately an amiable lady in whom she takes an interest) for companionship and conversation.

A great crowd assembles in Lincoln's Inn Fields on the day of the funeral. Sir Leicester Dedlock attends the ceremony in person; strictly speaking, there are only three other human followers, that is to say, Lord Doodle, William Buffy, and the debilitated cousin (thrown in as a make-weight), but the amount of inconsolable carriages is immense. The Peerage contributes more four-wheeled affliction than has ever been seen in that neighbourhood. Such is the assemblage of armorial bearings on coach panels, that the Herald's College might be supposed to have lost its father and mother at a blow. The Duke of Foodle sends a splendid pile of dust and ashes, with silver wheel-boxes, patent axles, all the last improvements, and three bereaved worms, six feet high, holding on behind, in a bunch of woe. All the state coachmen in London seem plunged into mourning; and if that dead old man of the rusty garb, be not beyond a taste in horse-flesh (which appears impossible), it must be highly gratified this day.

Quiet among the undertakers and the equipages, and the calves of so many legs all steeped in grief, Mr. Bucket sits concealed in one of the inconsolable carriages, and at his ease surveys the crowd through the lattice blinds. He has a keen eye for a crowd—as for what not?—and looking here and there, now from this side of the carriage, now from the other, now up at the house windows, now along the people's heads, nothing escapes him.

"And there you are, my partner, eh?" says Mr. Bucket to himself, apostrophising Mrs. Bucket, stationed, by his favour, on the steps of the deceased's house. "And so you are. And so you are! And very well indeed you are looking, Mrs. Bucket!"

The procession has not started yet, but is waiting for the cause of its assemblage to be brought out. Mr. Bucket, in the foremost emblazoned carriage, uses his two fat forefingers to hold the lattice a hair's-breadth open while he looks.

And it says a great deal for his attachment, as a husband, that he is still occupied with Mrs. B. "There you are, my partner, eh?" he murmuringly repeats. "And our lodger with you. I'm taking notice of you, Mrs. Bucket; I hope you're all right in your health, my dear!"

Not another word does Mr. Bucket say; but sits with most attentive eyes, until the sacked depository of noble secrets is brought down— where are all those secrets now? Does he keep them yet? Did they fly with him on that sudden journey?—and until the procession moves, and Mr. Bucket's view is changed. After which, he composes himself for an easy ride; and takes note of the fittings of the carriage, in case he should ever find such knowledge useful.

Contrast enough between Mr. Tulkinghorn shut up in his dark carriage, and Mr. Bucket shut up in *his*. Between the immeasurable track of space beyond the little wound that has thrown the one into the fixed sleep which jolts so heavily over the stones of the streets, and the narrow track of blood which keeps the other in the watchful state expressed in every hair of his head! But it is all one to both; neither is troubled about that.

Mr. Bucket sits out the procession, in his own easy manner, and glides from the carriage when the opportunity he has settled with himself arrives. He makes for Sir Leicester Dedlock's, which is at present a sort of home to him, where he comes and goes as he likes at all hours, where he is always welcome and made much of, where he knows the whole establishment, and walks in an atmosphere of mysterious greatness.

No knocking or ringing for Mr. Bucket. He has caused himself to be provided with a key, and can pass in at his pleasure. As he is crossing the hall, Mercury informs him, "Here's another letter for you, Mr. Bucket, come by post," and gives it him.

"Another one, eh?" says Mr. Bucket.

If Mercury should chance to be possessed by any lingering curiosity as to Mr. Bucket's letters, that wary person is not the man to gratify it. Mr. Bucket looks at him, as if his face were a vista of some miles in length, and he were leisurely contemplating the same.

"Do you happen to carry a box?" says Mr. Bucket.

Unfortunately Mercury is no snuff-taker.

"Could you fetch me a pinch from anywheres?" says Mr. Bucket. "Thankee. It don't matter what it is; I'm not particular as to the kind. Thankee!"

Having leisurely helped himself from a canister borrowed from somebody downstairs for the purpose, and having made a considerable show of tasting it, first with one side of his nose and then with the other, Mr. Bucket, with much deliberation, pronounces it of the right sort, and goes on, letter in hand.

Now, although Mr. Bucket walks upstairs to the little library within the larger one, with the face of a man who receives some scores of letters every day, it happens that much correspondence is not incidental to his life. He is no great scribe; rather handling his pen like the pocket-staff he carries about with him always convenient to his grasp; and discourages correspondence with himself in others, as being too artless and direct a way of doing delicate business. Further, he often sees damaging letters produced in evidence, and has occasion to reflect that it was a green thing to write them. For these reasons he has very little to do with letters, either as sender or receiver. And yet he has received a round half-dozen, within the last twenty-four hours.

"And this," says Mr. Bucket, spreading it out on the table, "is in the same hand, and consists of the same two words."

What two words?

He turns the key in the door, ungirdles his black pocket-book (book of fate to many), lays another letter by it, and reads, boldly written in each, "LADY DEDLOCK."

"Yes, yes," says Mr. Bucket. "But I could have made the money without this anonymous information."

Having put the letters in his book of Fate, and girdled it up again, he unlocks the door just in time to admit his dinner, which is brought upon a goodly tray, with a decanter of sherry. Mr. Bucket frequently observes, in friendly circles where there is no restraint, that he likes a toothful of your fine old brown East Inder sherry better than anything you can offer him. Consequently he fills and empties his glass, with a smack of his lips; and is proceeding with his refreshment, when an idea enters his mind.

Mr. Bucket softly opens the door of communication between that room and the next, and looks in. The library is deserted, and the fire is sinking low. Mr. Bucket's eye, after taking a pigeon-flight round the room, alights upon a table where letters are usually put as they arrive. Several letters for Sir Leicester are upon it. Mr. Bucket draws near, and examines the directions. "No," he says, "there's none in that hand. It's only me as is written to. I can break it to Sir Leicester Dedlock, Baronet, to-morrow."

With that he returns to finish his dinner with a good appetite; and after a light nap, is summoned into the drawing-room. Sir Leicester has received him there these several evenings past, to know whether he has anything to report. The debilitated cousin (much exhausted by the funeral), and Volumnia, are in attendance.

Mr. Bucket makes three distinctly different bows to these three people. A bow of homage to Sir Leicester, a bow of gallantry to Volumnia, and a bow of recognition to the debilitated cousin; to whom it airily says, "You are a swell about town, and you know me, and I know you." Having distributed these little specimens of his tact, Mr. Bucket rubs his hands.

"Have you anything new to communicate, officer?" inquires Sir Leicester. "Do you wish to hold any conversation with me in private?"

"Why—not to-night, Sir Leicester Dedlock, Baronet."

"Because my time," pursues Sir Leicester, "is wholly at your disposal, with a view to the vindication of the outraged majesty of the law."

Mr. Bucket coughs, and glances at Volumnia, rouged and necklaced, as though he would respectfully observe, "I do assure you, you're a pretty creetur. I've seen hundreds worse-looking at your time of life, I have indeed."

The fair Volumnia, not quite unconscious perhaps of the humanising influence of her charms, pauses in the writing of cocked-hat notes, and meditatively adjusts the pearl necklace. Mr. Bucket prices that decoration in his mind, and thinks it as likely as not that Volumnia is writing poetry.

"If I have not," pursues Sir Leicester, "in the most emphatic manner, adjured you, officer, to exercise your utmost skill in this atrocious case, I particularly desire to take the present opportunity of rectifying any omission I may have made. Let no expense be a consideration. I am prepared to defray all charges. You can incur none, in pursuit of the object you have undertaken, that I shall hesitate for a moment to bear."

Mr. Bucket made Sir Leicester's bow again, as a response to this liberality.

"My mind," Sir Leicester adds, with generous warmth, "has not, as may be easily supposed, recovered its tone since the late diabolical occurrence. It is not likely ever to recover its tone. But it is full of indignation to-night, after undergoing the ordeal of consigning to the tomb the remains of a faithful, a zealous, a devoted adherent."

Sir Leicester's voice trembles, and his grey hair stirs upon his head. Tears are in his eyes; the best part of his nature is aroused.

"I declare," he says, "I solemnly declare, that until this crime is discovered and, in the course of justice, punished, I almost feel as if there were a stain upon my name. A gentleman who has devoted a large portion of his life to me, a gentleman who has devoted the last day of his life to me, a gentleman who has constantly sat at my table and slept under my roof, goes from my house to his own, and is struck down within an hour of his leaving my house. I cannot say but that he may have been followed from my house, watched at my house, even first marked because of his association with my house—which may have suggested his possessing greater wealth, and being altogether of greater importance than his own retiring demeanour would have indicated. If I cannot, with my means, and my influence, and my position, bring all the perpetrators of such a crime to light, I fail in the assertion of my respect for that gentleman's memory, and of my fidelity towards one who was ever faithful to me."

While he makes this protestation with great emotion and earnestness, looking round the room as if he were addressing an assembly, Mr. Bucket glances at him with an observant gravity in which there might be, but for the audacity of the thought, a touch of compassion.

"The ceremony of to-day," continues Sir Leicester, "strikingly illustrative of the respect in which my deceased friend;" he lays a stress upon the word, for death levels all distinctions; "was held by the flower of the land, has, I say, aggravated the shock I have received from this most horrible and audacious crime. If it were my brother who had committed it, I would not spare him."

Mr. Bucket looks very grave. Volumnia remarks of the deceased that he was the trustiest and dearest person!

"You must feel it as a deprivation to you, miss," replies Mr. Bucket soothingly, "no doubt. He was calculated to *be* a deprivation, I'm sure he was."

Volumnia gives Mr. Bucket to understand, in reply, that her sensitive mind is fully made up never to get the better of it as long as she lives; that her nerves are unstrung for ever; and that she has not the least expectation of ever smiling again. Meanwhile she folds up a cocked hat for that redoubtable old general at Bath, descriptive of her melancholy condition.

"It gives a start to a delicate female," says Mr. Bucket, sympathetically, "but it'll wear off."

Volumnia wishes of all things to know what is doing? Whether they are going to convict, or whatever it is, that dreadful soldier? Whether he had any accomplices, or whatever the thing is called in the law? And a great deal more to the like artless purpose.

"Why you see, miss," returns Mr. Bucket, bringing the finger into persuasive action—and such is his natural gallantry, that he had almost said, my dear; "it ain't easy to answer those questions at the present moment. Not at the present moment. I've kept myself on this case, Sir Leicester Dedlock, Baronet," whom Mr. Bucket takes into the conversation in right of his importance, "morning, noon, and night. But for a glass or two of sherry, I don't think I could have had my mind so much upon the stretch as it has been. I *could* answer your questions, miss, but duty forbids it. Sir Leicester Dedlock, Baronet, will very soon be made acquainted with all that has been traced. And I hope that he may find it;" Mr. Bucket again looks grave; "to his satisfaction."

The debilitated cousin only hopes some fler'll be executed—zample. Thinks more interest's wanted—get man hanged presentime—than get man place ten thousand a year. Hasn't a doubt—zample—far better hang wrong fler than no fler.

"*You* know life, you know, sir," says Mr. Bucket, with a complimentary twinkle of his eye and crook of his finger, "and you can confirm what I've mentioned to this lady. *You* don't want to be told, that, from information I have received, I have gone to work. You're up to what a lady can't be expected to be up to. Lord! especially in your elevated station of society, miss," says Mr. Bucket, quite reddening at another narrow escape from my dear.

"The officer, Volumnia," observes Sir Leicester, "is faithful to his duty, and perfectly right."

Mr. Bucket murmurs, "Glad to have the honour of your approbation, Sir Leicester Dedlock, Baronet."

"In fact, Volumnia," proceeds Sir Leicester, "it is not holding up a good model for imitation, to ask the officer any such questions as you have put to him. He is the best judge of his own responsibility; he acts upon his responsibility. And it does not become us, who assist in making the laws, to impede or interfere with those who carry them into execution. Or," says Sir Leicester, somewhat sternly, for Volumnia was going to cut in before he had rounded his sentence; "or who vindicate their outraged majesty."

Volumnia with all humility explains that she has not merely the plea of curiosity to urge (in common with the giddy youth of her sex in general), but that she is perfectly dying with regret and interest for the darling man whose loss they all deplore.

"Very well, Volumnia," returns Sir Leicester. "Then you cannot be too discreet."

Mr. Bucket takes the opportunity of a pause to be heard again.

"Sir Leicester Dedlock, Baronet, I have no objections to telling this lady, with your leave and among ourselves, that I look upon the case as pretty well complete. It is a beautiful case—a beautiful case—and what little is wanting to complete it, I expect to be able to supply in a few hours."

"I am very glad indeed to hear it," says Sir Leicester. "Highly creditable to you."

"Sir Leicester Dedlock, Baronet," returns Mr. Bucket, very seriously, "I hope it may at one and the same time do me credit, and prove satisfactory to all. When I depict it as a beautiful case, you see, miss," Mr. Bucket goes on, glancing gravely at Sir Leicester, "I mean from my point of view. As considered from other points of view, such cases will always involve more or less unpleasantness. Very strange things comes to our knowledge in families, miss; bless your heart, what you would think to be phenomenons, quite."

Volumnia, with her innocent little scream, supposes so.

"Ay, and even in gen-teel families, in high families, in great families," says Mr. Bucket, again gravely eyeing Sir Leicester aside. "I have had the honour of being employed in high families before; and you have no idea—come, I'll go so far as to say not even *you* have any idea, sir," this to the debilitated cousin, "what game goes on!"

The cousin, who has been casting sofa-pillows on his head, in a prostration of boredom, yawns, "Vayli"—being the used-up for "very likely."

Sir Leicester, deeming it time to dismiss the officer, here majestically interposes with the words, "Very good. Thank you!" and also with a wave of his hand, implying not only that there is an end of the discourse, but that if high families fall into low habits they must take the consequences. "You will not forget, officer," he adds, with condescension, "that I am at your disposal when you please."

Mr. Bucket (still grave) inquires if to-morrow morning, now, would suit, in case he should be as for'ard as he expects to be? Sir Leicester replies, "All times are alike to me." Mr. Bucket makes his three bows, and is withdrawing, when a forgotten point occurs to him.

"Might I ask, by-the-bye," he says, in a low voice, cautiously returning, "who posted the Reward-bill on the staircase."

"*I* ordered it to be put up there," replies Sir Leicester.

"Would it be considered a liberty, Sir Leicester Dedlock, Baronet, if I was to ask you why?"

"Not at all. I chose it as a conspicuous part of the house. I think it cannot be too prominently kept before the whole establishment. I wish my people to be impressed with the enormity of the crime, the determination to punish it, and the hopelessness of escape. At the same time, officer, if you in your better knowledge of the subject see any objection——"

Mr. Bucket sees none now; the bill having been put up, had better not be taken down. Repeating his three bows he withdraws: closing the door on Volumnia's little scream, which is a preliminary to her remarking that that charmingly horrible person is a perfect Blue Chamber.

In his fondness for society, and his adaptability to all grades, Mr. Bucket is presently standing before the hall-fire—bright and warm on the early winter night—admiring Mercury.

"Why, you're six foot two, I suppose?" says Mr. Bucket.

"Three," says Mercury.

"Are you so much? But then, you see, you're broad in proportion, and don't look it. You're not one of the weak-legged ones, you ain't. Was you ever modelled now?" Mr. Bucket asks, conveying the expression of an artist into the turn of his eye and head.

Mercury never was modelled.

"Then you ought to be, you know," says Mr. Bucket; "and a friend of mine that you'll hear of one day as a Royal Academy Sculptor, would stand something handsome to make a drawing of your proportions for the marble. My Lady's out, ain't she?"

"Out to dinner."

"Goes out pretty well every day, don't she?"

"Yes."

"Not to be wondered at!" says Mr. Bucket. "Such a fine woman as her, so handsome and so graceful and so elegant, is like a fresh lemon on a dinner-table, ornamental wherever she goes. Was your father in the same way of life as yourself?"

Answer in the negative.

"Mine was," says Mr. Bucket. "My father was first a page, then a footman, then a butler, then a steward, then an innkeeper. Lived universally respected, and died lamented. Said with his last breath that he considered service the most honourable part of his career, and so it was. I've a brother in service, *and* a brother-in-law. My Lady a good temper?"

Mercury replies, "As good as you can expect."

"Ah!" says Mr. Bucket, "a little spoilt? A little capricious? Lord! What can you anticipate when they're so handsome as that? And we like 'em all the better for it, don't we?"

Mercury, with his hands in the pockets of his bright peach-blossom small-clothes, stretches his symmetrical silk legs with the air of a man of gallantry. And can't deny it. Come the roll of wheels and a violent ringing at the bell. "Talk of the angels," says Mr. Bucket. "Here she is!"

The doors are thrown open, and she passes through the hall. Still very pale, she is dressed in slight mourning, and wears two beautiful bracelets. Either their beauty, or the beauty of her arms, is particularly attractive to Mr. Bucket. He looks at them with an eager eye, and rattles something in his pocket—halfpence perhaps.

Noticing him at his distance, she turns an inquiring look on the other Mercury who has brought her home.

"Mr. Bucket, my Lady."

Mr. Bucket makes a leg, and comes forward, passing his familiar demon over the region of his mouth.

"Are you waiting to see Sir Leicester?"

"No, my Lady, I've seen him!"

"Have you anything to say to me?"

"Not just at present, my Lady."

"Have you made any new discoveries?"

"A few, my Lady."

This is merely in passing. She scarcely makes a stop, and sweeps upstairs alone. Mr. Bucket, moving towards the staircase-foot, watches her as she goes up the steps the old man came down to his grave; past murderous groups of statuary, repeated with their shadowy weapons on the wall; past the printed bill, which she looks at going by; out of view.

"She's a lovely woman, too, she really is," says Mr. Bucket, coming back to Mercury. "Don't look quite healthy though."

Is not quite healthy, Mercury informs him. Suffers much from headaches.

Really? That's a pity? Walking, Mr. Bucket would recommend for that. Well, she tries walking, Mercury rejoins. Walks sometimes for two hours, when she has them bad. By night, too.

"Are you sure you're quite so much as six foot three?" asks Mr. Bucket, "begging your pardon for interrupting you a moment?"

Not a doubt about it.

"You're so well put together that I shouldn't have thought it. But the household troops, though considered fine men, are built so straggling.—Walks by night, does she? When it's moonlight, though?"

Oh yes. When it's moonlight? Of course. Oh, of course. Conversational and acquiescent on both sides.

"I suppsoe you ain't in the habit of walking, yourself?" says Mr. Bucket. "Not much time for it, I should say?"

Besides which, Mercury don't like it. Prefers carriage exercise.

"To be sure," says Mr. Bucket. "That makes a difference. Now I think of it," says Mr. Bucket, warming his hands, and looking pleasantly at the blaze, "she went out walking the very night of this business."

"To be sure she did! I let her into the garden over the way."

"And left her there. Certainly you did. I saw you doing it."

"I didn't see *you*," says Mercury.

"I was rather in a hurry," returns Mr. Bucket, "for I was going to visit an aunt of mine that lives at Chelsea—next door but two to the old original Bun House—ninety year old the old lady is, a single woman, and got a little property. Yes, I chanced to be passing at the time. Let's see. What time might it be? It wasn't ten."

"Half-past nine."

"You're right. So it was. And if I don't deceive myself, my Lady was muffled in a loose black mantle, with a deep fringe to it?"

"Of course she was."

Of course she was. Mr. Bucket must return to a little work he has to get on with upstairs; but he must shake hands with Mercury in acknowledgment of his agreeable conversation, and will he—this is all he asks—will he, when he has a leisure half-hour, think of bestowing it on that Royal Academy sculptor, for the advantage of both parties?

CHAPTER LIV

SPRINGING A MINE

REFRESHED by sleep, Mr. Bucket rises betimes in the morning, and prepares for a field-day. Smartened up by the aid of a clean shirt and a wet hair-brush, with which instrument, on occasions of ceremony, he lubricates such thin locks as remain to him after his life of severe study, Mr. Bucket lays in a breakfast of two mutton chops as a foundation to work upon, together with tea, eggs, toast, and marmalade, on a corresponding scale. Having much enjoyed these strengthening matters, and having held subtle conference with his familiar demon, he confidently instructs Mercury "just to mention quietly to Sir Leicester Dedlock, Baronet, that whenever he is ready for me, I'm ready for him." A gracious message being returned, that Sir Leicester will expedite his dressing and join Mr. Bucket in the library within ten minutes, Mr. Bucket repairs to that apartment; and stands before the fire, with his finger on his chin, looking at the blazing coals.

Thoughtful Mr. Bucket is; as a man may be, with weighty work to do; but composed, sure, confident. From the expression of his face, he might be a famous whist-player for a large stake—say a hundred guineas certain—with the game in his hand, but with a high reputation involved in his playing his hand out to the last card, in a masterly way. Not in the least anxious or disturbed is Mr. Bucket, when Sir Leicester appears; but he eyes the baronet aside as he comes slowly to his easy-chair, with that observant gravity of yesterday, in which there might have been yesterday, but for the audacity of the idea, a touch of compassion.

"I am sorry to have kept you waiting, officer, but I am rather later than my usual hour this morning. I am not well. The agitation, and the indignation from which I have recently suffered, have been too much for me. I am subject to—gout;" Sir Leicester was going to say indisposition, and would have said it to anybody else, but Mr. Bucket palpably knows all about it; "and recent circumstances have brought it on."

As he takes his seat with some difficulty, and with an air of pain, Mr. Bucket draws a little nearer, standing with one of his large hands on the library-table.

"I am not aware, officer," Sir Leicester observes, raising his eyes to his face, "whether you wish us to be alone; but that is entirely as you please. If you do, well and good. If not, Miss Dedlock would be interested——"

"Why, Sir Leicester Dedlock, Baronet," returns Mr. Bucket, with his head persuasively on one side, and his forefinger pendant at one ear like an earring, "we can't be too private, just at present. You will presently see that we can't be too private. A lady, under any circumstances, and especially in Miss Dedlock's elevated station of society, can't but be agreeable to me; but speaking without a view to myself, I will take the liberty of assuring you that I know we can't be too private."

"That is enough."

"So much so, Sir Leicester Dedlock, Baronet," Mr. Bucket resumes, "that I was on the point of asking your permission to turn the key in the door."

"By all means." Mr. Bucket skilfully and softly takes that precaution; stooping on his knee for a moment, from mere force of habit, so to adjust the key in the lock as that no one shall peep in from the outer side.

"Sir Leicester Dedlock, Baronet, I mentioned yesterday evening, that I wanted but a very little to complete this case. I have now completed it, and collected proof against the person who did this crime."

"Against the soldier?"

"No, Sir Leicester Dedlock; not the soldier."

Sir Leicester looks astounded, and inquires, "Is the man in custody?"

Mr. Bucket tells him, after a pause, "It was a woman."

Sir Leicester leans back in his chair, and breathlessly ejaculates, "Good Heaven!"

"Now, Sir Leicester Dedlock, Baronet," Mr. Bucket begins, standing over him with one hand spread out on the library-table, and the forefinger of the other in impressive use, "it's my duty to prepare you for a train of circumstances that may, and I go so far as to say that will, give you a shock. But Sir Leicester Dedlock, Baronet, you are a gentleman; and I know what a gentleman is, and what a gentleman is capable of. A gentleman can bear a shock, when it must come, boldly and steadily. A gentleman can make up his mind to stand up against almost any blow. Why, take yourself, Sir Leicester Dedlock, Baronet. If there's a blow to be inflicted on you, you naturally think of your family. You ask yourself, how would all them ancestors of yours, away to Julius Cæsar—not to go beyond him at present—have borne that blow; you remember scores of them that would have borne it well; and you bear it well on their accounts, and to maintain the family credit. That's the way you argue, and that's the way you act, Sir Leicester Dedlock, Baronet."

Sir Leicester, leaning back in his chair, and grasping the elbow, sits looking at him with a stony face.

"Now, Sir Leicester Dedlock," proceeds Mr. Bucket, "thus preparing you, let me beg of you not to trouble your mind, for a moment, as to anything having come to *my* knowledge. I know so much about so many characters, high and low, that a piece of information more or less, don't signify a straw. I don't suppose there's a move on the board that would surprise *me;* and as to this or that move having taken place, why my knowing it is no odds at all; any possible move whatever (provided it's in a wrong direction) being a probable move according to my experience. Therefore, what I say to you, Sir Leicester Dedlock, Baronet, is, don't you go and let yourself be put out of the way, because of my knowing anything of your family affairs."

"I thank you for your preparation," returns Sir Leicester, after a silence, without moving hand, foot, or feature; "which I hope is not necessary, though I give it credit for being well intended. Be so good as to go on. Also;" Sir Leicester seems to shrink in the shadow of his figure; "also, to take a seat, if you have no objection."

None at all. Mr. Bucket brings a chair, and diminishes his shadow. "Now, Sir Leicester Dedlock, Baronet, with this short preface I come to the point. Lady Dedlock——"

Sir Leicester raises himself in his seat, and stares at him fiercely. Mr. Bucket brings the finger into play as an emollient.

"Lady Dedlock, you see, she's universally admired. That's what her Ladyship is; she's universally admired," says Mr. Bucket.

"I would greatly prefer, officer," Sir Leicester returns stiffly, "my Lady's name being entirely omitted from this discussion."

"So would I, Sir Leicester Dedlock, Baronet, but—it's impossible."

"Impossible?"

Mr. Bucket shakes his relentless head.

"Sir Leicester Dedlock, Baronet, it's altogether impossible. What I have got to say, is about her Ladyship. She is the pivot it all turns on."

"Officer," retorts Sir Leicester, with a fiery eye, and a quivering lip, "you know your duty. Do your duty; but be careful not to overstep it. I would not suffer it. I would not endure it. You bring my Lady's name into this communication upon your responsibility — upon your responsibility. My Lady's name is not a name for common persons to trifle with!"

"Sir Leicester Dedlock, Baronet, I say what I must say; and no more."

"I hope it may prove so. Very well. Go on. Go on, sir!"

Glancing at the angry eyes which now avoid him, and at the angry figure trembling from head to foot, yet striving to be still, Mr. Bucket feels his way with his forefinger, and in a low voice proceeds.

"Sir Leicester Dedlock, Baronet, it becomes my duty to tell you that the deceased Mr. Tulkinghorn long entertained mistrusts and suspicions of Lady Dedlock."

"If he had dared to breathe them to me, sir—which he never did—I would have killed him myself!" exclaims Sir Leicester, striking his hand upon the table. But, in the very heat and fury of the act, he stops, fixed by the knowing eyes of Mr. Bucket, whose forefinger is slowly going, and who, with mingled confidence and patience, shakes his head.

"Sir Leicester Dedlock, the deceased Mr. Tulkinghorn was deep and close; and what he fully had in his mind in the very beginning, I can't quite take upon myself to say. But I know from his lips, that he long ago suspected Lady Dedlock of having discovered, through the sight of some handwriting—in this very house, and when you yourself, Sir Leicester Dedlock, were present—the existence, in great poverty, of a certain person, who had been her lover before you courted her, and who ought to have been her husband;" Mr. Bucket stops, and deliberately repeats, "ought to have been her husband; not a doubt about it. I know from his lips, that when that person soon afterwards died, he suspected Lady Dedlock of visiting his wretched lodging, and his wretcheder grave, alone and in secret. I know from my own inquiries, and through my eyes and ears, that Lady Dedlock did make such visit, in the dress of her own maid; for the deceased Mr. Tulkinghorn employed me to reckon up her Ladyship—if you'll excuse my making use of the term we commonly employ—and I reckoned her up, so far, completely. I confronted the maid, in the chambers in Lincoln's Inn Fields, with a witness who had been Lady Dedlock's guide: and there couldn't be the shadow of a doubt that she had worn the young woman's dress, unknown to her. Sir Leicester Dedlock, Baronet, I did endeavour to pave the way a little towards these unpleasant disclosures, yesterday, by saying that very strange things happened even in high families sometimes. All this, and more, has happened in your own family, and to and through your own Lady. It's my belief that the deceased Mr. Tulkinghorn followed up these inquiries to the hour of his death; and that he and Lady Dedlock even had bad blood between them upon the matter, that very night. Now, only you put that to Lady Dedlock, Sir Leicester Dedlock, Baronet; and ask her Ladyship whether, even after he had left here, she didn't go down to his chambers with the intention of saying something further to him, dressed in a loose black mantle with a deep fringe to it."

Sir Leicester sits like a statue, gazing at the cruel finger that is probing the life-blood of his heart.

"You put that to her Ladyship, Sir Leicester Dedlock, Baronet, from me, Inspector Bucket of the Detective. And if her Ladyship makes any difficulty about admitting of it, you tell her that it's no use; that Inspector Bucket knows it, and knows that she passed the soldier as you called him (though he's not in the army now), and knows that she knows she passed him, on the staircase. Now, Sir Leicester Dedlock, Baronet, why do I relate all this?"

Sir Leicester, who has covered his face with his hands, uttering a single groan, requests him to pause for a moment. By-and-by he takes his hands away; and so preserves his dignity and outward calmness, though there is no more colour in his face than in his white hair, that Mr. Bucket is a little awed by him. Something frozen and fixed is upon his manner, over and above its usual shell of haughtiness; and Mr. Bucket soon detects an unusual slowness in his speech, with now and then a curious trouble in beginning, which occasioned him to utter inarticulate sounds. With such sounds he now breaks silence; soon, however, controlling himself to say, that he does not comprehend why a gentleman so faithful and zealous as the late Mr. Tulkinghorn should have communicated to him nothing of this painful, this distressing, this unlooked-for, this overwhelming, this incredible intelligence.

"Again, Sir Leicester Dedlock, Baronet," returns Mr. Bucket, "put it to her Ladyship to clear that up. Put it to her Ladyship, if you think right, from Inspector Bucket of the Detective. You'll find, or I'm much mistaken, that the deceased Mr. Tulkinghorn had the intention of communicating the whole to you, as soon as he considered it ripe; and further, that he had given her Ladyship so to understand. Why, he might have been going to reveal it on the very morning when I examined the body! You don't know what I'm going to say and do, five minutes from this present time, Sir Leicester Dedlock, Baronet; and supposing I was to be picked off now, you might wonder why I hadn't done it, don't you see?"

True. Sir Leicester avoiding, with some trouble, those obtrusive sounds, says, "True." At this juncture, a considerable noise of voices is heard in the hall. Mr. Bucket, after listening, goes to the library-door, softly unlocks and opens it, and listens again. Then he draws in his head, and whispers, hurriedly, but composedly, "Sir Leicester Dedlock, Baronet, this unfortunate family affair has taken air, as I expected it might; the deceased Mr. Tulkinghorn being cut down so sudden. The chance to hush it, is to let in these people, now in a wrangle with your footmen. Would you mind sitting quiet—on the family account—while I reckon 'em up? And would you just throw in a nod, when I seem to ask you for it?"

Sir Leicester indistinctly answers, "Officer. The best you can, the best you can!" and Mr. Bucket, with a nod and a sagacious crook of the forefinger, slips down into the hall, where the voices quickly die away. He is not long in returning, a few paces ahead of Mercury, and a brother deity also powdered and in peach-blossomed smalls, who bear between them a chair in which is an incapable old man. Another man and two women come behind. Directing the pitching of the chair, in an affable and easy manner, Mr. Bucket dismisses the Mercuries, and locks the door again. Sir Leicester looks on at this invasion of the sacred precincts with an icy stare.

"Now, perhaps you may know me, ladies and gentlemen," says Mr. Bucket, in a confidential voice. "I am Inspector Bucket of the Detective, I am; and this," producing the tip of his convenient little staff from his breast-pocket, "is my authority. Now, you wanted to see Sir Leicester Dedlock, Baronet. Well! You do see him; and, mind you, it ain't every one as is admitted to that honour. Your name, old gentleman, is Smallweed; that's what your name is; I know it well."

"Well, and you never heard any harm of it!" cries Mr. Smallweed in a shrill loud voice.

"You don't happen to know why they killed the pig, do you?" retorts Mr. Bucket, with a steadfast look, but without loss of temper.

"No!"

"Why, they killed him," says Mr. Bucket, "on account of his having so much cheek. Don't *you* get into the same position, because it isn't worthy of you. You ain't in the habit of conversing with a deaf person, are you?"

"Yes," snarls Mr. Smallweed, "my wife's deaf."

"That accounts for your pitching your voice so high. But as she ain't here, just pitch it an octave or two lower, will you, and I'll not only be obliged to you, but it'll do you more credit," says Mr. Bucket. "This other gentleman is in the preaching line, I think?"

"Name of Chadband," Mr. Smallweed puts in, speaking henceforth in a much lower key.

"Once had a friend and brother serjeant of the same name," says Mr. Bucket, offering his hand, "and consequently feel a liking for it. Mrs. Chadband, no doubt?"

"And Mrs. Snagsby," Mr. Smallweed introduces.

"Husband a law-stationer, and a friend of my own," says Mr. Bucket. "Love him like a brother!—Now, what's up?"

"Do you mean what business have we come upon?" Mr. Smallweed asks, a little dashed by the suddenness of this turn.

"Ah! You know what I mean. Let us hear what it's all about in presence of Sir Leicester Dedlock, Baronet. Come!"

Mr. Smallweed, beckoning Mr. Chadband, takes a moment's counsel with him in a whisper. Mr. Chadband, expressing a considerable amount of oil from the pores of his forehead and the palms of his hands, says aloud, "Yes. You first!" and retires to his former place.

"I was the client and friend of Mr. Tulkinghorn," pipes Grandfather Smallweed, then; "I did business with him. I was useful to him, and he was useful to me. Krook, dead and gone, was my brother-in-law. He was own brother to a brimstone magpie—leastways Mrs. Smallweed. I come into Krook's property. I examined all his papers and all his effects. They was all dug out under my eyes. There was a bundle of letters belonging to a dead and gone lodger, as was hid away at the back of a shelf in the side of Lady Jane's bed—his cat's bed. He hid all manner of things away, everywheres. Mr. Tulkinghorn wanted 'em and got 'em, but I looked 'em over first. I'm a man of business, and I took a squint at 'em. They was letters from the lodger's sweetheart, and she signed Honoria. Dear me, that's not a common name, Honoria, is it? There's no lady in this house that signs Honoria, is there? Oh no, I don't think so! Oh no, I don't think so! And not in the same hand, perhaps? Oh no, I don't think so!"

Here Mr. Smallweed, seized with a fit of coughing in the midst of his triumph, breaks off to ejaculate, "Oh dear me! O Lord! I'm shaken all to pieces!"

"Now, when you're ready," says Mr. Bucket, after awaiting his recovery, "to come to anything that concerns Sir Leicester Dedlock, Baronet, here the gentleman sits, you know."

"Haven't I come to it, Mr. Bucket?" cries Grandfather Smallweed. "Isn't the gentleman concerned yet! Not with Captain Hawdon and his ever affectionate Honoria, and their child into the bargain? Come, then, I want to know where those letters are. That concerns me, if it don't concern Sir Leicester Dedlock. I will know where they are. I won't have 'em disappear so quietly. I handed 'em over to my friend and solicitor, Mr. Tulkinghorn; not to anybody else."

"Why, he paid you for them, you know, and handsome too," says Mr. Bucket.

"I don't care for that. I want to know who's got 'em. And I tell you what we want—what we all here want, Mr. Bucket. We want more painstaking and search-making into this murder. We know where the interest and the motive was, and you have not done enough. If George the vagabond dragoon had any hand in it, he was only an accomplice, and was set on. You know what I mean as well as any man."

"Now I tell you what," says Mr. Bucket, instantaneously altering his manner, coming close to him, and communicating an extraordinary fascination to the forefinger, "I am damned if I am a-going to have my case spoilt, or interfered with, or anticipated by so much as half a second of time, by any human being in creation. *You* want more painstaking and search-making? *You* do? Do you see this hand, and do you think that *I* don't know the right time to stretch it out, and put it on the arm that fired that shot?"

Such is the dread power of the man, and so terribly evident it is that he makes no idle boast, that Mr. Smallweed begins to apologise. Mr. Bucket, dismissing his sudden anger, checks him.

"The advice I give you, is, don't you trouble your head about the murder. That's my affair. You keep half an eye on the newspapers; and I shouldn't wonder if you was to read something about it before long, if you look sharp. I know my business, and that's all I've got to say to you on that subject. Now about those letters. You want to know who's got 'em. I don't mind telling you. *I* have got 'em. Is that the packet?"

Mr. Smallweed looks, with greedy eyes, at the little bundle Mr. Bucket produces from a mysterious part of his coat, and identifies it as the same.

"What have you got to say next?" asks Mr. Bucket. "Now don't open your mouth too wide, because you don't look handsome when you do it."

"I want five hundred pound."

"No, you don't; you mean fifty," says Mr. Bucket humorously.

It appears, however, that Mr. Smallweed means five hundred.

"That is, I am deputed by Sir Leicester Dedlock, Baronet, to consider (without admitting or promising anything) this bit of business," says Mr. Bucket; Sir Leicester mechanically bows his head; "and you ask me to consider a proposal of five hundred pounds. Why, it's an unreasonable proposal? Two fifty would be bad enough, but better than that. Hadn't you better say two fifty?"

Mr. Smallweed is quite clear that he had better not.

"Then," says Mr. Bucket, "let's hear Mr. Chadband. Lord! Many a time I've heard my old fellow-serjeant of that name; and a moderate man he was in all respects, as ever I come across!"

Thus invited, Mr. Chadband steps forth, and, after a little sleek smiling and a little oil-grinding with the palms of his hands, delivers himself as follows:

"My friends, we are now—Rachel my wife, and I—in the mansions of the rich and great. Why are we now in the mansions of the rich and great, my friends? Is it because we are invited? Because we are bidden to feast with them, because we are bidden to rejoice with them, because we are bidden to play the lute with them, because we are bidden to dance with them? No. Then why are we here, my friends? Air we in possession of a sinful secret, and doe we require corn, and wine, and oil—or, what is much the same thing, money—for the keeping thereof? Probably so, my friends."

"You're a man of business, you are," returns Mr. Bucket, very attentive; "and consequently you're going on to mention what the nature of your secret is. You are right. You couldn't do better."

"Let us then, my brother, in a spirit of love," says Mr. Chadband, with a cunning eye, "proceed untoe it. Rachel, my wife, advance!"

Mrs. Chadband, more than ready, so advances as to jostle her husband into the background, and confronts Mr. Bucket with a hard frowning smile.

"Since you want to know what we know," says she, "I'll tell you. I helped to bring up Miss Hawdon, her Ladyship's daughter. I was in the service of her Ladyship's sister, who was very sensitive to the disgrace her Ladyship brought upon her, and gave out, even to her Ladyship, that the child was dead—she *was* very nearly so—when she was born. But she's alive, and I know her." With these words, and a laugh, and laying a bitter stress on the word "Ladyship," Mrs. Chadband folds her arms, and looks implacably at Mr. Bucket.

"I suppose now," returns that officer, "*you* will be expecting a twenty-pound note, or a present of about that figure?"

Mrs. Chadband merely laughs, and contemptuously tells him he can "offer" twenty pence.

"My friend the law-stationer's good lady, over there," says Mr. Bucket, luring Mrs. Snagsby forward with the finger. "What may *your* game be, ma'am?"

Mrs. Snagsby is at first prevented, by tears and lamentations, from stating the nature of her game: but by degrees it confusedly comes to light, that she is a woman overwhelmed with injuries and wrongs, whom

Mr. Snagsby has habitually deceived, abandoned, and sought to keep in darkness, and whose chief comfort, under her afflictions, has been the sympathy of the late Mr. Tulkinghorn; who showed so much commiseration for her, on one occasion of his calling in Cook's Court in the absence of her perjured husband, that she has of late habitually carried to him all her woes. Everybody it appears, the present company excepted, has plotted against Mrs. Snagsby's peace. There is Mr. Guppy, clerk to Kenge and Carboy, who was at first as open as the sun at noon, but who suddenly shut up as close as midnight, under the influence—no doubt— of Mr. Snagsby's suborning and tampering. There is Mr. Weevle, friend of Mr. Guppy, who lived mysteriously up a court, owing to the like coherent causes. There was Krook, deceased; there was Nimrod, deceased; and there was Jo, deceased; and they were "all in it." In what, Mrs. Snagsby does not with particularity express; but she knows that Jo was Mr. Snagsby's son, "as well as if a trumpet had spoken it," and she followed Mr. Snagsby when he went on his last visit to the boy, and if he was not his son why did he go? The one occupation of her life has been, for some time back, to follow Mr. Snagsby to and fro, and up and down, and to piece suspicious circumstances together—and every circumstance that has happened has been most suspicious; and in this way she has pursued her object of detecting and confounding her false husband, night and day. Thus did it come to pass that she brought the Chadbands and Mr. Tulkinghorn together, and conferred with Mr. Tulkinghorn on the change in Mr. Guppy, and helped to turn up the circumstances in which the present company are interested, casually, by the wayside: being still, and ever, on the great high road that is to terminate in Mr. Snagsby's full exposure and a matrimonial separation. All this, Mrs. Snagsby, as an injured woman, and the friend of Mrs. Chadband, and the follower of Mr. Chadband, and the mourner of the late Mr. Tulkinghorn, is here to certify under the seal of confidence, with every possible confusion and involvement possible and impossible; having no pecuniary motive whatever, no scheme or project but the one mentioned; and bringing here, and taking everywhere, her own dense atmosphere of dust, arising from the ceaseless working of her mill of jealousy.

While this exordium is in hand—and it takes some time—Mr. Bucket, who has seen through the transparency of Mrs. Snagsby's vinegar at a glance, confers with his familiar demon, and bestows his shrewd attention on the Chadbands and Mr. Smallweed. Sir Leicester Dedlock remains immovable, with the same icy surface upon him; except that he once or twice looks towards Mr. Bucket, as relying on that officer alone of all mankind.

"Very good," says Mr. Bucket. "Now I understand you, you know; and, being deputed by Sir Leicester Dedlock, Baronet, to look into this little matter," again Sir Leicester mechanically bows in confirmation of the statement, "can give it my fair and full attention. Now I won't allude to conspiring to extort money, or anything of that sort, because we are men and women of the world here, and our object is to make things pleasant. But I tell you what I *do* wonder at; I am surprised that you should think of making a noise below in the hall. It was so opposed to your interests. That's what I look at."

"We wanted to get in," pleads Mr. Smallweed.

"Why, of course, you wanted to get in," Mr. Bucket assents with cheerfulness; "but for a old gentleman at your time of life—what I call truly venerable, mind you!—with his wits sharpened, as I have no doubt they are, by the loss of the use of his limbs, which occasions all his animation to mount up into his head—not to consider, that if he don't keep such a business as the present as close as possible it can't be worth a mag to him, is so curious! You see your temper got the better of you; that's where you lost ground," says Mr. Bucket in an argumentative and friendly way.

"I only said I wouldn't go, without one of the servants came up to Sir Leicester Dedlock," returns Mr. Smallweed.

"That's it! That's where your temper got the better of you. Now, you keep it under another time, and you'll make money by it. Shall I ring for them to carry you down?"

"When are we to hear more of this?" Mrs. Chadband sternly demands.

"Bless your heart for a true woman! Always curious, your delightful sex is!" replies Mr. Bucket, with gallantry. "I shall have the pleasure of giving you a call to-morrow or next day—not forgetting Mr. Smallweed and his proposal of two fifty."

"Five hundred!" exclaims Mr. Smallweed.

"All right! Nominally five hundred;" Mr. Bucket has his hand on the bell-rope; "*shall* I wish you good day for the present, on the part of myself and the gentleman of the house?" he asks in an insinuating tone.

Nobody having the hardihood to object to his doing so, he does it, and the party retire as they came up. Mr. Bucket follows them to the door; and, returning, says with an air of serious business:

"Sir Leicester Dedlock, Baronet, it's for you to consider whether or not to buy this up. I should recommend, on the whole, its being bought up myself; and I think it may be bought pretty cheap. You see, that little pickled cowcumber of a Mrs. Snagsby has been used by all sides of the speculation, and has done a deal more harm in bringing odds and ends together than if she had meant it. Mr. Tulkinghorn, deceased, he held all these horses in his hand, and could have drove 'em his own way, I haven't a doubt; but he was fetched off the box head-foremost, and now they have got their legs over the traces, and are all dragging and pulling their own ways. So it is, and such is life. The cat's away, and the mice they play; the frost breaks up, and the water runs. Now, with regard to the party to be apprehended."

Sir Leicester seems to wake, though his eyes have been wide open; and he looks intently at Mr. Bucket, as Mr. Bucket refers to his watch.

"The party to be apprehended is now in this house," proceeds Mr. Bucket, putting up his watch with a steady hand, and with rising spirits, "and I'm about to take her into custody in your presence. Sir Leicester Dedlock, Baronet, don't you say a word, nor yet stir. There'll be no noise, and no disturbance at all. I'll come back in the course of the evening, if agreeable to you, and endeavour to meet your wishes respecting this unfortunate family matter, and the nobbiest way of keeping it quiet. Now, Sir Leicester Dedlock, Baronet, don't you be nervous on account of the apprehension at present coming off. You shall see the whole case clear, from first to last."

Mr. Bucket rings, goes to the door, briefly whispers Mercury, shuts the door, and stands behind it with his arms folded. After a suspense of a minute or two, the door slowly opens, and a French woman enters. Mademoiselle Hortense.

The moment she is in the room, Mr. Bucket claps the door to, and puts his back against it. The suddenness of the noise occasions her to turn ; and then, for the first time she sees Sir Leicester Dedlock in his chair.

"I ask your pardon," she mutters hurriedly. "They tell me there was no one here."

Her step towards the door brings her front to front with Mr. Bucket. Suddenly a spasm shoots across her face, and she turns deadly pale.

"This is my lodger, Sir Leicester Dedlock," says Mr. Bucket, nodding at her. "This foreign young woman has been my lodger for some weeks back."

"What do Sir Leicester care for that, you think, my angel?" returns Mademoiselle, in a jocular strain.

"Why, my angel," returns Mr. Bucket, "we shall see."

Mademoiselle Hortense eyes him with a scowl upon her tight face, which gradually changes into a smile of scorn. "You are very mysterieuse. Are you drunk?"

"Tolerable sober, my angel," returns Mr. Bucket.

"I come from arriving at this so detestable house with your wife. Your wife have left me, since some minutes. They tell me downstairs that your wife is here. I come here, and your wife is not here. What is the intention of this fool's play, say then?" Mademoiselle demands, with her arms composedly crossed, but with something in her dark cheek beating like a clock.

Mr. Bucket merely shakes the finger at her.

"Ah my God, you are an unhappy idiot !" cries Mademoiselle, with a toss of her head and a laugh.—"Leave me to pass downstairs, great pig." With a stamp of her foot and a menace.

"Now, Mademoiselle," says Mr. Bucket, in a cool determined way, "you go and sit down upon that sofy."

"I will not sit down upon nothing," she replies, with a shower of nods.

"Now, Mademoiselle," repeats Mr. Bucket, making no demonstration, except with the finger; "you sit down upon that sofy."

"Why?"

"Because I take you into custody on a charge of murder, and you don't need to be told it. Now, I want to be polite to one of your sex and a foreigner, if I can. If I can't, I must be rough ; and there's rougher ones outside. What I am to be, depends on you. So I recommend you, as a friend, afore another half a blessed moment has passed over your head, to go and sit down upon that sofy."

Mademoiselle complies, saying in a concentrated voice, while that something in her cheek beats fast and hard, "You are a Devil."

"Now, you see," Mr. Bucket proceeds approvingly, "you're comfortable, and conducting yourself as I should expect a foreign young woman of your sense to do. So I'll give you a piece of advice, and it's this, Don't you talk too much. You're not expected to say anything here, and you can't keep too quiet a tongue in your head. In short, the less you Parlay, the better, you know." Mr. Bucket is very complacent over this French explanation.

Mademoiselle, with that tigerish expansion of the mouth, and her black eyes darting fire upon him, sits upright on the sofa in a rigid state, with her hands clenched—and her feet too, one might suppose—muttering, "Oh, you Bucket, you are a Devil !"

"Now, Sir Leicester Dedlock, Baronet," says Mr. Bucket, and from this time forth the finger never rests, "this young woman, my lodger, was her Ladyship's maid at the time I have mentioned to you ; and this young woman, besides being extraordinary vehement and passionate against her Ladyship after being discharged——"

"Lie !" cries Mademoiselle. "I discharge myself."

"Now, why don't you take my advice?" returns Mr. Bucket, in an impressive, almost in an imploring tone. "I'm surprised at the indiscreetness you commit. You'll say something that'll be used against you, you know. You're sure to come to it. Never you mind what I say, till it's given in evidence. It is not addressed to you."

"Discharge, too !" cries Mademoiselle furiously, "by her Ladyship ! Eh, my faith, a pretty Ladyship ! Why, I r-r-r-ruin my character by remaining with a Ladyship so infame !"

"Upon my soul I wonder at you !" Mr. Bucket remonstrates. "I thought the French were a polite nation, I did, really. Yet to hear a female going on like that, before Sir Leicester Dedlock, Baronet !"

"He is a poor abused !" cries Mademoiselle. "I spit upon his house, upon his name, upon his imbecility," all of which she makes the carpet represent. "Oh, that he is a great man ! Oh yes, superb ! Oh Heaven ! Bah !"

"Well, Sir Leicester Dedlock," proceeds Mr. Bucket, "this intemperate foreigner also angrily took it into her head that she had established a claim upon Mr. Tulkinghorn, deceased, by attending on the occasion I told you of, at his chambers ; though she was liberally paid for her time and trouble."

"Lie !" cries Mademoiselle. "I ref-use his money altogezzer."

("If you *will* Parlay, you know," says Mr. Bucket parenthetically, "you must take the consequences.) Now, whether she became my lodger,

Sir Leicester Dedlock, with any deliberate intention then of doing this deed and blinding me, I give no opinion on; but she lived in my house, in that capacity, at the time that she was hovering about the chambers of the deceased Mr. Tulkinghorn with a view to a wrangle, and likewise persecuting and half-frightening the life out of an unfortunate stationer."

"Lie!" cries Mademoiselle. "All lie!"

"The murder was committed, Sir Leicester Dedlock, Baronet, and you know under what circumstances. Now, I beg of you to follow me close with your attention for a minute or two. I was sent for, and the case was entrusted to me. I examined the place, and the body, and the papers, and everything. From information I received (from a clerk in the same house) I took George into custody, as having been seen hanging about there, on the night, and at very nigh the time, of the murder; also, as having been overheard in high words with the deceased on former occasions —even threatening him, as the witness made out. If you ask me, Sir Leicester Dedlock, whether from the first I believed George to be the murderer, I tell you candidly No; but he might be, notwithstanding; and there was enough against him to make it my duty to take him, and get him kept under remand. Now, observe!"

As Mr. Bucket bends forward in some excitement—for him—and inaugurates what he is going to say with one ghostly beat of his forefinger in the air, Mademoiselle Hortense fixes her black eyes upon him with a dark frown, and sets her dry lips closely and firmly together.

"I went home, Sir Leicester Dedlock, Baronet, at night, and found this young woman having supper with my wife, Mrs. Bucket. She had made a mighty show of being fond of Mrs. Bucket from her first offering herself as our lodger, but that night she made more than ever—in fact, overdid it. Likewise she overdid her respect, and all that, for the lamented memory of the deceased Mr. Tulkinghorn. By the living Lord it flashed upon me, as I sat opposite to her at the table and saw her with a knife in her hand, that she had done it!"

Mademoiselle is hardly audible, in straining through her teeth and lips the words "You are a Devil."

"Now where," pursues Mr. Bucket, "had she been on the night of the murder? She had been to the theayter. (She really was there, I have since found, both before the deed and after it.) I knew I had an artful customer to deal with, and that proof would be very difficult; and I laid a trap for her—such a trap as I never laid yet, and such a ventur as I never made yet. I worked it out in my mind while I was talking to her at supper. When I went upstairs to bed, our house being small and this young woman's ears sharp, I stuffed the sheet into Mrs. Bucket's mouth that she shouldn't say a word of surprise, and told her all about it.—My dear, don't you give your mind to that again, or I shall link your feet together at the ankles." Mr. Bucket, breaking off, has made a noiseless descent upon Mademoiselle, and laid his heavy hand upon her shoulder.

"What is the matter with you now?" she asks him.

"Don't you think any more," returns Mr. Bucket, with admonitory finger, "of throwing yourself out of window. That's what's the matter with me. Come! Just take my arm. You needn't get up; I'll sit down by you. Now, take my arm, will you? I'm a married man, you know; you're acquainted with my wife. Just take my arm."

Vainly endeavouring to moisten those dry lips, with a painful sound, she struggles with herself and complies.

"Now we're all right again. Sir Leicester Dedlock, Baronet, this case could never have been the case it is, but for Mrs. Bucket, who is a woman in fifty thousand—in a hundred and fifty thousand! To throw this young woman off her guard, I have never set foot in our house since; though I've communicated with Mrs. Bucket, in the baker's loaves and in the milk, as often as required. My whispered words to Mrs. Bucket, when she had the sheet in her mouth, were, 'My dear, can you throw her off continually with natural accounts of my suspicions against George, and this, and that, and t'other? Can you do without rest, and keep watch upon her, night and day? Can you undertake to say, She shall do nothing without my knowledge, she shall be my prisoner without suspecting it, she shall no more escape from me than from death, and her life shall be my life, and her soul my soul, till I have got her, if she did this murder?' Mrs. Bucket says to me, as well as she could speak, on account of the sheet, 'Bucket, I can!' And she has acted up to it glorious!"

"Lies!" Mademoiselle interposes. "All lies, my friend!"

"Sir Leicester Dedlock, Baronet, how did my calculations come out under these circumstances? When I calculated that this impetuous young woman would overdo it in new directions, was I wrong or right? I was right. What does she try to do? Don't let it give you a turn. To throw the murder on her Ladyship."

Sir Leicester rises from his chair, and staggers down again.

"And she got encouragement in it from hearing that I was always here, which was done a' purpose. Now, open that pocket-book of mine, Sir Leicester Dedlock, if I may take the liberty of throwing it towards you, and look at the letters sent to me, each with the two words, LADY DEDLOCK, in it. Open the one directed to yourself, which I stopped this very morning, and read the three words, LADY DEDLOCK, MURDERESS, in it. These letters have been falling about like a shower of lady-birds. What do you say now to Mrs. Bucket, from her spy-place, having seen them all written by this young woman? What do you say to Mrs. Bucket having, within this half-hour, secured the corresponding ink and paper, fellow half-sheets and what not? What do you say to Mrs. Bucket having watched the posting of 'em every one by this young woman, Sir Leicester Dedlock, Baronet?" Mr. Bucket asks, triumphant in his admiration of his lady's genius.

Two things are especially observable, as Mr. Bucket proceeds to a conclusion. First, that he seems imperceptibly to establish a dreadful right of property in Mademoiselle. Secondly, that the very atmosphere she breathes seems to narrow and contract about her, as if a close net, or a pall, were being drawn nearer and yet nearer around her breathless figure.

"There is no doubt that her Ladyship was on the spot at the eventful period," says Mr. Bucket; "and my foreign friend here saw her, I believe, from the upper part of the staircase. Her Ladyship and George and my foreign friend were all pretty close on one another's heels. But that don't signify any more, so I'll not go into it. I found the wadding of the pistol with which the deceased Mr. Tulkinghorn was shot. It was a bit of the printed description of your house at Chesney Wold. Not much in that, you'll say, Sir Leicester Dedlock, Baronet. No. But when my foreign friend here is so thoroughly off her guard as to think it a safe time to tear up the rest of that leaf, and when Mrs. Bucket puts the pieces together and finds the wadding wanting, it begins to look like Queer Street."

"These are very long lies," Mademoiselle interposes. "You prose great deal. Is it that you have almost all finished, or are you speaking always?"

"Sir Leicester Dedlock, Baronet," proceeds Mr. Bucket, who delights in a full title, and does violence to himself when he dispenses with any fragment of it, "the last point in the case which I am now going to mention, shows the necessity of patience in our business, and never doing a thing in a hurry. I watched this young woman yesterday, without her knowledge, when she was looking at the funeral, in company with my wife, who planned to take her there; and I had so much to convict her, and I saw such an expression in her face, and my mind so rose against her malice towards her Ladyship, and the time was altogether such a time for bringing down what you may call retribution upon her, that if I had been a younger hand with less experience, I should have taken her, certain. Equally, last night, when her Ladyship, as is so universally admired I am sure, come home, looking—why, Lord! a man might almost say like Venus rising from the ocean, it was so unpleasant and inconsistent to think of her being charged with a murder of which she was innocent, that I felt quite to want to put an end to the job. What should I have lost? Sir Leicester Dedlock, Baronet, I should have lost the weapon. My prisoner here proposed to Mrs. Bucket, after the departure of the funeral, that they should go, per bus, a little ways into the country, and take tea at a very decent house of entertainment. Now, near that house of entertainment there's a piece of water. At tea, my prisoner got up to fetch her pocket-handkercher from the bedroom where the bonnets was; she was rather a long time gone, and came back a little out of wind. As soon as they came home this was reported to me by Mrs. Bucket, along with her observations and suspicions. I had the piece of water dragged by moonlight, in presence of a couple of our men, and the pocket-pistol was brought up before it had been there half-a-dozen hours. Now, my dear, put your arm a little further through mine, and hold it steady, and I shan't hurt you!"

In a trice Mr. Bucket snaps a handcuff on her wrist. "That's one," says Mr. Bucket. "Now the other, darling. Two, and all told!"

He rises; she rises too. "Where," she asks him, darkening her large eyes until their drooping lids almost conceal them—and yet they stare, "where is your false, your treacherous and cursed wife?"

"She's gone forrard to the Police Office," returns Mr. Bucket. "You'll see her there, my dear."

"I would like to kiss her!" exclaims Mademoiselle Hortense, panting tigress-like.

"You'd bite her, I suspect," says Mr. Bucket.

"I would!" making her eyes very large. "I would love to tear her, limb from limb."

"Bless you, darling," says Mr. Bucket, with the greatest composure; "I'm fully prepared to hear that. Your sex have such a surprising animosity against one another, when you do differ. You don't mind me half so much, do you?"

"No. Though you are a Devil still."

"Angel and devil by turns, eh?" cries Mr. Bucket. "But I am in my regular employment, you must consider. Let me put your shawl tidy. I've been lady's maid to a good many before now. Anything wanting to the bonnet? There's a cab at the door."

Mademoiselle Hortense, casting an indignant eye at the glass, shakes herself perfectly neat in one shake, and looks, to do her justice, uncommonly genteel.

"Listen then, my angel," says she, after several sarcastic nods. "You are very spiritual. But can you restore him back to life?"

Mr. Bucket answers, "Not exactly."

"That is droll. Listen yet one time. You are very spiritual. Can you make an honourable lady of Her?"

"Don't be so malicious," says Mr. Bucket.

"Or a haughty gentleman of *Him*?" cries Mademoiselle, referring to Sir Leicester with ineffable disdain. "Eh! Oh then regard him! The poor infant! Ha! ha! ha!"

"Come, come, why this is worse Parlaying than the other," says Mr. Bucket. "Come along!"

"You cannot do these things? Then you can do as you please with me. It is but the death, it is all the same. Let us go, my angel. Adieu you old man, grey. I pity you, and I des-pise you!"

With these last words, she snaps her teeth together, as if her mouth closed with a spring. It is impossible to describe how Mr. Bucket gets her out, but he accomplishes that feat in a manner peculiar to himself; enfolding and pervading her like a cloud, and hovering away with her as if he were a homely Jupiter, and she the object of his affections.

Sir Leicester, left alone, remains in the same attitude as though he were still listening, and his attention were still occupied. At length he gazes round the empty room, and finding it deserted, rises unsteadily to his feet, pushes back his chair, and walks a few steps, supporting himself by the table. Then he stops; and, with more of those inarticulate sounds, lifts up his eyes and seems to stare at something.

Heaven knows what he sees. The green, green woods of Chesney Wold, the noble house, the pictures of his forefathers, strangers defacing them, officers of police coarsely handling his most precious heirlooms, thousands of fingers pointing at him, thousands of faces sneering at him. But if such shadows flit before him to his bewilderment, there is one other shadow which he can name with something like distinctness even yet, and to which alone he addresses his tearing of his white hair, and his extended arms.

It is she, in association with whom, saving that she has been for years a main fibre of the root of his dignity and pride, he has never had a selfish thought. It is she whom he has loved, admired, honoured, and set up for the world to respect. It is she, who, at the core of all the constrained formalities and conventionalities of his life, has been a stock of living tenderness and love, susceptible as nothing else is of being struck with the agony he feels. He sees her, almost to the exclusion of himself; and cannot bear to look upon her cast down from the high place she has graced so well.

And, even to the point of his sinking on the ground, oblivious of his suffering, he can yet pronounce her name with something like distinctness in the midst of those intrusive sounds, and in a tone of mourning and compassion rather than reproach.

CHAPTER LV

FLIGHT

INSPECTOR BUCKET of the Detective has not yet struck his great blow, as just now chronicled, but is yet refreshing himself with sleep preparatory to his field-day, when, through the night and along the freezing wintry roads, a chaise and pair comes out of Lincolnshire, making its way towards London.

Railroads shall soon traverse all this country, and with a rattle and a glare the engines and trains shall shoot like a meteor over the wide night-landscape, turning the moon paler; but, as yet, such things are non-existent in these parts, though not wholly unexpected. Preparations are afoot, measurements are made, ground is staked out. Bridges are begun, and their not yet united piers desolately look at one another over roads and streams, like brick and mortar couples with an obstacle to their union; fragments of embankments are thrown up, and left as precipices with torrents of rusty carts and barrows tumbling over them; tripods of tall poles appear on hilltops, where there are rumours of tunnels; everything looks chaotic, and abandoned in fell hopelessness. Along the freezing roads, and through the night, the post-chaise makes its way without a railroad on its mind.

Mrs. Rouncewell, so many years housekeeper at Chesney Wold, sits within the chaise ; and by her side sits Mrs. Bagnet with her grey cloak and umbrella. The old girl would prefer the bar in front, as being exposed to the weather, and a primitive sort of perch more in accordance with her usual course of travelling ; but Mrs. Rouncewell is too thoughtful of her comfort to admit of her proposing it. The old lady cannot make enough of the old girl. She sits, in her stately manner, holding her hand, and, regardless of its roughness, puts it often to her lips. " You are a mother, my dear soul," says she many times, " and you found out my George's mother ! "

" Why, George," returns Mrs. Bagnet, " was always free with me, ma'am, and when he said at our house to my Woolwich, that of all the things my Woolwich could have to think of when he grew to be a man, the comfortablest would be that he had never brought a sorrowful line into his mother's face, or turned a hair of her head grey, then I felt sure, from his way, that something fresh had brought his own mother into his mind. I had often known him say to me, in past times, that he had behaved bad to her."

" Never, my dear ! " returns Mrs. Rouncewell, bursting into tears. " My blessing on him, never ! He was always fond of me, and loving to me, was my George ! But he had a bold spirit, and he ran a little wild, and went for a soldier. And I know he waited at first, in letting us know about himself, till he should rise to be an officer ; and when he didn't rise, I know he considered himself beneath us, and wouldn't be a disgrace to us. For he had a lion heart, had my George, always from a baby ! "

The old lady's hands stray about her as of yore, while she recalls, all in a tremble, what a likely lad, what a fine lad, what a gay good-humoured clever lad he was ; how they all took to him, down at Chesney Wold ; how Sir Leicester took to him when he was a young gentleman ; how the dogs took to him ; how even the people, who had been angry with him, forgave him the moment he was gone, poor boy. And now to see him after all, and in a prison too ! And the broad stomacher heaves, and the quaint upright old-fashioned figure bends under its load of affectionate distress.

Mrs. Bagnet, with the instinctive skill of a good warm heart, leaves the old housekeeper to her emotions for a little while—not without passing the back of her hand across her own motherly eyes—and presently chirps up in her cheery manner :

" So I says to George when I goes to call him in to tea (he pretended to be smoking his pipe outside), ' What ails you this afternoon, George, for gracious sake ? I have seen all sorts, and I have seen you pretty often in season and out of season, abroad and at home, and I never see you so melancholy penitent.' ' Why, Mrs. Bagnet,' says George, ' it's because I *am* melancholy and penitent both, this afternoon, that you see me so.' ' What have you done, old fellow ? ' I says. ' Why, Mrs. Bagnet,' says George, shaking his head, ' what I have done has been done this many a long year, and is best not tried to be undone now. If I ever get to Heaven, it won't be for being a good son to a widowed mother; I say no more.' Now, ma'am, when George says to me that it's best not tried to be undone now, I have my thoughts as I have often had before, and I draw it out of George how he comes to have such things on him that afternoon. Then George tells me that he has seen by chance, at the lawyer's office, a fine old lady that has brought his mother plain before him; and he runs on about that old lady till he quite forgets himself, and paints her picture to me as she used to be, years upon years back. So I says to George when he has done, who is this old lady he has seen? And George tells me it's Mrs. Rouncewell, house-keeper for more than half a century to the Dedlock family down at Chesney Wold in Lincolnshire. George has frequently told me before that he's a Lincolnshire man, and I says to my old Lignum that night, 'Lignum, that's his mother for five-and-for-ty pound!'"

All this Mrs. Bagnet now relates for the twentieth time at least within the last four hours. Trilling it out, like a kind of bird; with a pretty high note, that it may be audible to the old lady above the hum of the wheels.

"Bless you, and thank you," says Mrs. Rouncewell. "Bless you, and thank you, my worthy soul!"

"Dear heart!" cries Mrs. Bagnet, in the most natural manner. "No thanks to me, I am sure. Thanks to yourself, ma'am, for being so ready to pay 'em! And mind once more, ma'am, what you had best do on finding George to be your own son, is, to make him—for your sake—have every sort of help to put himself in the right, and clear himself of a charge of which he is as innocent as you or me. It won't do to have truth and justice on his side; he must have law and lawyers," exclaims the old girl, apparently persuaded that the latter form a separate establishment, and have dissolved partnership with truth and justice for ever and a day.

"He shall have," says Mrs. Rouncewell, "all the help that can be got for him in the world, my dear. I will spend all I have, and thankfully, to procure it. Sir Leicester will do his best, the whole family will do their best. I—I know something, my dear; and will make my own appeal, as his mother parted from him all these years, and finding him in a jail at last."

The extreme disquietude of the old housekeeper's manner in saying this, her broken words, and her wringing of her hands, make a powerful im-pression on Mrs. Bagnet, and would astonish her but that she refers them all to her sorrow for her son's condition. And yet Mrs. Bagnet wonders, too, why Mrs. Rouncewell should murmur so distractedly, "My Lady, my Lady, my Lady!" over and over again.

The frosty night wears away, and the dawn breaks, and the post-chaise comes rolling on through the early mist, like the ghost of a chaise departed. It has plenty of spectral company, in ghosts of trees and hedges, slowly vanishing and giving place to the realities of day. London reached, the travellers alight; the old housekeeper in great tribulation and confusion; Mrs. Bagnet, quite fresh and collected—as she would be, if her next point, with no new equipage and outfit, were the Cape of Good Hope, the Island of Ascension, Hong Kong, or any other military station.

But when they set out for the prison where the trooper is confined, the old lady has managed to draw about her, with her lavender-coloured dress, much of the staid calmness which is its usual accompaniment. A wonderfully grave, precise, and handsome piece of old china she looks; though her heart beats fast, and her stomacher is ruffled, more than even the remembrance of this wayward son has ruffled it these many years.

Approaching the cell, they find the door opening and a warder in the act of coming out. The old girl promptly makes a sign of entreaty to him to say nothing; assenting, with a nod, he suffers them to enter as he shuts the door.

So George, who is writing at his table, supposing himself to be alone, does not raise his eyes, but remains absorbed. The old housekeeper looks at him, and those wandering hands of hers are quite enough for Mrs. Bagnet's confirmation; even if she could see the mother and the son together, knowing what she knows, and doubt their relationship.

Not a rustle of the housekeeper's dress, not a gesture, not a word betrays her. She stands looking at him as he writes on, all unconscious, and only her fluttering hands give utterance to her emotions. But they are very eloquent; very, very eloquent. Mrs. Bagnet understands them. They speak of gratitude, of joy, of grief, of hope; of inextinguishable affection, cherished with no return since this stalwart man was a stripling; of a better son loved less, and this son loved so fondly and so proudly; and they speak in such touching language, that Mrs. Bagnet's eyes brim up with tears, and they run glistening down her sun-brown face.

"George Rouncewell! O my dear child, turn and look at me!"

The trooper starts up, clasps his mother round the neck, and falls down on his knees before her. Whether in a late repentance, whether in the first association that comes back upon him, he puts his hands together as a child does when it says its prayers, and raising them towards her breast, bows down his head, and cries.

"My George, my dearest son! Always my favourite, and my favourite still, where have you been these cruel years and years? Grown such a man, too, grown such a fine strong man. Grown so like what I knew he must be, if it pleased God he was alive!"

She can ask, and he can answer, nothing connected for a time. All that time the old girl, turned away, leans one arm against the whitened wall, leans her honest forehead upon it, wipes her eyes with her serviceable grey cloak, and quite enjoys herself like the best of old girls as she is.

"Mother," says the trooper, when they are more composed; "forgive me first of all, for I know my need of it."

Forgive him! She does it with all her heart and soul. She always has done it. She tells him how she has had it written in her will, these many years, that he was her beloved son George. She has never believed any ill of him, never. If she had died without this happiness—and she is an old woman now, and can't look to live very long—she would have blessed him with her last breath, if she had had her senses, as her beloved son George.

"Mother, I have been an undutiful trouble to you, and I have my reward; but of late years I have had a kind of glimmering of a purpose in me, too. When I left home I didn't care much, mother—I am afraid not a great deal—for leaving; and went away and 'listed, harum-scarum, making believe to think that I cared for nobody, no not I, and that nobody cared for me."

The trooper has dried his eyes, and put away his handkerchief; but there is an extraordinary contrast between his habitual manner of expressing himself and carrying himself, and the softened tone in which he speaks, interrupted occasionally by a half-stifled sob.

"So I wrote a line home, mother, as you too well know, to say I had 'listed under another name, and I went abroad. Abroad, at one time I thought I would write home next year, when I might be better off; and when that year was out, I thought I would write home next year, when I might be better off; and when that year was out again, perhaps I didn't think much about it. So on, from year to year, through a service of ten years, till I began to get older, and to ask myself why should I ever write?"

"I don't find any fault, child—but not to ease my mind, George? Not a word to your loving mother, who was growing older, too?"

This almost overturns the trooper afresh; but he sets himself up with a great, rough, sounding clearance of his throat.

"Heaven forgive me, mother, but I thought there would be small consolation then in hearing anything about me. There were you, respected and esteemed. There was my brother, as I read in chance north-country papers now and then, rising to be prosperous and famous. There was I a dragoon, roving, unsettled, not self-made like him, but self-unmade— all my earlier advantages thrown away, all my little learning unlearnt, nothing picked up but what unfitted me for most things that I could think of. What business had *I* to make myself known? After letting all that time go by me, what good could come of it? The worst was past with you, mother. I knew by that time (being a man) how you had mourned for me, and wept for me; and prayed for me; and the pain was over, or was softened down, and I was better in your mind as it was."

The old lady sorrowfully shakes her head; and taking one of his powerful hands, lays it lovingly upon her shoulder.

"No, I don't say that it was so, mother, but that I made it out to be so. I said just now, what good could come of it? Well, my dear mother, some good might have come of it to myself—and there was the meanness of it. You would have sought me out; you would have purchased my discharge; you would have taken me down to Chesney Wold; you would have brought me and my brother and my brother's family together; you would all have considered anxiously how to do something for me, and set me up as a respectable civilian. But how could any of you feel sure of me, when I couldn't so much as feel sure of myself? How could you help regarding as an incumbrance and a discredit to you, an idle dragooning chap, who was an incumbrance and a discredit to himself, excepting under discipline? How could I look my brother's children in the face, and pretend to set them an example—I, the vagabond boy, who had run away from home, and been the grief and unhappiness of my mother's life? 'No, George.' Such were my words, mother, when I passed this in review before me: 'You have made your bed. Now, lie upon it.'"

Mrs. Rouncewell, drawing up her stately form, shakes her head at the old girl with a swelling pride upon her, as much as to say, "I told you so!" The old girl relieves her feelings, and testifies her interest in the conversation, by giving the trooper a great poke between the shoulders with her umbrella; this action she afterwards repeats, at intervals, in a species of affectionate lunacy: never failing, after the administration of each of these remonstrances, to resort to the whitened wall and the grey cloak again.

"This was the way I brought myself to think, mother, that my best amends was to lie upon that bed I had made, and die upon it. And I should have done it (though I have been to see you more than once down at Chesney Wold, when you little thought of me), but for my old comrade's wife here, who I find has been too many for me. But I thank her for it. I thank you for it, Mrs. Bagnet, with all my heart and might."

To which Mrs. Bagnet responds with two pokes.

And now the old lady impresses upon her son George, her own dear recovered boy, her joy and pride, the light of her eyes, the happy close of her life, and every fond name she can think of, that he must be governed by the best advice obtainable by money and influence; that he must yield up his case to the greatest lawyers that can be got; that he must act, in this serious plight, as he shall be advised to act; and must not be self-willed, however right, but must promise to think only of his poor old mother's anxiety and suffering until he is released, or he will break her heart.

"Mother, 'tis little enough to consent to," returns the trooper, stopping her with a kiss; "tell me what I shall do, and I'll make a late beginning, and do it. Mrs. Bagnet, you'll take care of my mother, I know?"

A very hard poke from the old girl's umbrella.

"If you'll bring her acquainted with Mr. Jarndyce and Miss Summerson, she will find them of her way of thinking, and they will give her the best advice and assistance."

"And, George," says the old lady, "we must send with all haste for your brother. He is a sensible sound man as they tell me—out in the world beyond Chesney Wold, my dear, though I don't know much of it myself—and will be of great service."

"Mother," returns the trooper, "is it too soon to ask a favour?"

"Surely not, my dear."

"Then grant me this one great favour. Don't let my brother know."

"Not know what, my dear?"

"Not know of me. In fact, mother, I can't bear it; I can't make up my mind to it. He has proved himself so different from me, and has done so much to raise himself while I've been soldiering, that I haven't brass enough in my composition, to see him in this place and under this charge. How could a man like him be expected to have any pleasure in such a discovery? It's impossible. No, keep my secret from him, mother; do me a greater kindness than I deserve, and keep my secret from my brother, of all men."

"But not always, dear George?"

"Why, mother, perhaps not for good and all—though I may come to ask that too—but keep it now, I do entreat you. If it's ever broke to him that his Rip of a brother has turned up, I could wish," says the trooper, shaking his head very doubtfully, "to break it myself; and be governed, as to advancing or retreating, by the way in which he seems to take it."

As he evidently has a rooted feeling on this point, and as the depth of it is recognised in Mrs. Bagnet's face, his mother yields her implicit assent to what he asks. For this he thanks her kindly.

"In all other respects, my dear mother, I'll be as tractable and obedient as you can wish; on this one alone, I stand out. So now I am ready even for the lawyers. I have been drawing up," he glances at his writing on the table, "an exact account of what I knew of the deceased, and how I came to be involved in this unfortunate affair. It's entered, plain and regular, like an orderly-book; not a word in it but what's wanted for the facts. I did intend to read it, straight on end, whensoever I was called upon to say anything in my defence. I hope I may be let to do it still; but I have no longer a will of my own in this case, and whatever is said or done, I give my promise not to have any."

Matters being brought to this so far satisfactory pass, and time being on the wane, Mrs. Bagnet proposes a departure. Again and again the old lady hangs upon her son's neck, and again and again the trooper holds her to his broad chest.

"Where are you going to take my mother, Mrs. Bagnet?"

"I am going to the town house, my dear, the family house. I have some business there, that must be looked to directly," Mrs. Rouncewell answers.

"Will you see my mother safe there, in a coach, Mrs. Bagnet? But of course I know you will. Why should I ask it!"

Why indeed, Mrs. Bagnet expresses with the umbrella.

"Take her, my old friend, and take my gratitude along with you. Kisses to Quebec and Malta, love to my godson, a hearty shake of the hand to Lignum, and this for yourself, and I wish it was ten thousand pound in gold, my dear!" So saying, the trooper puts his lips to the old girl's tanned forehead, and the door shuts upon him in his cell.

No entreaties on the part of the good old housekeeper will induce Mrs. Bagnet to retain the coach for her own conveyance home. Jumping out cheerfully at the door of the Dedlock mansion, and handing Mrs. Rouncewell up the steps, the old girl shakes hands and trudges off;

arriving soon afterwards in the bosom of the Bagnet family, and falling to washing the greens, as if nothing had happened.

My Lady is in that room in which she held her last conference with the murdered man, and is sitting where she sat that night, and is looking at the spot where he stood upon the hearth, studying her so leisurely, when a tap comes at the door. Who is it? Mrs. Rouncewell. What has brought Mrs. Rouncewell to town so unexpectedly?

"Trouble, my Lady. Sad trouble. Oh, my Lady, may I beg a word with you?"

What new occurrence is it that makes this tranquil old woman tremble so? Far happier than her Lady, as her Lady has often thought, why does she falter in this manner, and look at her with such strange mistrust?

"What is the matter? Sit down and take your breath."

"Oh, my Lady, my Lady. I have found my son—my youngest, who went away for a soldier so long ago. And he is in prison."

"For debt?"

"Oh no, my Lady; I would have paid any debt, and joyful."

"For what is he in prison then?"

"Charged with a murder, my Lady, of which he is as innocent as—as I am. Accused of the murder of Mr. Tulkinghorn."

What does she mean by this look and this imploring gesture? Why does she come so close? What is the letter that she holds?

"Lady Dedlock, my dear Lady, my good Lady, my kind Lady! You must have a heart to feel for me, you must have a heart to forgive me. I was in this family before you were born. I am devoted to it. But think of my dear son wrongfully accused."

"*I* do not accuse him."

"No, my Lady, no. But others do, and he is in prison and in danger. O Lady Dedlock, if you can say but a word to help to clear him, say it!"

What delusion can this be? What power does she suppose is in the person she petitions, to avert this unjust suspicion, if it be unjust? Her Lady's handsome eyes regard her with astonishment, almost with fear.

"My Lady, I came away last night from Chesney Wold to find my son in my old age, and the step upon the Ghost's Walk was so constant and so solemn that I never heard the like in all these years. Night after night, as it has fallen dark, the sound has echoed through your rooms, but last night it was awfullest. And as it fell dark last night, my Lady, I got this letter."

"What letter is it?"

"Hush! Hush!" The housekeeper looks round, and answers in a frightened whisper: "My Lady, I have not breathed a word of it, I don't believe what's written in it, I know it can't be true, I am sure and certain that it is not true. But my son is in danger, and you must have a heart to pity me. If you know of anything that is not known to others, if you have any suspicion, if you have any clue at all, and any reason for keeping it in your own breast, O my dear Lady, think of me, and conquer that reason, and let it be known! This is the most I consider possible. I know you are not a hard lady, but you go your own way always, without help, and you are not familiar with your friends ; and all who admire you—and all do—as a beautiful and elegant lady, know you to be one far away from themselves, who can't be approached close. My Lady, you may have some proud or angry reasons for disdaining to utter something that you know ; if so, pray, oh pray, think of a faithful servant whose whole life has been passed in this family which she dearly loves, and relent, and help to clear my son ! My Lady, my good Lady," the old housekeeper pleads with genuine simplicity, "I am so humble in my place, and you are by nature so high and distant, that you may not think what I feel for my child; but I feel so much, that I have come here to make so bold as to beg and pray you not to be scornful of us, if you can do us any right or justice at this fearful time !"

Lady Dedlock raises her without one word, until she takes the letter from her hand.

"Am I to read this?"

"When I am gone, my Lady, if you please; and then remembering the most that I consider possible."

"I know of nothing I can do. I know of nothing I reserve, that can affect your son. I have never accused him."

"My Lady, you may pity him the more, under a false accusation, after reading the letter."

The old housekeeper leaves her with the letter in her hand. In truth she is not a hard lady naturally ; and the time has been when the sight of the venerable figure suing to her with such strong earnestness would have moved her to great compassion. But, so long accustomed to suppress emotion, and keep down reality ; so long schooled for her own purposes, in that destructive school which shuts up the natural feelings of the heart, like flies in amber, and spreads one uniform and dreary gloss over the good and bad, the feeling and the unfeeling, the sensible and the senseless ; she had subdued even her wonder until now.

She opens the letter. Spread out upon the paper is a printed account of the discovery of the body, as it lay face downward on the floor, shot through the heart; and underneath is written her own name, with the word Murderess attached.

It falls out of her hand. How long it may have lain upon the ground, she knows not ; but it lies where it fell, when a servant stands before her announcing a young man of the name of Guppy. The words have probably been repeated several times, for they are ringing in her head before she begins to understand them.

"Let him come in !"

He comes in. Holding the letter in her hand, which she has taken from the floor, she tries to collect her thoughts. In the eyes of Mr. Guppy she is the same Lady Dedlock, holding the same prepared, proud, chilling state.

"Your Ladyship may not be at first disposed to excuse this visit from one who has never been very welcome to your Ladyship—which he don't

complain of, for he is bound to confess that there never has been any
particular reason on the face of things, why he should be; but I hope
when I mention my motives to your Ladyship, you will not find fault
with me," says Mr. Guppy.

"Do so."

"Thank your Ladyship. I ought first to explain to your Ladyship,"
Mr. Guppy sits on the edge of a chair, and puts his hat on the carpet at
his feet, "that Miss Summerson, whose image, as I formerly mentioned
to your Ladyship, was at one period of my life imprinted on my art until
erased by circumstances over which I had no control, communicated to
me, after I had the pleasure of waiting on your Ladyship last, that she
particularly wished me to take no steps whatever in any matter at all
relating to her. And Miss Summerson's wishes being to me a law (except
as connected with circumstances over which I have no control), I consequently never expected to have the distinguished honour of waiting on
your Ladyship again."

And yet he is here now, Lady Dedlock moodily reminds him.

"And yet I am here now," Mr. Guppy admits. "My object being to
communicate to your Ladyship, under the seal of confidence, why I am
here."

He cannot do so, she tells him, too plainly or too briefly.

"Nor can I," Mr. Guppy returns, with a sense of injury upon him,
"too particularly request your Ladyship to take particular notice that
it's no personal affair of mine that brings me here. I have no interested
views of my own to serve in coming here. If it was not for my promise
to Miss Summerson, and my keeping of it sacred—I, in point of fact,
shouldn't have darkened these doors again, but should have seen 'em
further first."

Mr. Guppy considers this a favourable moment for sticking up his hair
with both hands.

"Your Ladyship will remember when I mention it, that the last time
I was here, I run against a party very eminent in our profession, and
whose loss we all deplore. That party certainly did from that time apply
himself to cutting in against me in a way that I will call sharp practice,
and did make it, at every turn and point, extremely difficult for me to be
sure that I hadn't inadvertently led up to something contrary to Miss
Summerson's wishes. Self-praise is no recommendation; but I may say
for myself that I am not so bad a man of business either."

Lady Dedlock looks at him in stern inquiry. Mr. Guppy immediately
withdraws his eyes from her face, and looks anywhere else.

"Indeed, it has been made so hard," he goes on, "to have any idea
what that party was up to in combination with others, that until the loss
which we all deplore, I was gravelled—an expression which your Ladyship, moving in the higher circles, will be so good as to consider tantamount to knocked over. Small likewise—a name by which I refer to
another party, a friend of mine that your Ladyship is not acquainted
with—got to be so close and double-faced that at times it wasn't easy

2 o

to keep one's hands off his ed. However, what with the exertion of my humble abilities, and what with the help of a mutual friend by the name of Mr. Tony Weevle (who is of a high aristocratic turn, and has your Ladyship's portrait always hanging up in his room), I have now reasons for an apprehension, as to which I come to put your Ladyship upon your guard. First, will your Ladyship allow me to ask you whether you have had any strange visitors this morning? I don't mean fashionable visitors, but such visitors, for instance, as Miss Barbary's old servant, or as a person without the use of his lower extremities, carried upstairs similarly to a Guy?"

" No ! "

" Then I assure your Ladyship that such visitors have been here, and have been received here. Because I saw them at the door, and waited at the corner of the square till they came out, and took half-an-hour's turn afterwards to avoid them."

" What have I to do with that, or what have you? I do not understand you. What do you mean?"

" Your Ladyship, I come to put you on your guard. There may be no occasion for it. Very well. Then I have only done my best to keep my promise to Miss Summerson. I strongly suspect (from what Small has dropped, and from what we have corkscrewed out of him) that those letters I was to have brought to your Ladyship were not destroyed when I supposed they were. That if there was anything to be blown upon, it *is* blown upon. That the visitors I have alluded to have been here this morning to make money of it. And that the money is made, or making."

Mr. Guppy picks up his hat and rises.

" Your Ladyship, you know best, whether there's anything in what I say, or whether there's nothing. Something or nothing, I have acted up to Miss Summerson's wishes in letting things alone, and in undoing what I had begun to do, as far as possible; that's sufficient for me. In case I should be taking a liberty in putting your Ladyship on your guard when there's no necessity for it, you will endeavour, I should hope, to outlive my presumption, and I shall endeavour to outlive your disapprobation. I now take my farewell of your Ladyship, and assure you that there's no danger of your ever being waited on by me again."

She scarcely acknowledges these parting words by any look ; but when he has been gone a little while, she rings her bell.

" Where is Sir Leicester? "

Mercury reports that he is at present shut up in the library, alone.

" Has Sir Leicester had any visitors this morning? "

Several, on business. Mercury proceeds to a description of them, which has been anticipated by Mr. Guppy. Enough ; he may go.

So ! All is broken down. Her name is in these many mouths, her husband knows his wrongs, her shame will be published—may be spreading while she thinks about it—and in addition to the thunderbolt so long foreseen by her, so unforeseen by him, she is denounced by an invisible accuser as the murderess of her enemy.

Her enemy he was, and she has often, often, often, wished him dead.

Her enemy he is, even in his grave. This dreadful accusation comes upon her, like a new torment at his lifeless hand. And when she recalls how she was secretly at his door that night, and how she may be represented to have sent her favourite girl away, so soon before, merely to release herself from observation, she shudders as if the hangman's hands were at her neck.

She has thrown herself upon the floor, and lies with her hair all wildly scattered, and her face buried in the cushions of a couch. She rises up, hurries to and fro, flings herself down again, and rocks and moans. The horror that is upon her, is unutterable. If she really were the murderess, it could hardly be, for the moment, more intense.

For, as her murderous perspective, before the doing of the deed, however subtle the precautions for its commission, would have been closed up by a gigantic dilatation of the hateful figure, preventing her from seeing any consequences beyond it ; and as those consequences would have rushed in, in an unimagined flood, the moment the figure was laid low—which always happens when a murder is done ; so, now she sees that when he used to be on the watch before her, and she used to think, " if some mortal stroke would but fall on this old man and take him from my way ! " it was but wishing that all he held against her in his hand might be flung to the winds, and chance-sown in many places. So, too, with the wicked relief she has felt in his death. What was his death but the key-stone of a gloomy arch removed, and now the arch begins to fall in a thousand fragments, each crushing and mangling piecemeal !

Thus, a terrible impression steals upon and overshadows her, that from this pursuer, living or dead—obdurate and imperturbable before her in his well-remembered shape, or not more obdurate and imperturbable in his coffin-bed,—there is no escape but in death. Hunted, she flies. The complication of her shame, her dread, remorse, and misery, overwhelms her at its height ; and even her strength of self-reliance is overturned and whirled way, like a leaf before a mighty wind.

She hurriedly addresses these lines to her husband, seals, and leaves them on her table.

"If I am sought for, or accused of, his murder, believe that I am wholly innocent. Believe no other good of me, for I am innocent of nothing else that you have heard, or will hear, laid to my charge. He prepared me, on that fatal night, for his disclosure of my guilt to you. After he had left me, I went out, on pretence of walking in the garden where I sometimes walk, but really to follow him, and make one last petition that he would not protract the dreadful suspense on which I have been racked by him, you do not know how long, but would mercifully strike next morning.

"I found his house dark and silent. I rang twice at his door, but there was no reply, and I came home.

"I have no home left. I will encumber you no more. May you, in your just resentment, be able to forget the unworthy woman on whom you have wasted a most generous devotion—who avoids you, only with a deeper shame than that with which she hurries from herself—and who writes this last adieu."

She veils and dresses quickly, leaves all her jewels and her money, listens, goes downstairs at a moment when the hall is empty, opens and shuts the great door; flutters away, in the shrill frosty wind.

CHAPTER LVI

PURSUIT

IMPASSIVE, as behoves its high breeding, the Dedlock town house stares at the other houses in the street of dismal grandeur, and gives no outward sign of anything going wrong within. Carriages rattle, doors are battered at, the world exchanges calls; ancient charmers with skeleton throats, and peachy cheeks that have a rather ghastly bloom upon them seen by daylight, when indeed these fascinating creatures look like Death and the Lady fused together, dazzle the eyes of men. Forth from the frigid Mews come easily swinging carriages guided by short-legged coachmen in flaxen wigs, deep sunk into downy hammercloths; and up behind mount luscious Mercuries, bearing sticks of state, and wearing cocked hats broadwise : a spectacle for the Angels.

The Dedlock town house changes not externally, and hours pass before its exalted dulness is disturbed within. But Volumnia the fair, being subject to the prevalent complaint of boredom, and finding that disorder attacking her spirits with some virulence, ventures at length to repair to the library for change of scene. Her gentle tapping at the door producing no response, she opens it and peeps in; seeing no one there, takes possession.

The sprightly Dedlock is reputed, in that grass-grown city of the ancients, Bath, to be stimulated by an ardent curiosity, which impels her on all convenient and inconvenient occasions to sidle about with a golden glass at her eye, peering into objects of every description. Certain it is that she avails herself of the present opportunity of hovering over her kinsman's letters and papers, like a bird; taking a short peck at this document, and a blink with her head on one side at that document, and hopping about from table to table, with her glass at her eye in an in- quisitive and restless manner. In the course of these researches, she stumbles over something; and turning her glass in that direction, sees her kinsman lying on the ground like a felled tree.

Volumnia's pet little scream acquires a considerable augmentation of reality from this surprise, and the house is quickly in commotion. Servants tear up and downstairs, bells are violently rung, doctors are sent for, and Lady Dedlock is sought in all directions, but not found. Nobody has seen or heard her since she last rang her bell. Her letter to Sir Leicester is discovered on her table;—but it is doubtful yet whether he has not received another missive from another world, requiring to be personally answered; and all the living languages, and all the dead, are as one to him.

They lay him down upon his bed, and chafe, and rub, and fan, and put ice to his head, and try every means of restoration. Howbeit, the day has ebbed away, and it is night in his room, before his stertorous breathing lulls, or his fixed eyes show any consciousness of the candle that is occasionally passed before them. But when this change begins, it goes on; and by-and-by he nods, or moves his eyes, or even his hand, in token that he hears and comprehends.

He fell down, this morning, a handsome stately gentleman; somewhat infirm, but of a fine presence, and with a well-filled face. He lies upon his bed, an aged man with sunken cheeks, the decrepit shadow of himself. His voice was rich and mellow; and he had so long been thoroughly persuaded of the weight and import to mankind of any word he said, that his words really had come to sound as if there were something in them. But now he can only whisper; and what he whispers sounds like what it is—mere jumble and jargon.

His favourite and faithful housekeeper stands at his bedside. It is the first fact he notices, and he clearly derives pleasure from it. After vainly trying to make himself understood in speech, he makes signs for a pencil. So inexpressively, that they cannot at first understand him; it is his old housekeeper who makes out what he wants, and brings him a slate.

After pausing for some time, he slowly scrawls upon it, in a hand that is not his, "Chesney Wold?"

No, she tells him; he is in London. He was taken ill in the library, this morning. Right thankful she is that she happened to come to London, and is able to attend upon him.

"It is not an illness of any serious consequence, Sir Leicester. You will be much better to-morrow, Sir Leicester. All the gentlemen say so." This, with the tears coursing down her fair old face.

After making a survey of the room, and looking with particular attention all round the bed where the doctors stand, he writes, "My Lady."

"My Lady went out, Sir Leicester, before you were taken ill, and don't know of your illness yet."

He points again, in great agitation, at the two words. They all try to quiet him, but he points again with increased agitation. On their looking at one another, not knowing what to say, he takes the slate once more, and writes, "My Lady. For God's sake, where?" And makes an imploring moan.

It is thought better that his old housekeeper should give him Lady Dedlock's letter, the contents of which no one knows or can surmise. She opens it for him, and puts it out for his perusal. Having read it twice by a great effort, he turns it down so that it shall not be seen, and lies moaning. He passes into a kind of relapse, or into a swoon; and it is an hour before he opens his eyes, reclining on his faithful and attached old servant's arm. The doctors know that he is best with her; and, when not actively engaged about him, stand aloof.

The slate comes into requisition again; but the word he wants to write, he cannot remember. His anxiety, his eagerness, and affliction at this pass, are pitiable to behold. It seems as if he must go mad, in the necessity he feels for haste, and the inability under which he labours of expressing to do what, or to fetch whom. He has written the letter B, and there stopped. Of a sudden, in the height of his misery he puts Mr. before it. The old housekeeper suggests Bucket. Thank Heaven! That's his meaning.

Mr. Bucket is found to be downstairs, by appointment. Shall he come up?

There is no possibility of misconstruing Sir Leicester's burning wish to see him, or the desire he signifies to have the room cleared of every one but the housekeeper. It is speedily done; and Mr. Bucket appears. Of all men upon earth, Sir Leicester seems fallen from his high estate to place his sole trust and reliance upon this man.

"Sir Leicester Dedlock, Baronet, I'm sorry to see you like this. I hope you'll cheer up. I'm sure you will, on account of the family credit."

Sir Leicester puts her letter in his hand, and looks intently in his face while he reads it. A new intelligence comes into Mr. Bucket's eye, as he reads on; with one hook of his finger, while that eye is still glancing over the words, he indicates, "Sir Leicester Dedlock, Baronet, I understand you."

Sir Leicester writes upon the slate. "Full forgiveness. Find——" Mr. Bucket stops his hand.

"Sir Leicester Dedlock, Baronet, I'll find her. But my search after her must be begun out of hand. Not a minute must be lost."

With the quickness of thought he follows Sir Leicester Dedlock's look towards a little box upon a table.

"Bring it here, Sir Leicester Dedlock, Baronet? Certainly. Open it with one of these here keys? Certainly. The littlest key? *To* be sure. Take the notes out? So I will. Count 'em? That's soon done. Twenty and thirty's fifty, and twenty's seventy, and fifty's one twenty, and forty's one sixty. Take 'em for expenses? That I'll do, and render an account of course. Don't spare money. No, I won't."

The velocity and certainty of Mr. Bucket's interpretation on all these heads is little short of miraculous. Mrs. Rouncewell, who holds the light, is giddy with the swiftness of his eyes and hands, as he starts up, furnished for his journey.

"You're George's mother, old lady; that's about what you are, I believe?" says Mr. Bucket, aside, with his hat already on, and buttoning up his coat.

"Yes, sir, I am his distressed mother."

"So I thought, according to what he mentioned to me just now.

Well, then, I'll tell you something. You needn't be distressed no more.
Your son's all right. Now, don't you begin a-crying; because what
you've got to do is to take care of Sir Leicester Dedlock, Baronet, and
you won't do that by crying. As to your son, he's all right, I tell you;
and he sends his loving duty, and hoping you're the same. He's discharged honourable; that's about what *he* is; with no more imputation
on his character than there is on yours, and yours is a tidy one, *I'll*
bet a pound. You may trust me, for I took your son. He conducted
himself in a game way, too, on that occasion; and he's a fine-made man,
and you're a fine-made old lady, and you're a mother and son, the pair
of you, as might be showed for models in a caravan. Sir Leicester
Dedlock, Baronet, what you've trusted to me, I'll go through with.
Don't you be afraid of my turning out of my way, right or left; or
taking a sleep, or a wash, or a shave, till I have found what I go in
search of. Say everything as is kind and forgiving on your part? Sir
Leicester Dedlock, Baronet, I will. And I wish you better, and these
family affairs smoothed over—as, Lord! many other family affairs equally
has been, and equally will be, to the end of time."

With this peroration, Mr. Bucket, buttoned up, goes quietly out,
looking steadily before him as if he were already piercing the night, in
quest of the fugitive.

His first step is to take himself to Lady Dedlock's rooms, and look all
over them for any trifling indication that may help him. The rooms
are in darkness now; and to see Mr. Bucket with a wax-light in his
hand, holding it above his head, and taking a sharp mental inventory of
the many delicate objects so curiously at variance with himself, would
be to see a sight—which nobody *does* see, as he is particular to lock
himself in.

"A spicy boudoir this," says Mr. Bucket, who feels in a manner
furbished up in his French by the blow of the morning. "Must have
cost a sight of money. Rum articles to cut away from, these; she must
have been hard put to it!"

Opening and shutting table-drawers, and looking into caskets and
jewel-cases, he sees the reflection of himself in various mirrors, and
moralises thereon.

"One might suppose I was a-moving in the fashionable circles, and
getting myself up for Almack's," says Mr. Bucket. "I begin to think
I must be a swell in the Guards, without knowing it."

Ever looking about, he has opened a dainty little chest in an inner
drawer. His great hand, turning over some gloves which it can scarcely
feel, they are so light and soft within it, comes upon a white handkerchief.

"Hum! Let's have a look at *you*," says Mr. Bucket, putting down
the light. "What should *you* be kept by yourself for? What's *your*
motive? Are you her ladyship's property, or somebody else's? You've
got a mark upon you, somewheres or another, I suppose?"

He finds it as he speaks, "Esther Summerson."

"Oh!" says Mr. Bucket, pausing, with his finger at his ear, "Come, I'll take *you*."

He completes his observations as quietly and carefully as he has carried them on, leaves everything else precisely as he found it, glides away after some five minutes in all, and passes into the street. With a glance upward at the dimly lighted windows of Sir Leicester's room, he sets off, full swing, to the nearest coach-stand, picks out the horse for his money, and directs to be driven to the Shooting Gallery. Mr. Bucket does not claim to be a scientific judge of horses; but he lays out a little money on the principal events in that line, and generally sums up his knowledge of the subject in the remark, that when he sees a horse as can go, he knows him.

His knowledge is not at fault in the present instance. Clattering over the stones at a dangerous pace, yet thoughtfully bringing his keen eyes to bear on every slinking creature whom he passes in the midnight streets, and even on the lights in upper windows where people are going or gone to bed, and on all the turnings that he rattles by, and alike on the heavy sky, and on the earth where the snow lies thin—for something may present itself to assist him, anywhere—he dashes to his destination at such a speed, that when he stops, the horse half smothers him in a cloud of steam.

"Unbear him half a moment to freshen him up, and I'll be back."

He runs up the long wooden entry, and finds the trooper smoking his pipe.

"I thought I should, George, after what you have gone through, my lad. I haven't a word to spare. Now, honour! All to save a woman. Miss Summerson that was here when Gridley died—that was the name, I know—all right!—where does she live?"

The trooper has just come from there, and gives him the address near Oxford Street.

"You won't repent it, George. Good night!"

He is off again, with an impression of having seen Phil sitting by the frosty fire, staring at him open-mouthed; and gallops away again, and gets out in a cloud of steam again.

Mr. Jarndyce, the only person up in the house, is just going to bed; rises from his book, on hearing the rapid ringing at the bell; and comes down to the door in his dressing-gown.

"Don't be alarmed, sir." In a moment his visitor is confidential with him in the hall, has shut the door, and stands with his hand upon the lock. "I've had the pleasure of seeing you before. Inspector Bucket. Look at that handkerchief, sir, Miss Esther Summerson's. Found it myself put away in a drawer of Lady Dedlock's, quarter of an hour ago. Not a moment to lose. Matter of life or death. You know Lady Dedlock?"

"Yes."

"There has been a discovery there, to-day. Family affairs have come out. Sir Leicester Dedlock, Baronet, has had a fit—apoplexy or paralysis—and couldn't be brought to, and precious time has been lost. Lady Dedlock disappeared this afternoon, and left a letter for him that looks bad. Run your eye over it. Here it is!"

Mr. Jarndyce having read it, asks him what he thinks?

"I don't know. It looks like suicide. Anyways, there's more and more danger, every minute, of its drawing to that. I'd give a hundred pound an hour to have got the start of the present time. Now, Mr. Jarndyce, I am employed by Sir Leicester Dedlock, Baronet, to follow her and find her—to save her, and take her his forgiveness. I have money and full power, but I want something else. I want Miss Summerson."

Mr. Jarndyce, in a troubled voice, repeats "Miss Summerson?"

"Now, Mr. Jarndyce;" Mr. Bucket has read his face with the greatest attention all along; "I speak to you as a gentleman of a humane heart, and under such pressing circumstances as don't often happen. If ever delay was dangerous, it's dangerous now; and if ever you couldn't afterwards forgive yourself for causing it, this is the time. Eight or ten hours' worth, as I tell you, a hundred pound a-piece at least, have been lost since Lady Dedlock disappeared. I am charged to find her. I am Inspector Bucket. Besides all the rest that's heavy on her, she has upon her, as she believes, suspicion of murder. If I follow her alone, she, being in ignorance of what Sir Leicester Dedlock, Baronet, has communicated to me, may be driven to desperation. But if I follow her in company with a young lady, answering to the description of a young lady that she has a tenderness for—I ask no question, and I say no more than that—she will give me credit for being friendly. Let me come up with her, and be able to have the hold upon her of putting that young lady for'ard, and I'll save her and prevail with her if she is alive. Let me come up with her, alone—a harder matter—and I'll do my best; but I don't answer for what the best may be. Time flies; it's getting on for one o'clock. When one strikes, there's another hour gone; and it's worth a thousand pound now, instead of a hundred."

This is all true, and the pressing nature of the case cannot be questioned. Mr. Jarndyce begs him to remain there, while he speaks to Miss Summerson. Mr. Bucket says he will; but acting on his usual principle, does no such thing—following upstairs instead, and keeping his man in sight. So he remains, dodging and lurking about in the gloom of the staircase, while they confer. In a very little time, Mr. Jarndyce comes down, and tells him that Miss Summerson will join him directly, and place herself under his protection, to accompany him where he pleases. Mr. Bucket, satisfied, expresses high approval; and awaits her coming at the door.

There, he mounts a high tower in his mind, and looks out, far and wide. Many solitary figures he perceives, creeping through the streets; many solitary figures out on heaths, and roads, and lying under haystacks. But the figure that he seeks is not among them. Other solitaries he perceives, in nooks of bridges, looking over; and in shadowed places down by the river's level ; and a dark, dark, shapeless object drift-ing with the tide, more solitary than all, clings with a drowning hold on his attention.

Where is she? Living or dead, where is she? If, as he folds the handkerchief and carefully puts it up, it were able, with an enchanted power, to bring before him the place where she found it, and the night landscape near the cottage where it covered the little child, would he descry her there? On the waste, where the brick-kilns are burning with a pale blue flare ; where the straw-roofs of the wretched huts in which the bricks are made, are being scattered by the wind ; where the clay and water are hard frozen, and the mill in which the gaunt blind horse goes round all day, looks like an instrument of human torture ;—travers-ing this deserted blighted spot, there is a lonely figure with the sad world to itself, pelted by the snow and driven by the wind, and cast out, it would seem, from all companionship. It is the figure of a woman, too ; but it is miserably dressed, and no such clothes ever came through the hall, and out at the great door of the Dedlock mansion.

CHAPTER LVII

ESTHER'S NARRATIVE

I HAD gone to bed and fallen asleep, when my guardian knocked at the door of my room and begged me to get up directly. On my hurrying to speak to him and learn what had happened, he told me, after a word or two of preparation, that there had been a discovery at Sir Leicester Dedlock's. That my mother had fled ; that a person was now at our door who was empowered to convey to her the fullest assur-ances of affectionate protection and forgiveness, if he could possibly find her ; and that I was sought for to accompany him, in the hope that my entreaties might prevail upon her, if his failed. Something to this general purpose I made out ; but I was thrown into such a tumult of alarm, and hurry and distress, that, in spite of every effort I could make to subdue my agitation, I did not seem, to myself, fully to recover my right mind until hours had passed.

But I dressed and wrapped up expeditiously without waking Charley, or any one ; and went down to Mr. Bucket, who was the person entrusted with the secret. In taking me to him my guardian told me this, and also explained how it was that he had come to think of me. Mr. Bucket, in a low voice, by the light of my guardian's candle, read to me, in the hall, a letter that my mother had left upon her table ; and, I suppose within ten minutes of my having been aroused, I was sitting beside him, rolling swiftly through the streets.

His manner was very keen, and yet considerate when he explained to me that a great deal might depend on my being able to answer, without confusion, a few questions that he wished to ask me. These were, chiefly, whether I had had much communication with my mother (to whom he only referred as Lady Dedlock); when and where I had spoken with her last; and how she had become possessed of my handkerchief. When I had satisfied him on these points, he asked me particularly to consider—taking time to think—whether, within my knowledge, there was any one, no matter where, in whom she might be at all likely to confide, under circumstances of the last necessity. I could think of no one but my guardian. But, by-and-by, I mentioned Mr. Boythorn. He came into my mind, as connected with his old chivalrous manner of mentioning my mother's name; and with what my guardian had informed me of his engagement to her sister, and his unconscious connection with her unhappy story.

My companion had stopped the driver while we held this conversation, that we might the better hear each other. He now told him to go on again; and said to me, after considering within himself for a few moments, that he had made up his mind how to proceed. He was quite willing to tell me what his plan was, but I did not feel clear enough to understand it.

We had not driven very far from our lodgings, when we stopped in a by-street, at a public-looking place lighted up with gas. Mr. Bucket took me in and sat me in an arm-chair, by a bright fire. It was now past one, as I saw by the clock against the wall. Two police officers, looking in their perfectly neat uniform not at all like people who were up all night, were quietly writing at a desk; and the place seemed very quiet, altogether, except for some beating and calling out at distant doors underground, to which nobody paid any attention.

A third man in uniform, whom Mr. Bucket called, and to whom he whispered his instructions, went out; and then the two others advised together, while one wrote from Mr. Bucket's subdued dictation. It was a description of my mother that they were busy with; for Mr. Bucket brought it to me when it was done, and read it in a whisper. It was very accurate indeed.

The second officer, who had attended to it closely, then copied it out, and called in another man in uniform (there were several in an outer room) who took it up and went away with it. All this was done with the greatest despatch, and without the waste of a moment; yet nobody was at all hurried. As soon as the paper was sent out upon its travels, the two officers resumed their former quiet work of writing with neatness and care. Mr. Bucket thoughtfully came and warmed the soles of his boots, first one and then the other, at the fire.

"Are you well wrapped up, Miss Summerson?" he asked me, as his eyes met mine. "It's a desperate sharp night for a young lady to be out in."

I told him I cared for no weather, and was warmly clothed.

"It may be a long job," he observed; "but so that it ends well, never mind, miss."

"I pray to Heaven it may end well!" said I.

He nodded comfortingly. "You see, whatever you do, don't you go and fret yourself. You keep yourself cool, and equal for anything that may happen; and it'll be the better for you, the better for me, the better for Lady Dedlock, and the better for Sir Leicester Dedlock, Baronet."

He was really very kind and gentle; and as he stood before the fire warming his boots, and rubbing his face with his forefinger, I felt a confidence in his sagacity which reassured me. It was not yet a quarter to two, when I heard horses' feet and wheels outside. "Now, Miss Summerson," said he, "we are off, if you please!"

He gave me his arm, and the two officers courteously bowed me out, and we found at the door a phaeton or barouche, with a postillion and post horses. Mr. Bucket handed me in, and took his own seat on the box. The man in uniform whom he had sent to fetch this equipage, then handed him up a dark lantern at his request; and when he had given a few directions to the driver, we rattled away.

I was far from sure that I was not in a dream. We rattled with great rapidity through such a labyrinth of streets, that I soon lost all idea where we were; except that we had crossed and re-crossed the river, and still seemed to be traversing a low-lying, waterside, dense neighbourhood of narrow thoroughfares, chequered by docks and basins, high piles of warehouses, swing-bridges, and masts of ships. At length we stopped at the corner of a little slimy turning, which the wind from the river, rushing up it, did not purify; and I saw my companion, by the light of his lantern, in conference with several men, who looked like a mixture of police and sailors. Against the mouldering wall by which they stood, there was a bill, on which I could discern the words, "FOUND DROWNED;" and this, and an inscription about Drags, possessed me with the awful suspicion shadowed forth in our visit to that place.

I had no need to remind myself that I was not there, by the indulgence of any feeling of mine, to increase the difficulties of the search, or to lessen its hopes, or enhance its delays. I remained quiet; but what I suffered in that dreadful spot I never can forget. And still it was like the horror of a dream. A man yet dark and muddy, in long swollen sodden boots and a hat like them, was called out of a boat, and whispered with Mr. Bucket, who went away with him down some slippery steps— as if to look at something secret that he had to show. They came back, wiping their hands upon their coats, after turning over something wet; but thank God it was not what I feared!

After some further conference, Mr. Bucket (whom everybody seemed to know and defer to) went in with the others at a door, and left me in the carriage; while the driver walked up and down by his horses, to warm himself. The tide was coming in, as I judged from the sound it made; and I could hear it break at the end of the alley, with a little rush towards me. It never did so—and I thought it did so, hundreds of times, in what can have been at the most a quarter of an hour, and probably was less—but the thought shuddered through me that it would cast my mother at the horses' feet.

Mr. Bucket came out again, exhorting the others to be vigilant, darkened his lantern, and once more took his seat. "Don't you be alarmed, Miss Summerson, on account of our coming down here," he said, turning to me, "I only want to have everything in train, and to know that it is in train by looking after it myself. Get on, my lad!"

We appeared to retrace the way we had come. Not that I had taken note of any particular objects in my perturbed state of mind, but judging from the general character of the streets. We called at another office or station for a minute, and crossed the river again. During the whole of this time, and during the whole search, my companion, wrapped up on the box, never relaxed in his vigilance a single moment; but when we crossed the bridge he seemed, if possible, to be more on the alert than before. He stood up to look over the parapet; he alighted, and went back after a shadowy female figure that flitted past us; and he gazed into the profound black pit of water, with a face that made my heart die within me. The river had a fearful look, so overcast and secret, creeping away so fast between the low flat lines of shore : so heavy with indistinct and awful shapes, both of substance and shadow : so deathlike and mysterious. I have seen it many times since then, by sunlight and by moonlight, but never free from the impressions of that journey. In my memory, the lights upon the bridge are always burning dim ; the cutting wind is eddying round the homeless woman whom we pass ; the monotonous wheels are whirling on ; and the light of the carriage-lamps reflected back, looks palely in upon me—a face, rising out of the dreaded water.

Clattering and clattering through the empty streets, we came at length from the pavement on to the dark smooth roads, and began to leave the houses behind us. After awhile, I recognised the familiar way to Saint Albans. At Barnet, fresh horses were ready for us, and we changed and went on. It was very cold indeed; and the open country was white with snow, though none was falling then.

"An old acquaintance of yours, this road, Miss Summerson," said Mr. Bucket cheerfully.

"Yes," I returned. "Have you gathered any intelligence?"

"None that can be quite depended on as yet," he answered ; "but it's early times as yet."

He had gone into every late or early public-house where there was a light (they were not a few at that time, the road being then much frequented by drovers), and had got down to talk to the turnpike-keepers. I had heard him ordering drink, and chinking money, and making himself agreeable and merry everywhere ; but whenever he took his seat upon the box again, his face resumed its watchful steady look, and he always said to the driver in the same business tone, "Get on, my lad!"

With all these stoppages, it was between five and six o'clock and we were yet a few miles short of Saint Albans, when he came out of one of these houses and handed me in a cup of tea.

"Drink it, Miss Summerson, it'll do you good. You're beginning to get more yourself now, ain't you?"

I thanked him, and said I hoped so.

"You was what you may call stunned at first," he returned; "and Lord! no wonder. Don't speak loud, my dear. It's all right. She's on ahead."

I don't know what joyful exclamation I made, or was going to make, but he put up his finger, and I stopped myself.

"Passed through here on foot, this evening, about eight or nine. I heard of her first at the archway toll, over at Highgate, but couldn't make quite sure. Traced her all along, on and off. Picked her up at one place, and dropped her at another; but she's before us now, safe. Take hold of this cup and saucer, Ostler. Now, if you wasn't brought up to the butter trade, look out and see if you can catch half-a-crown in your t'other hand. One, two, three, and there you are! Now, my lad, try a gallop!"

We were soon in Saint Albans, and alighted a little before day, when I was just beginning to arrange and comprehend the occurrences of the night, and really to believe that they were not a dream. Leaving the carriage at the posting-house, and ordering fresh horses to be ready, my companion gave me his arm, and we went towards home.

"As this is your regular abode, Miss Summerson, you see," he observed, "I should like to know whether you've been asked for by any stranger answering the description, or whether Mr. Jarndyce has. I don't much expect it, but it might be."

As we ascended the hill, he looked about him with a sharp eye—the day was now breaking—and reminded me that I had come down it one night, as I had reason for remembering, with my little servant and poor Jo: whom he called Toughey.

I wondered how he knew that.

"When you passed a man upon the road, just yonder, you know," said Mr. Bucket.

Yes, I remembered that too, very well.

"That was me," said Mr. Bucket.

Seeing my surprise, he went on:

"I drove down in a gig that afternoon, to look after that boy. You might have heard my wheels when you came out to look after him yourself, for I was aware of you and your little maid going up, when I was walking the horse down. Making an inquiry or two about him in the town, I soon heard what company he was in; and was coming among the brick-fields to look for him, when I observed you bringing him home here."

"Had he committed any crime?" I asked.

"None was charged against him," said Mr. Bucket, coolly lifting off his hat; "but I suppose he wasn't over-particular. No. What I wanted him for, was in connection with keeping this very matter of Lady Dedlock quiet. He had been making his tongue more free than welcome, as to a small accidental service he had been paid for by the deceased Mr. Tulkinghorn; and it wouldn't do, at any sort of price, to have him playing those games. So having warned him out of London, I made an afternoon of it to warn him to keep out of it now he *was* away, and go farther from it, and maintain a bright look out that I didn't catch him coming back again."

"Poor creature!" said I.

"Poor enough," assented Mr. Bucket, "and trouble enough, and well enough away from London, or anywhere else. I was regularly turned on my back when I found him taken up by your establishment, I do assure you."

I asked him why? "Why, my dear?" said Mr. Bucket. "Naturally there was no end to his tongue then. He might as well have been born with a yard and a half of it, and a remnant over."

Although I remember this conversation now, my head was in confusion at the time, and my power of attention hardly did more than enable me to understand that he entered into these particulars to divert me. With the same kind intention, manifestly, he often spoke to me of indifferent things, while his face was busy with the one object that he had in view. He still pursued this subject, as we turned in at the garden-gate.

"Ah!" said Mr. Bucket. "Here we are, and a nice retired place it is. Puts a man in mind of the country-house in the Woodpecker-tapping, that was known by the smoke which so gracefully curled. They're early with the kitchen fire, and that denotes good servants. But what you've always got to be careful of with servants, is, who comes to see 'em; you never know what they're up to, if you don't know that. And another thing, my dear. Whenever you find a young man behind the kitchen-door, you give that young man in charge on suspicion of being secreted in a dwelling-house with an unlawful purpose."

We were now in front of the house; he looked attentively and closely at the gravel for footprints, before he raised his eyes to the windows.

"Do you generally put that elderly young gentleman in the same room, when he's on a visit here, Miss Summerson?" he inquired, glancing at Mr. Skimpole's usual chamber.

"You know Mr. Skimpole!" said I.

"What do you call him again?" returned Mr. Bucket, bending down his ear. "Skimpole, is it? I've often wondered what his name might be. Skimpole. Not John. I should say, nor yet Jacob?"

"Harold," I told him.

"Harold. Yes. He's a queer bird is Harold," said Mr. Bucket, eyeing me with great expression.

"He is a singular character," said I.

"No idea of money," observed Mr. Bucket.—"He takes it though!"

I involuntarily returned for answer, that I perceived Mr. Bucket knew him.

"Why, now I'll tell you, Miss Summerson," he rejoined. "Your mind will be all the better for not running on one point too continually, and I'll tell you for a change. It was him as pointed out to me where Toughey was. I made up my mind, that night, to come to the door and ask for Toughey, if that was all; but, willing to try a move or so first, if any such was on the board, I just pitched up a morsel of gravel at that window where I saw a shadow. As soon as Harold opens it and I have had a look at him, thinks I, you're the man for me. So I smoothed him down a bit, about not wanting to disturb the family after they was gone to bed, and about its being a thing to be regretted that charitable young ladies should harbour vagrants; and then, when I pretty well understood his ways, I said, I should consider a fypunnote well bestowed if I could relieve the premises of Toughey without causing any noise or trouble. Then says he, lifting up his eyebrows in the gayest way, 'It's no use mentioning a fypunnote to me, my friend, because I'm a mere child in such matters, and have no idea of money.' Of course I understood what his taking it so easy meant; and being now quite sure he was the man for me, I wrapped the note round a little stone and threw it up to him. Well! He laughs and beams, and looks as innocent as you like, and says, 'But I don't know the value of these things. What am I to *do* with this?' 'Spend it, sir,' says I. 'But I shall be taken in,' he says, 'they won't give me the right change, I shall lose it, it's no use to me.' Lord, you never saw such a face as he carried it with! Of course he told me where to find Toughey, and I found him."

I regarded this as very treacherous on the part of Mr. Skimpole towards my guardian, and as passing the usual bounds of his childish innocence.

"Bounds, my dear?" returned Mr. Bucket. "Bounds? Now, Miss Summerson, I'll give you a piece of advice that your husband will find useful when you are happily married and have got a family about you. Whenever a person says to you that they are as innocent as can be in all concerning money, look well after your own money, for they are dead certain to collar it, if they can. Whenever a person proclaims to you, 'In worldly matters I'm a child,' you consider that that person is only a-crying off from being held accountable, and that you have got that person's number, and it's Number One. Now, I am not a poetical man myself, except in a vocal way when it goes round a company, but I'm a practical one, and that's my experience. So's this rule. Fast and loose in one thing, Fast and loose in everything. I never knew it fail. No more will you. Nor no one. With which caution to the unwary, my dear, I take the liberty of pulling this here bell, and so go back to our business."

I believe it had not been for a moment out of his mind, any more than it had been out of my mind, or out of his face. The whole household were amazed to see me, without any notice, at that time in the morning, and so accompanied; and their surprise was not diminished by my inquiries. No one, however, had been there. It could not be doubted that this was the truth.

"Then, Miss Summerson," said my companion, "we can't be too soon at the cottage where those brickmakers are to be found. Most inquiries there I leave to you, if you'll be so good as to make 'em. The naturalest way is the best way, and the naturalest way is your own way."

We set off again immediately. On arriving at the cottage, we found it shut up, and apparently deserted; but one of the neighbours who knew me, and who came out when I was trying to make some one hear, informed me that the two women and their husbands now lived together in another house, made of loose rough bricks, which stood on the margin of the piece of ground where the kilns were, and where the long rows of bricks were drying. We lost no time in repairing to this place, which was within a few hundred yards; and as the door stood ajar, I pushed it open.

There were only three of them sitting at breakfast; the child lying asleep on a bed in the corner. It was Jenny, the mother of the dead child, who was absent. The other woman rose on seeing me; and the men, though they were, as usual, sulky and silent, each gave me a morose nod of recognition. A look passed between them when Mr. Bucket followed me in, and I was surprised to see that the woman evidently knew him.

I had asked leave to enter of course. Liz (the only name by which I knew her) rose to give me her own chair, but I sat down on a stool near the fire, and Mr. Bucket took a corner of the bedstead. Now that I had to speak, and was among people with whom I was not familiar, I became conscious of being hurried and giddy. It was very difficult to begin, and I could not help bursting into tears.

"Liz," said I, "I have come a long way in the night and through the snow, to inquire after a lady——"

"Who has been here, you know," Mr. Bucket struck in, addressing the whole group, with a composed propitiatory face; "that's the lady the young lady means. The lady that was here last night, you know."

"And who told *you* as there was anybody here?" inquired Jenny's husband, who had made a surly stop in his eating, to listen, and now measured him with his eye.

"A person of the name of Michael Jackson, with a blue welveteen waistcoat with a double row of mother of pearl buttons," Mr. Bucket immediately answered.

"He had as good mind his own business, whoever he is," growled the man.

"He's out of employment, I believe," said Mr. Bucket, apologetically for Michael Jackson, "and so gets talking."

The woman had not resumed her chair, but stood faltering with her hand upon its broken back, looking at me. I thought she would have spoken to me privately, if she had dared. She was still in this attitude of uncertainty, when her husband, who was eating with a lump of bread and fat in one hand, and his clasp-knife in the other, struck the handle of his knife violently on the table, and told her with an oath to mind *her* business at any rate, and sit down.

2 P

"I should like to have seen Jenny very much," said I, "for I am sure she would have told me all she could about this lady, whom I am very anxious indeed—you cannot think how anxious—to overtake. Will Jenny be here soon? Where is she?"

The woman had a great desire to answer, but the man, with another oath, openly kicked at her foot with his heavy boot. He left it to Jenny's husband to say what he chose, and after a dogged silence the latter turned his shaggy head towards me.

"I'm not partial to gentlefolks coming into my place, as you've heerd me say afore now, I think, miss. I let their places be, and it's curious they can't let my place be. There'd be a pretty shine made if I was to go a-wisiting *them*, I think. Howsoever, I don't so much complain of you as of some others; and I'm agreeable to make you a civil answer, though I give notice that I'm not agoing to be drawed like a badger. Will Jenny be here soon? No she won't. Where is she? She's gone up to Lunnun."

"Did she go last night?" I asked.

"Did she go last night? Ah! she went last night," he answered, with a sulky jerk of his head.

"But was she here when the lady came? And what did the lady say to her? And where is the lady gone? I beg and pray you to be so kind as to tell me," said I, "for I am in great distress to know."

"If my master would let me speak, and not say a word of harm—" the woman timidly began.

"Your master," said her husband, muttering an imprecation with slow emphasis, "will break your neck, if you meddle with wot don't concern you."

After another silence, the husband of the absent woman, turning to me again, answered me with his usual grumbling unwillingness.

"Wos Jenny here when the lady come? Yes, she wos here when the lady come. Wot did the lady say to her? Well, I'll tell you wot the lady said to her. She said, 'You remember me as come one time to talk to you about the young lady as had been a-wisiting of you? You remember me as give you somethink handsome for a handkercher wot she had left?' Ah, she remembered. So we all did. Well, then, wos that young lady up at the house now? No, she warn't up at the house now. Well, then, lookee here. The lady was upon a journey all alone, strange as we might think it, and could she rest herself where you're a-setten, for a hour or so? Yes she could, and so she did. Then she went —it might be at twenty minutes past eleven, and it might be at twenty minutes past twelve; we ain't got no watches here to know the time by, nor yet clocks. Where did she go? I don't know where she go'd. She went one way, and Jenny went another; one went right to Lunnun, and t'other went right from it. That's all about it. Ask this man. He heerd it all, and see it all. He knows."

The other man repeated, "That's all about it."

"Was the lady crying?" I inquired.

"Devil a bit," returned the first man. "Her shoes was the worse, and her clothes was the worse, but she warn't—not as I see."

The woman sat with her arms crossed, and her eyes upon the ground. Her husband had turned his seat a little, so as to face her; and kept his hammer-like hand upon the table, as if it were in readiness to execute his threat if she disobeyed him.

"I hope you will not object to my asking your wife," said I, "how the lady looked?"

"Come, then!" he gruffly cried to her. "You hear what she says. Cut it short, and tell her."

"Bad," replied the woman. "Pale and exhausted. Very bad."

"Did she speak much?"

"Not much, but her voice was hoarse."

She answered, looking all the while at her husband for leave.

"Was she faint?" said I. "Did she eat or drink here?"

"Go on!" said the husband, in answer to her look. "Tell her and cut it short."

"She had a little water, miss, and Jenny fetched her some bread and tea. But she hardly touched it."

"And when she went from here"—I was proceeding, when Jenny's husband impatiently took me up.

"When she went from here, she went right away Nor'ard by the high road. Ask on the road if you doubt me, and see if it warn't so. Now, there's the end. That's all about it."

I glanced at my companion; and finding that he had already risen and was ready to depart, thanked them for what they had told me, and took my leave. The woman looked full at Mr. Bucket as he went out, and he looked full at her.

"Now, Miss Summerson," he said to me, as we walked quickly away. "They've got her ladyship's watch among 'em. That's a positive fact."

"You saw it?" I exclaimed.

"Just as good as saw it," he returned. "Else why should he talk about his 'twenty minutes past,' and about his having no watch to tell the time by? Twenty minutes! He don't usually cut his time so fine as that. If he comes to half-hours, it's as much as *he* does. Now, you see, either her ladyship gave him that watch, or he took it. I think she gave it him. Now, what should she give it him for? What should she give it him for?"

He repeated this question to himself several times, as we hurried on; appearing to balance between a variety of answers that arose in his mind.

"If time could be spared," said Mr. Bucket—"which is the only thing that can't be spared in this case—I might get it out of that woman; but it's too doubtful a chance to trust to, under present circumstances. They are up to keeping a close eye upon her, and any fool knows that a poor creetur like her, beaten and kicked and scarred and bruised from head to foot, will stand by the husband that ill uses her, through thick and thin.

There's something kept back. It's a pity but what we had seen the other woman."

I regretted it exceedingly; for she was very grateful, and I felt sure would have resisted no entreaty of mine.

"It's possible, Miss Summerson," said Mr. Bucket, pondering on it, "that her Ladyship sent her up to London with some word for you, and it's possible that her husband got the watch to let her go. It don't come out altogether so plain as to please me, but it's on the cards. Now, I don't take kindly to laying out the money of Sir Leicester Dedlock, Baronet, on these Roughs, and I don't see my way to the usefulness of it at present. No! So far, our road, Miss Summerson, is for'ard—straight ahead—and keeping everything quiet!"

We called at home once more, that I might send a hasty note to my guardian, and then we hurried back to where we had left the carriage. The horses were brought out as soon as we were seen coming, and we were on the road again in a few minutes.

It had set in snowing at daybreak, and it now snowed hard. The air was so thick with the darkness of the day, and the density of the fall, that we could see but a very little way in any direction. Although it was extremely cold, the snow was but partially frozen, and it churned—with a sound as if it were a beach of small shells—under the hoofs of the horses, into mire and water. They sometimes slipped and floundered for a mile together, and we were obliged to come to a standstill to rest them. One horse fell three times in this first stage, and trembled so, and was so shaken, that the driver had to dismount from his saddle and lead him at last.

I could eat nothing, and could not sleep; and I grew so nervous under those delays, and the slow pace at which we travelled, that I had an unreasonable desire upon me to get out and walk. Yielding to my companion's better sense, however, I remained where I was. All this time, kept fresh by a certain enjoyment of the work in which he was engaged, he was up and down at every house we came to; addressing people whom he had never beheld before, as old acquaintances; running in to warm himself at every fire he saw; talking and drinking and shaking hands at every bar and tap; friendly with every waggoner, wheelwright, blacksmith, and toll-taker; yet never seeming to lose time, and always mounting to the box again with his watchful, steady face, and his business-like "Get on, my lad!"

When we were changing horses the next time, he came from the stable-yard, and with the wet snow encrusted upon him, and dropping off him—plashing and crashing through it to his wet knees, as he had been doing frequently since we left Saint Albans—and spoke to me at the carriage side.

"Keep up your spirits. It's certainly true that she came on here, Miss Summerson. There's not a doubt of the dress by this time, and the dress has been seen here."

"Still on foot?" said I.

"Still on foot. I think the gentleman you mentioned must be the point she's aiming at; and yet I don't like his living down in her own part of the country, neither."

"I know so little," said I. "There may be some one else nearer here, of whom I never heard."

"That's true. But whatever you do, don't you fall a-crying, my dear; and don't you worry yourself no more than you can help. Get on, my lad!"

The sleet fell all that day unceasingly, a thick mist came on early, and it never rose or lightened for a moment. Such roads I had never seen. I sometimes feared we had missed the way and got into the ploughed grounds, or the marshes. If I ever thought of the time I had been out, it presented itself as an indefinite period of great duration; and I seemed, in a strange way, never to have been free from the anxiety under which I then laboured."

As we advanced, I began to feel misgivings that my companion lost confidence. He was the same as before with all the roadside people, but he looked graver when he sat by himself on the box. I saw his finger uneasily going across and across his mouth, during the whole of one long weary stage. I overheard that he began to ask the drivers of coaches and other vehicles coming towards us, what passengers they had seen in other coaches and vehicles that were in advance. Their replies did not encourage him. He always gave me a reassuring beck of his finger, and lift of his eyelid, as he got upon the box again; but he seemed perplexed now, when he said, "Get on, my lad!"

At last, when we were changing, he told me that he had lost the track of the dress so long that he began to be surprised. It was nothing, he said, to lose such a track for one while, and to take it up for another while, and so on; but it had disappeared here in an unaccountable manner, and we had not come upon it since. This corroborated the apprehensions I had formed, when he began to look at direction-posts, and to leave the carriage at cross roads for a quarter of an hour at a time, while he explored them. But, I was not to be downhearted, he told me; for it was as likely as not that the next stage might set us right again.

The next stage, however, ended, as that one ended; we had no new clue. There was a spacious inn here, solitary, but a comfortable, substantial building, and as we drove in under a large gateway before I knew it, where a landlady and her pretty daughters came to the carriage-door, entreating me to alight and refresh myself while the horses were making ready, I thought it would be uncharitable to refuse. They took me upstairs to a warm room, and left me there.

It was at the corner of the house, I remember, looking two ways. On one side, to a stable-yard open to a by-road, where the hostlers were un-harnessing the splashed and tired horses from the muddy carriage; and beyond that, to the by-road itself, across which the sign was heavily swinging; on the other side, to a wood of dark pine-trees. Their branches were encumbered with snow, and it silently dropped off in wet heaps while I stood at the window. Night was setting in, and its bleakness was enhanced by the contrast of the pictured fire glowing and gleaming in the window-pane. As I looked among the stems of the trees, and followed the discoloured marks in the snow where the thaw was sinking into it and undermining it, I thought of the motherly face brightly set off by daughters that had just now welcomed me, and of *my* mother lying down in such a wood to die.

I was frightened when I found them all about me, but I remember that before I fainted I tried very hard not to do it; and that was some little comfort. They cushioned me up, on a large sofa by the fire; and then the comely landlady told me that I must travel no further to-night, but must go to bed. But this put me into such a tremble lest they should detain me there, that she soon recalled her words, and compromised for a rest of half-an-hour.

A good endearing creature she was. She, and her three fair girls, all so busy about me. I was to take hot soup and broiled fowl, while Mr. Bucket dried himself and dined elsewhere; but I could not do it when a snug round table was presently spread by the fireside, though I was very unwilling to disappoint them. However, I could take some toast and some hot negus; and as I really enjoyed that refreshment, it made some recompense.

Punctual to the time, at the half-hour's end the carriage came rumbling under the gateway, and they took me down, warmed, refreshed, comforted by kindness, and safe (I assured them) not to faint any more. After I had got in and had taken a grateful leave of them all, the youngest daughter—a blooming girl of nineteen, who was to be the first married, they had told me—got upon the carriage step, reached in, and kissed me. I have never seen her, from that hour, but I think of her to this hour as my friend.

The transparent windows with the fire and light, looking so bright and warm from the cold darkness out of doors, were soon gone, and again we were crushing and churning the loose snow. We went on with toil enough; but the dismal roads were not much worse than they had been, and the stage was only nine miles. My companion smoking on the box —I had thought at the last inn of begging him to do so, when I saw him standing at a great fire in a comfortable cloud of tobacco—was as vigilant as ever; and as quickly down and up again, when we came to any human abode or any human creature. He had lighted his little dark lantern, which seemed to be a favourite with him, for we had lamps to the carriage; and every now and then he turned it upon me, to see that I was doing well. There was a folding-window to the carriage-head, but I never closed it, for it seemed like shutting out hope.

We came to the end of the stage, and still the lost trace was not re-covered. I looked at him anxiously when we stopped to change; but I knew by his yet graver face, as he stood watching the hostlers, that he had heard nothing. Almost in an instant afterwards, as I leaned back in my seat, he looked in, with his lighted lantern in his hand, an excited and quite different man.

"What is it?" said I, starting. "Is she here?"

"No, no. Don't deceive yourself, my dear. Nobody's here. But I've got it!"

The crystallised snow was in his eyelashes, in his hair, lying in ridges on his dress. He had to shake it from his face, and get his breath, before he spoke to me.

"Now, Miss Summerson," said he, beating his finger on the apron, "don't you be disappointed at what I'm agoing to do. You know me. I'm Inspector Bucket, and you can trust me. We've come a long way; never mind. Four horses out there for the next stage up! Quick!"

There was a commotion in the yard, and a man came running out of the stables to know "if he meant up or down?"

"Up, I tell you! Up! Ain't it English? Up!"

"Up?" said I, astonished. "To London! Are we going back?"

"Miss Summerson," he answered, "back. Straight back as a die. You know me. Don't be afraid. I'll follow the other, by G——."

"The other?" I repeated. "Who?"

"You called her Jenny, didn't you? I'll follow her. Bring those two pair out here, for a crown a man. Wake up, some of you!"

"You will not desert this lady we are in search of; you will not abandon her on such a night, and in such a state of mind as I know her to be in!" said I, in an agony, and grasping his hand.

"You are right, my dear, I won't. But I'll follow the other. Look alive here with them horses. Send a man for'ard in the saddle to the next stage, and let him send another for'ard again, and order four on, up, right through. My darling, don't you be afraid!"

These orders, and the way in which he ran about the yard, urging them, caused a general excitement that was scarcely less bewildering to me than the sudden change. But in the height of the confusion, a mounted man galloped away to order the relays, and our horses were put to with great speed.

"My dear," said Mr. Bucket, jumping to his seat, and looking in again—"you'll excuse me if I'm too familiar—don't you fret and worry yourself no more than you can help. I say nothing else at present; but you know me, my dear; now, don't you?"

I endeavoured to say that I knew he was far more capable than I of deciding what we ought to do; but was he sure that this was right? Could I not go forward by myself in search of—— I grasped his hand again in my distress, and whispered it to him—of my own mother.

"My dear," he answered, "I know, I know, and would I put you wrong, do you think? Inspector Bucket. Now you know me, don't you?"

What could I say but yes!

"Then you keep up as good a heart as you can, and you rely upon me for standing by you, no less than by Sir Leicester Dedlock, Baronet. Now, are you right there?"

" All right, sir!"

" Off she goes, then. And get on, my lads!"

We were again upon the melancholy road by which we had come; tearing up the miry sleet and thawing snow, as if they were torn up by a water-wheel.

CHAPTER LVIII

A WINTRY DAY AND NIGHT

STILL impassive, as behoves its breeding, the Dedlock town-house carries itself as usual towards the street of dismal grandeur. There are powdered heads from time to time in the little windows of the hall, looking out at the untaxed powder falling all day from the sky; and, in the same conservatory, there is peach-blossom turning itself exotically to the great hall fire from the nipping weather out of doors. It is given out that my Lady has gone down into Lincolnshire, but is expected to return presently.

Rumour, busy overmuch, however, will not go down into Lincolnshire. It persists in flitting and chattering about town. It knows that that poor unfortunate man, Sir Leicester, has been sadly used. It hears, my dear child, all sorts of shocking things. It makes the world of five miles round, quite merry. Not to know that there is something wrong at the Dedlocks' is to augur yourself unknown. One of the peachy-cheeked charmers with the skeleton throats, is already apprised of all the principal circumstances that will come out before the Lords, on Sir Leicester's application for a bill of divorce.

At Blaze and Sparkle's the jewellers, and at Sheen and Gloss's the mercers, it is and will be for several hours the topic of the age, the feature of the century. The patronesses of those establishments, albeit so loftily inscrutable, being as nicely weighed and measured there as any other article of the stock-in-trade, are perfectly understood in this new fashion by the rawest hand behind the counter. " Our people, Mr. Jones," said Blaze and Sparkle to the hand in question on engaging him, " our people, sir, are sheep—mere sheep. Where two or three marked ones go, the rest follow. Keep those two or three in your eye, Mr. Jones, and you have the flock." So, likewise, Sheen and Gloss to *their* Jones, in reference to knowing where to have the fashionable people, and how to bring what they (Sheen and Gloss) choose, into fashion. On similar unerring principles, Mr. Sladdery the librarian, and indeed the great farmer of gorgeous sheep, admits this very day, " Why yes, sir, there certainly *are* reports concerning Lady Dedlock, very current indeed among my high connection, sir. You see, my high connection must talk about something, sir; and it's only to get a subject into vogue with one or two ladies I could name, to make it go down with the whole. Just what I should have done with those ladies, sir, in the case of any novelty you had left to me to bring in, they have done of themselves in this case through knowing Lady Dedlock, and being perhaps a little innocently jealous of her too, sir. You'll find, sir, that this topic will be very popular among my high connection. If it had been a speculation, sir, it would have brought money. And when I say so, you may trust to my being right, sir; for I have made it my business to study my high connection, and to be able to wind it up like a clock, sir."

Thus rumour thrives in the capital, and will not go down into Lincoln-shire. By half-past five, post meridian, Horse Guards' time, it has even elicited a new remark from the Honourable Mr. Stables, which bids fair to outshine the old one, on which he has so long rested his colloquial reputation. This sparkling sally is to the effect that, although he always knew she was the best-groomed woman in the stud, he had no idea she was a bolter. It is immensely received in turf-circles.

At feasts and festivals also: in firmaments she has often graced, and among constellations she outshone but yesterday, she is still the prevalent subject. What is it? Who is it? When was it? Where was it? How was it? She is discussed by her dear friends with all the genteelest slang in vogue, with the last new word, the last new manner, the last new drawl, and the perfection of polite indifference. A remarkable feature of the theme is, that it is found to be so inspiring that several people come out upon it who never came out before—positively say things! William Buffy carries one of these smartnesses from the place where he dines, down to the House, where the Whip for his party hands it about with his snuff-box, to keep men together who want to be off, with such effect that the Speaker (who has had it privately insinuated into his own ear under the corner of his wig) cries "Order at the bar!" three times without making an impression.

And not the least amazing circumstance connected with her being vaguely the town talk, is, that people hovering on the confines of Mr. Sladdery's high connection, people who know nothing and ever did know nothing about her, think it essential to their reputation to pretend that she is their topic too; and to retail her at second-hand with the last new word and the last new manner, and the last new drawl, and the last new polite indifference, and all the rest of it, all at second-hand but con-sidered equal to new, in inferior systems and to fainter stars. If there be any man of letters, art, or science among these little dealers, how noble in him to support the feeble sisters on such majestic crutches!

So goes the wintry day outside the Dedlock mansion. How within it?

Sir Leicester lying in his bed can speak a little, though with difficulty and indistinctness. He is enjoined to silence and to rest, and they have given him some opiate to lull his pain; for his old enemy is very hard with him. He is never asleep, though sometimes he seems to fall into a dull waking doze. He caused his bedstead to be moved out nearer to the window, when he heard it was such inclement weather; and his head to be so adjusted that he could see the driving snow and sleet. He watches it as it falls, throughout the whole wintry day.

Upon the least noise in the house, which is kept hushed, his hand is at the pencil. The old housekeeper, sitting by him, knows what he would write, and whispers, "No, he has not come back yet, Sir Leicester. It was late last night when he went. He has been but a little time gone yet."

He withdraws his hand, and falls to looking at the sleet and snow again, until they seem, by being long looked at, to fall so thick and fast, that he is obliged to close his eyes for a minute on the giddy whirl of white flakes and icy blots.

He began to look at them as soon as it was light. The day is not yet far spent, when he conceives it to be necessary that her rooms should be prepared for her. It is very cold and wet. Let there be good fires. Let them know that she is expected. Please see to it yourself. He writes to this purpose on his slate, and Mrs. Rouncewell with a heavy heart obeys.

"For I dread, George," the old lady says to her son, who waits below to keep her company when she has a little leisure; "I dread, my dear, that my Lady will never more set foot within these walls."

"That's a bad presentiment, mother."

"Nor yet within the walls of Chesney Wold, my dear."

"That's worse. But why, mother?"

"When I saw my Lady yesterday, George, she looked to me—and I may say at me too—as if the step on the Ghost's Walk had almost walked her down."

"Come, come! You alarm yourself with old-story fears, mother."

"No I don't, my dear. No I don't. It's going on for sixty year that I have been in this family, and I never had any fears for it before. But it's breaking up, my dear; the great old Dedlock family is breaking up."

"I hope not, mother."

"I am thankful I have lived long enough to be with Sir Leicester in this illness and trouble; for I know I am not too old, nor too useless, to be a welcomer sight to him than anybody else in my place would be. But the step on the Ghost's Walk will walk my Lady down, George; it has been many a day behind her, and now it will pass her, and go on."

"Well, mother dear, I say again, I hope not."

"Ah, so do I, George," the old lady returns, shaking her head, and parting her folded hands. "But if my fears come true, and he has to know it, who will tell him?"

"Are these her rooms?"

"These are my Lady's rooms, just as she left them."

"Why now," says the trooper, glancing round him, and speaking in a lower voice, "I begin to understand how you come to think as you do think, mother. Rooms get an awful look about them when they are fitted up, like these, for one person you are used to see in them, and that person is away under any shadow: let alone being God knows where."

He is not far out. As all partings foreshadow the great final one—so, empty rooms, bereft of a familiar presence, mournfully whisper what your room and what mine must one day be. My Lady's state has a hollow look, thus gloomy and abandoned; and in the inner apartment, where Mr. Bucket last night made his secret perquisition, the traces of her dresses and her ornaments, even the mirrors accustomed to reflect them when they were a portion of herself, have a desolate and vacant air. Dark and cold as the wintry day is, it is darker and colder in these deserted chambers than in many a hut that will barely exclude the weather; and though the servants heap fires in the grates, and set the couches and the chairs within the warm glass screens that let their ruddy light shoot through to the furthest corners, there is a heavy cloud upon the rooms which no light will dispel.

The old housekeeper and her son remain until the preparations are complete, and then she returns upstairs. Volumnia has taken Mrs. Rouncewell's place in the meantime: though pearl necklaces and rouge pots, however calculated to embellish Bath, are but indifferent comforts to the invalid under present circumstances. Volumnia not being supposed to know (and indeed not knowing) what is the matter, has found it a ticklish task to offer appropriate observations; and consequently has supplied their place with distracting smoothings of the bed-linen, elaborate locomotion on tiptoe, vigilant peeping at her kinsman's eyes, and one exasperating whisper to herself of "He is asleep." In disproof of which superfluous remark, Sir Leicester has indignantly written on the slate, "I am not."

Yielding, therefore, the chair at the bedside to the quaint old housekeeper, Volumnia sits at a table a little removed, sympathetically sighing. Sir Leicester watches the sleet and snow, and listens for the returning steps that he expects. In the ears of his old servant, looking as if she had stepped out of an old picture-frame to attend a summoned Dedlock to another world, the silence is fraught with echoes of her own words, "Who will tell him?"

He has been under his valet's hands this morning, to be made presentable; and is as well got up as the circumstances will allow. He is propped with pillows, his grey hair is brushed in its usual manner, his linen is arranged to a nicety, and he is wrapped in a responsible dressing-gown. His eye-glass and his watch are ready to his hand. It is necessary—less to his own dignity now, perhaps, than for her sake—that he should be seen as little disturbed, and as much himself, as may be. Women will talk, and Volumnia, though a Dedlock, is no exceptional case. He keeps her here, there is little doubt, to prevent her talking somewhere else. He is very ill: but he makes his present stand against distress of mind and body, most courageously.

The fair Volumnia being one of those sprightly girls who cannot long continue silent without imminent peril of seizure by the dragon Boredom, soon indicates the approach of that monster with a series of undisguisable yawns. Finding it impossible to suppress those yawns by any other

process than conversation, she compliments Mrs. Rouncewell on her son ;
declaring that he positively is one of the finest figures she ever saw, and
as soldierly a looking person, she should think, as what's his name, her
favourite Life Guardsman—the man she doats on—the dearest of creatures
—who was killed at Waterloo.

Sir Leicester hears this tribute with so much surprise, and stares about
him in such a confused way, that Mrs. Rouncewell feels it necessary to
explain.

"Miss Dedlock don't speak of my eldest son, Sir Leicester, but my
youngest. I have found him. He has come home."

Sir Leicester breaks silence with a harsh cry. "George? Your son
George come home, Mrs. Rouncewell?"

The old housekeeper wipes her eyes. "Thank God. Yes, Sir
Leicester."

Does this discovery of some one lost, this return of some one so long
gone, come upon him as a strong confirmation of his hopes? Does he
think, "Shall I not, with the aid I have, recall her safely after this ;
there being fewer hours in her case than there are years in his?"

It is of no use entreating him ; he is determined to speak now, and
he does. In a thick crowd of sounds, but still intelligibly enough to be
understood.

"Why did you not tell me, Mrs. Rouncewell?"

"It happened only yesterday, Sir Leicester, and I doubted your being
well enough to be talked to of such things."

Besides, the giddy Volumnia now remembers with her little scream that
nobody was to have known of his being Mrs. Rouncewell's son, and that
she was not to have told. But Mrs. Rouncewell protests, with warmth
enough to swell the stomacher, that of course she would have told Sir
Leicester as soon as he got better.

"Where is your son George, Mrs. Rouncewell?" asks Sir Leicester.

Mrs. Rouncewell, not a little alarmed by his disregard of the doctor's
injunctions, replies, in London.

"Where in London?"

Mrs. Rouncewell is constrained to admit that he is in the house.

"Bring him here to my room. Bring him directly."

The old lady can do nothing but go in search of him. Sir Leicester,
with such power of movement as he has, arranges himself a little, to receive him. When he has done so, he looks out again at the falling sleet
and snow, and listens again for the returning steps. A quantity of straw
has been tumbled down in the street to deaden the noises there, and she
might be driven to the door perhaps without his hearing wheels.

He is lying thus, apparently forgetful of his newer and minor surprise,
when the housekeeper returns, accompanied by her trooper son. Mr.
George approaches softly to the bedside, makes his bow, squares his chest,
and stands, with his face flushed, very heartily ashamed of himself.

"Good Heaven, and it is really George Rouncewell!" exclaims Sir
Leicester. "Do you remember me, George?"

The trooper needs to look at him, and to separate this sound from that sound, before he knows what he has said; but doing this, and being a little helped by his mother, he replies:

"I must have a very bad memory, indeed, Sir Leicester, if I failed to remember you."

"When I look at you, George Rouncewell," Sir Leicester observes with difficulty, "I see something of a boy at Chesney Wold—I remember well—very well."

He looks at the trooper until tears come into his eyes, and then he looks at the sleet and snow again.

"I ask your pardon, Sir Leicester," says the trooper, "but would you accept of my arms to raise you up? You would lie easier, Sir Leicester, if you would allow me to move you."

"If you please, George Rouncewell; if you will be so good."

The trooper takes him in his arms like a child, lightly raises him, and turns him with his face more towards the window. "Thank you. You have your mother's gentleness," returns Sir Leicester, "and your own strength. Thank you."

He signs to him with his hand not to go away. George quietly remains at the bedside, waiting to be spoken to.

"Why did you wish for secrecy?" It takes Sir Leicester some time to ask this.

"Truly I am not much to boast of, Sir Leicester, and I—I should still, Sir Leicester, if you was not so indisposed—which I hope you will not be long—I should still hope for the favour of being allowed to remain unknown in general. That involves explanations not very hard to be guessed at, not very well timed here, and not very creditable to myself. However opinions may differ on a variety of subjects, I should think it would be universally agreed, Sir Leicester, that I am not much to boast of."

"You have been a soldier," observes Sir Leicester, "and a faithful one."

George makes his military bow. "As far as that goes, Sir Leicester, I have done my duty under discipline, and it was the least I could do."

"You find me," says Sir Leicester, whose eyes are much attracted towards him, "far from well, George Rouncewell."

"I am very sorry both to hear it and to see it, Sir Leicester."

"I am sure you are. No. In addition to my older malady, I have had a sudden and bad attack. Something that deadens—" making an endeavour to pass one hand down one side; "and confuses—" touching his lips.

George, with a look of assent and sympathy, makes another bow. The different times when they were both young men (the trooper much the younger of the two), and looked at one another down at Chesney Wold, arise before them both, and soften both.

Sir Leicester, evidently with a great determination to say, in his own manner, something that is on his mind before relapsing into silence, tries to raise himself among his pillows a little more. George, observant of the action, takes him in his arms again, and places him as he desires to be. "Thank you, George. You are another self to me. You have often carried my spare gun at Chesney Wold, George. You are familiar to me in these strange circumstances, very familiar." He has put Sir Leicester's sounder arm over his shoulder in lifting him up, and Sir Leicester is slow in drawing it away again, as he says these words.

"I was about to add," he presently goes on, "I was about to add, respecting this attack, that it was unfortunately simultaneous with a slight misunderstanding between my Lady and myself. I do not mean that there was any difference between us (for there has been none), but that there was a misunderstanding of certain circumstances important only to ourselves, which deprives me, for a little while, of my Lady's society. She has found it necessary to make a journey,—I trust will shortly return. Volumnia, do I make myself intelligible? The words are not quite under my command, in the manner of pronouncing them."

Volumnia understands him perfectly; and in truth he delivers himself with far greater plainness than could have been supposed possible a minute ago. The effort by which he does so, is written in the anxious and labouring expression of his face. Nothing but the strength of his purpose enables him to make it.

"Therefore, Volumnia, I desire to say in your presence—and in the presence of my old retainer and friend, Mrs. Rouncewell, whose truth and fidelity no one can question—and in the presence of her son, George, who comes back like a familiar recollection of my youth in the home of my ancestors at Chesney Wold—in case I should relapse, in case I should not recover, in case I should lose both my speech and the power of writing, though I hope for better things——"

The old housekeeper weeping silently; Volumnia in the greatest agitation, with the freshest bloom on her cheeks; the trooper with his arms folded and his head a little bent, respectfully attentive.

"Therefore I desire to say, and to call you all to witness—beginning, Volumnia, with yourself, most solemnly—that I am on unaltered terms with Lady Dedlock. That I assert no cause whatever of complaint against her. That I have ever had the strongest affection for her, and that I retain it undiminished. Say this to herself, and to every one. If you ever say less than this, you will be guilty of deliberate falsehood to me."

Volumnia tremblingly protests that she will observe his injunctions to the letter.

"My Lady is too high in position, too handsome, too accomplished, too superior in most respects to the best of those by whom she is surrounded, not to have her enemies and traducers, I dare say. Let it be known to them, as I make it known to you, that being of sound mind, memory, and understanding, I revoke no disposition I have made in her favour. I abridge nothing I have ever bestowed upon her. I am on unaltered terms with her, and I recall—having the full power to do it if I were so disposed, as you see—no act I have done for her advantage and happiness."

His formal array of words might have at any other time, as it has often had, something ludicrous in it; but at this time it is serious and affecting. His noble earnestness, his fidelity, his gallant shielding of her, his generous conquest of his own wrong and his own pride for her sake, are simply honourable, manly, and true. Nothing less worthy can be seen through the lustre of such qualities in the commonest mechanic, nothing less worthy can be seen in the best-born gentleman. In such a light both aspire alike, both rise alike, both children of the dust shine equally.

Overpowered by his exertions, he lays his head back on his pillows, and closes his eyes; for not more than a minute; when he again resumes his watching of the weather, and his attention to the muffled sounds. In the rendering of those little services, and in the manner of their acceptance, the trooper has become installed as necessary to him. Nothing has been said, but it is quite understood. He falls a step or two backward to be out of sight, and mounts guard a little behind his mother's chair.

The day is now beginning to decline. The mist, and the sleet into which the snow has all resolved itself, are darker, and the blaze begins to tell more vividly upon the room walls and furniture. The gloom augments; the bright gas springs up in the streets; and the pertinacious oil lamps which yet hold their ground there, with their source of life half frozen and half thawed, twinkle gaspingly, like fiery fish out of water— as they are. The world, which has been rumbling over the straw and pulling at the bell, "to inquire," begins to go home, begins to dress, to dine, to discuss its dear friend, with all the last new modes, as already mentioned.

Now, does Sir Leicester become worse; restless, uneasy, and in great pain. Volumnia lighting a candle (with a predestined aptitude for doing something objectionable) is bidden to put it out again, for it is not yet dark enough. Yet it is very dark too; as dark as it will be all night. By-and-by she tries again. No! Put it out. It is not dark enough yet.

His old housekeeper is the first to understand that he is striving to uphold the fiction with himself that it is not growing late.

"Dear Sir Leicester, my honoured master," she softly whispers, "I must, for your own good, and my duty, take the freedom of begging and praying that you will not lie here in the lone darkness, watching and waiting, and dragging through the time. Let me draw the curtains and light the candles, and make things more comfortable about you. The church-clocks will strike the hours just the same, Sir Leicester, and the night will pass away just the same. My Lady will come back, just the same."

"I know it, Mrs. Rouncewell, but I am weak—and he has been so long gone."

"Not so very long, Sir Leicester. Not twenty-four hours yet."

"But that is a long time. Oh it is a long time!"

He says it with a groan that wrings her heart.

She knows that this is not a period for bringing the rough light upon him; she thinks his tears too sacred to be seen, even by her. Therefore, she sits in the darkness for awhile, without a word; then gently begins to move about; now stiring the fire, now standing at the dark window looking out. Finally he tells her, with recovered self-command, "As you say, Mrs. Rouncewell, it is no worse for being confessed. It is getting late, and they are not come. Light the room!" When it is lighted, and the weather shut out, it is only left to him to listen.

But they find that, however dejected and ill he is, he brightens when a quiet pretence is made of looking at the fires in her rooms, and being sure that everything is ready to receive her. Poor pretence as it is, these allusions to her being expected keep up hope within him.

Midnight comes, and with it the same blank. The carriages in the streets are few, and other late sounds in that neighbourhood there are none, unless a man so very nomadically drunk as to stray into the frigid zone goes brawling and bellowing along the pavement. Upon this wintry night it is so still, that listening to the intense silence is like looking at intense darkness. If any distant sound be audible in this case, it departs through the gloom like a feeble light in that, and all is heavier than before.

The corporation of servants are dismissed to bed (not unwilling to go, for they were up all last night), and only Mrs. Rouncewell and George keep watch in Sir Leicester's room. As the night lags tardily on—or rather when it seems to stop altogether, at between two and three o'clock —they find a restless craving on him to know more about the weather, now he cannot see it. Hence George, patrolling regularly every half-hour to the rooms so carefully looked after, extends his march to the hall-door, looks about him, and brings back the best report he can make of the worst of nights; the sleet still falling, and even the stone footways lying ankle-deep in icy sludge.

Volumnia, in her room up a retired landing on the staircase—the second turning past the end of the carving and gilding—a cousinly room containing a fearful abortion of a portrait of Sir Leicester, banished for its crimes, and commanding in the day a solemn yard, planted with dried-up shrubs like antediluvian specimens of black tea—is a prey to horrors of many kinds. Not last nor least among them, possibly, is a horror of what may befall her little income, in the event, as she expresses it, "of anything happening" to Sir Leicester. Anything, in this sense, meaning one thing only, and that the last thing that can happen to the consciousness of any baronet in the known world.

An effect of these horrors is, that Volumnia finds she cannot go to bed in her own room, or sit by the fire in her own room, but must come forth with her fair head tied up in a profusion of shawl, and her fair form en-robed in drapery, and parade the mansion like a ghost: particularly haunting the rooms, warm and luxurious, prepared for one who still does not return. Solitude under such circumstances being not to be thought of, Volumnia is attended by her maid, who, impressed from her own bed for that purpose, extremely cold, very sleepy, and generally an injured maid as condemned by circumstances to take office with a cousin, when she had resolved to be maid to nothing less than ten thousand a year, has not a sweet expression of countenance.

The periodical visits of the trooper to these rooms, however, in the course of his patrolling, is an assurance of protection and company, both to mistress and maid, which renders them very acceptable in the small hours of the night. Whenever he is heard advancing, they both make some little decorative preparation to receive him; at other times, they divide their watches into short scraps of oblivion, and dialogues, not wholly free from acerbity, as to whether Miss Dedlock, sitting with her feet upon the fender, was or was not falling into the fire when rescued (to her great displeasure) by her guardian genius the maid.

"How is Sir Leicester now, Mr. George?" inquires Volumnia, adjusting her cowl over her head.

"Why, Sir Leicester is much the same, miss. He is very low and ill, and he even wanders a little sometimes."

"Has he asked for me?" inquires Volumnia tenderly.

"Why, no, I can't say he has, miss. Not within my hearing, that is to say."

"This is a truly sad time, Mr. George."

"It is indeed, miss. Hadn't you better go to bed?"

"You had a deal better go to bed, Miss Dedlock," quoth the maid sharply.

But Volumnia answers No! No! She may be asked for, she may be wanted at a moment's notice. She never should forgive herself "if anything was to happen" and she was not on the spot. She declines to enter on the question, mooted by the maid, how the spot comes to be there, and not in her own room (which is nearer to Sir Leicester's); but staunchly declares that on the spot she will remain. Volumnia further makes a merit of not having "closed an eye"—as if she had twenty or thirty—though it is hard to reconcile this statement with her having most indisputably opened two within five minutes.

But when it comes to four o'clock, and still the same blank, Volumnia's constancy begins to fail her, or rather it begins to strengthen; for she now considers that it is her duty to be ready for the morrow, when much may be expected of her; that, in fact, howsoever anxious to remain upon the spot, it may be required of her, as an act of self-devotion, to desert the spot. So, when the trooper reappears with his "Hadn't you better go to bed, miss?" and when the maid protests, more sharply than before, "You had a deal better go to bed, Miss Dedlock!" she meekly rises and says, "Do with me what you think best!"

Mr. George undoubtedly thinks it best to escort her on his arm to the door of her cousinly chamber, and the maid as undoubtedly thinks it best to hustle her into bed with mighty little ceremony. Accordingly, these steps are taken; and now the trooper, in his rounds, has the house to himself.

There is no improvement in the weather. From the portico, from the

2 Q

eaves, from the parapet, from every ledge and post and pillar, drips the thawed snow. It has crept, as if for shelter, into the lintels of the great door—under it, into the corners of the windows, into every chink and crevice of retreat, and there wastes and dies. It is falling still; upon the roof, upon the skylight; even through the skylight, and drip, drip, drip, with the regularity of the Ghost's Walk, on the stone floor below.

The trooper, his old recollections awakened by the solitary grandeur of a great house—no novelty to him once at Chesney Wold—goes up the stairs and through the chief rooms, holding up his light at arm's length. Thinking of his varied fortunes within the last few weeks, and of his rustic boyhood, and of the two periods of his life so strangely brought together across the wide intermediate space; thinking of the murdered man whose image is fresh in his mind; thinking of the lady who has disappeared from these very rooms, and the tokens of whose recent presence are all here; thinking of the master of the house upstairs, and of the foreboding "Who will tell him?" he looks here and looks there, and reflects how he *might* see something now, which it would tax his boldness to walk up to, lay his hand upon, and prove to be a fancy. But it is all blank; blank as the darkness above and below, while he goes up the great staircase again; blank as the oppressive silence.

"All is still in readiness, George Rouncewell?"

"Quite orderly and right, Sir Leicester."

"No word of any kind?"

The trooper shakes his head.

"No letter that can possibly have been overlooked?"

But he knows there is no such hope as that, and lays his head down without looking for an answer.

Very familiar to him, as he said himself some hours ago, George Rouncewell lifts him into easier positions through the long remainder of the blank wintry night; and, equally familiar with his unexpressed wish, extinguishes the light, and undraws the curtains at the first late break of day. The day comes like a phantom. Cold, colourless, and vague, it sends a warning streak before it of a deathlike hue, as if it cried out, "Look what I am bringing you, who watch there! Who will tell him?"

CHAPTER LIX

ESTHER'S NARRATIVE

IT was three o'clock in the morning when the houses outside London did at last begin to exclude the country, and to close us in with streets. We had made our way along roads in a far worse condition than when we had traversed them by daylight, both the fall and the thaw having lasted ever since; but the energy of my companion had never slackened. It had only been, as I thought, of less assistance than the horses in getting us on, and it had often aided them. They had stopped exhausted, half-way up hills, they had been driven through streams of turbulent water, they had slipped down and become entangled with the harness ; but he and his little lantern had been always ready, and when the mishap was set right, I had never heard any variation in his cool, " Get on, my lads ! "

The steadiness and confidence with which he had directed our journey back, I could not account for. Never wavering, he never even stopped to make an inquiry until we were within a few miles of London. A very few words, here and there, were then enough for him ; and thus we came, at between three and four o'clock in the morning, into Islington.

I will not dwell on the suspense and anxiety with which I reflected all this time, that we were leaving my mother farther and farther behind every minute. I think I had some strong hope that he must be right, and could not fail to have a satisfactory object in following this woman ; but I tormented myself with questioning it, and discussing it, during the whole journey. What was to ensue when we found her, and what could compensate us for this loss of time, were questions also that I could not possibly dismiss ; my mind was quite tortured by long dwelling on such reflections, when we stopped.

We stopped in a high-street, where there was a coach-stand. My companion paid our two drivers, who were as completely covered with splashes as if they had been dragged along the roads like the carriage itself; and giving them some brief direction where to take it, lifted me out of it, and into a hackney-coach he had chosen from the rest.

" Why, my dear ! " he said, as he did this. " How wet you are ! "

I had not been conscious of it. But the melted snow had found its way into the carriage ; and I had got out two or three times when a fallen horse was plunging and had to be got up ; and the wet had penetrated my dress. I assured him it was no matter ; but the driver, who knew him, would not be dissuaded by me from running down the street to his stable, whence he brought an armful of clean dry straw. They shook it out and strewed it well about me, and I found it warm and comfortable.

" Now, my dear," said Mr. Bucket, with his head in at the window after I was shut up. " We're a-going to mark this person down. It may take a little time, but you don't mind that. You're pretty sure that I've got a motive. Ain't you ? "

I little thought what it was—little thought in how short a time I should understand it better ; but I assured him that I had confidence in him.

" So you may have, my dear," he returned. " And I tell you what ! If you only repose half as much confidence in me as I repose in you, after what I've experienced of you, that'll do. Lord ! you're no trouble at all. I never see a young woman in any station of society—and I've seen many elevated ones too—conduct herself like you have conducted yourself, since you was called out of your bed. You're a pattern, you know, that's what you are," said Mr. Bucket warmly; "you're a pattern."

I told him I was very glad, as indeed I was, to have been no hindrance to him; and that I hoped I should be none now.

"My dear," he returned, "when a young lady is as mild as she's game, and as game as she's mild, that's all I ask, and more than I expect. She then becomes a Queen, and that's about what you are yourself."

With these encouraging words—they really were encouraging to me under those lonely and anxious circumstances—he got upon the box, and we once more drove away. Where we drove, I neither knew then, nor have ever known since; but we appeared to seek out the narrowest and worst streets in London. Whenever I saw him directing the driver, I was prepared for our descending into a deeper complication of such streets, and we never failed to do so.

Sometimes we emerged upon a wider thoroughfare, or came to a larger building than the generality, well lighted. Then we stopped at offices like those we had visited when we began our journey, and I saw him in consultation with others. Sometimes he would get down by an archway, or at a street corner, and mysteriously show the light of his little lantern. This would attract similar lights from various dark quarters, like so many insects, and a fresh consultation would be held. By degrees we appeared to contract our search within narrower and easier limits. Single police-officers on duty could now tell Mr. Bucket what he wanted to know, and point to him where to go. At last we stopped for a rather long conversation between him and one of these men, which I supposed to be satisfactory from his manner of nodding from time to time. When it was finished he came to me, looking very busy and very attentive.

"Now, Miss Summerson," he said to me, "you won't be alarmed whatever comes off, I know. It's not necessary for me to give you any further caution, than to tell you that we have marked this person down, and that you may be of use to me before I know it myself. I don't like to ask such a thing, my dear, but would you walk a little way?"

Of course I got out directly, and took his arm.

"It ain't so easy to keep your feet," said Mr. Bucket; "but take time."

Although I looked about me confusedly and hurriedly, as we crossed a street, I thought I knew the place. "Are we in Holborn?" I asked him.

"Yes," said Mr. Bucket. "Do you know this turning?"

"It looks like Chancery Lane."

"And was christened so, my dear," said Mr. Bucket.

We turned down it; and as we went, shuffling through the sleet, I heard the clocks strike half-past five. We passed on in silence, and as quickly as we could with such a foothold, when some one coming towards us on the narrow pavement, wrapped in a cloak, stopped and stood aside to give me room. In the same moment I heard an exclamation of wonder, and my own name, from Mr. Woodcourt. I knew his voice very well.

It was so unexpected, and so—I don't know what to call it, whether pleasant or painful—to come upon it after my feverish wandering journey, and in the midst of the night, that I could not keep back the tears from my eyes. It was like hearing his voice in a strange country.

"My dear Miss Summerson, that you should be out at this hour, and in such weather!"

He had heard from my guardian of my having been called away on some uncommon business, and said so to dispense with any explanation. I told him that we had but just left a coach, and were going—but then I was obliged to look at my companion.

"Why, you see, Mr. Woodcourt;" he had caught the name from me; "we are a-going at present into the next street—Inspector Bucket."

Mr. Woodcourt, disregarding my remonstrances, had hurriedly taken off his cloak, and was putting it about me. "That's a good move, too," said Mr. Bucket, assisting, "a very good move."

"May I go with you?" said Mr. Woodcourt. I don't know whether to me or my companion.

"Why, Lord!" exclaimed Mr. Bucket, taking the answer on himself. "Of course you may."

It was all said in a moment, and they took me between them, wrapped in the cloak.

"I have just left Richard," said Mr. Woodcourt. "I have been sitting with him since ten o'clock last night."

"Oh dear me, he is ill!"

"No, no, believe me; not ill, but not quite well. He was depressed and faint—you know he gets so worried and so worn sometimes—and Ada sent to me of course; and when I came home I found her note, and came straight here. Well! Richard revived so much after a little while, and Ada was so happy, and so convinced of its being my doing, though God knows I had little enough to do with it, that I remained with him until he had been fast asleep some hours. As fast asleep as she is now, I hope!"

His friendly and familiar way of speaking of them, his unaffected devotion to them, the grateful confidence with which I knew he had inspired my darling, and the comfort he was to her; could I separate all this from his promise to me? How thankless I must have been if it had not recalled the words he said to me, when he was so moved by the change in my appearance: "I will accept him as a trust, and it shall be a sacred one!"

We now turned into another narrow street. "Mr. Woodcourt," said Mr. Bucket, who had eyed him closely as we came along, "our business takes us to a law-stationer's here; a certain Mr. Snagsby's. What, you know him, do you?" He was so quick that he saw it in an instant.

"Yes, I know a little of him, and have called upon him at this place."

"Indeed, sir?" said Mr. Bucket. "Then will you be so good as to let me leave Miss Summerson with you for a moment, while I go and have half a word with him?"

The last police-officer with whom he had conferred was standing silently behind us. I was not aware of it until he struck in, on my saying I heard some one crying.

"Don't be alarmed, miss," he returned. "It's Snagsby's servant."

"Why, you see," said Mr. Bucket, "the girl's subject to fits, and has 'em bad upon her to-night. A most contrairy circumstance it is, for I want certain information out of that girl, and she must be brought to reason somehow."

"At all events, they wouldn't be up yet, if it wasn't for her, Mr. Bucket," said the other man. "She's been at it pretty well all night, sir."

"Well, that's true," he returned. "My light's burnt out. Show yours a moment."

All this passed in a whisper, a door or two from the house in which I could faintly hear crying and moaning. In the little round of light produced for the purpose, Mr. Bucket went up to the door and knocked. The door was opened, after he had knocked twice ; and he went in, leaving us standing in the street.

"Miss Summerson," said Mr. Woodcourt ; "if, without obtruding myself on your confidence, I may remain near you, pray let me do so."

"You are truly kind," I answered. "I need wish to keep no secret of my own from you ; if I keep any, it is another's."

"I quite understand. Trust me, I will remain near you only so long as I can fully respect it."

"I trust implicitly to you," I said. "I know and deeply feel how sacredly you keep your promise."

After a short time the little round of light shone out again, and Mr. Bucket advanced towards us in it with his earnest face. "Please to come in, Miss Summerson," he said, "and sit down by the fire. Mr. Woodcourt, from information I have received I understand you are a medical man. Would you look to this girl and see if anything can be done to bring her round ? She has a letter somewhere that I particularly want. It's not in her box, and I think it must be about her ; but she is so twisted and clenched up, that she is difficult to handle without hurting."

We all three went into the house together ; although it was cold and raw, it smelt close too from being up all night. In the passage, behind the door, stood a scared, sorrowful-looking little man in a grey coat, who seemed to have a naturally polite manner, and spoke meekly.

"Downstairs, if you please, Mr. Bucket," said he. "The lady will excuse the front kitchen ; we use it as our workaday sitting-room. The back is Guster's bedroom, and in it she's a-carrying on, poor thing, to a frightful extent !"

We went downstairs, followed by Mr. Snagsby, as I soon found the little man to be. In the front kitchen, sitting by the fire, was Mrs. Snagsby, with very red eyes and a very severe expression of face.

"My little woman," said Mr. Snagsby, entering behind us, "to waive—

not to put too fine a point upon it, my dear—hostilities, for one single moment, in the course of this prolonged night, here is Inspector Bucket, Mr. Woodcourt, and a lady."

She looked very much astonished, as she had reason for doing, and looked particularly hard at me.

"My little woman," said Mr. Snagsby, sitting down in the remotest corner by the door, as if he were taking a liberty, "it is not unlikely that you may inquire of me why Inspector Bucket, Mr. Woodcourt, and a lady, call upon us in Cook's Court, Cursitor Street, at the present hour. I don't know. I have not the least idea. If I was to be informed, I should despair of understanding, and I'd rather not be told."

He appeared so miserable, sitting with his head upon his hand, and I appeared so unwelcome, that I was going to offer an apology, when Mr. Bucket took the matter on himself.

"Now, Mr. Snagsby," said he, "the best thing you can do, is to go along with Mr. Woodcourt to look after your Guster——"

"My Guster, Mr. Bucket!" cried Mr. Snagsby. "Go on, sir, go on. I shall be charged with that next."

"And to hold the candle," pursued Mr. Bucket without correcting himself, "or hold her, or make yourself useful in any way you're asked. Which there's not a man alive more ready to do; for you're a man of urbanity and suavity, you know, and you've got the sort of heart that can feel for another. (Mr. Woodcourt, would you be so good as to see to her, and if you can get that letter from her, to let me have it as soon as ever you can?)"

As they went out, Mr. Bucket made me sit down in a corner by the fire, and take off my wet shoes, which he turned up to dry upon the fender; talking all the time.

"Don't you be at all put out, miss, by the want of a hospitable look from Mrs. Snagsby there, because she's under a mistake altogether. She'll find that out, sooner than will be agreeable to a lady of her generally correct manner of forming her thoughts, because I'm a-going to explain it to her." Here, standing on the hearth with his wet hat and shawls in his hand, himself a pile of wet, he turned to Mrs. Snagsby. "Now, the first thing that I say to you, as a married woman, possessing what you may call charms, you know—'Believe me, if all those endearing, and cetrer'—you're well acquainted with the song, because it's in vain for you to tell me that you and good society are strangers—charms —attractions, mind you, that ought to give you confidence in yourself— is, that you've done it."

Mrs. Snagsby looked rather alarmed, relented a little, and faltered, what did Mr. Bucket mean?

"What does Mr. Bucket mean?" he repeated; and I saw, by his face, that all the time he talked he was listening for the discovery of the letter—to my own great agitation; for I knew then how important it must be; "I'll tell you what he means, ma'am. Go and see Othello acted. That's the tragedy for you."

Mrs. Snagsby consciously asked why.

"Why?" said Mr. Bucket. "Because you'll come to that, if you don't look out. Why, at the very moment while I speak, I know what your mind's not wholly free from, respecting this young lady. But shall I tell you who this young lady is? Now, come, you're what I call an intellectual woman—with your soul too large for your body, if you come to that, and chafing it—and you know me, and you recollect where you saw me last, and what was talked of in that circle. Don't you? Yes! Very well. This young lady is that young lady."

Mrs. Snagsby appeared to understand the reference better than I did at the time.

"And Toughey—him as you call Jo—was mixed up in the same business, and no other; and the law-writer that you know of, was mixed up in the same business, and no other; and your husband, with no more knowledge of it than your great-grandfather, was mixed up (by Mr. Tulkinghorn, deceased, his best customer) in the same business, and no other; and the whole bileing of people was mixed up in the same business, and no other. And yet a married woman, possessing your attractions, shuts her eyes (and sparklers too), and goes and runs her delicate-formed head against a wall. Why, I am ashamed of you! (I expected Mr. Woodcourt might have got it, by this time.)"

Mrs. Snagsby shook her head, and put her handkerchief to her eyes.

"Is that all?" said Mr. Bucket excitely. "No. See what happens. Another person mixed up in that business and no other, a person in a wretched state, comes here to-night, and is seen a-speaking to your maid-servant; and between her and your maid-servant there passes a paper that I would give a hundred pound for, down. What do you do? You hide and you watch 'em, and you pounce upon that maid-servant—knowing what she's subject to, and what a little thing will bring 'em on—in that surprising manner, and with that severity, that, by the Lord, she goes off and keeps off, when a Life may be hanging upon that girl's words!"

He so thoroughly meant what he said now, that I involuntarily clasped my hands, and felt the room turning away from me. But it stopped. Mr. Woodcourt came in, put a paper into his hand, and went away again.

"Now, Mrs. Snagsby, the only amends you can make," said Mr. Bucket, rapidly glancing at it, "is to let me speak a word to this young lady in private here. And if you know of any help that you can give to that gentleman in the next kitchen there, or can think of any one thing that's likelier than another to bring the girl round, do your swiftest and best!" In an instant she was gone, and he had shut the door.

"Now, my dear, you're steady, and quite sure of yourself?"

"Quite," said I.

"Whose writing is that?"

It was my mother's. A pencil-writing, on a crushed and torn piece of paper, blotted with wet. Folded roughly like a letter, and directed to me, at my guardian's.

"You know the hand," he said; "and if you are firm enough to read it to me, do! But be particular to a word."

It had been written in portions, at different times. I read what follows:

"I came to the cottage with two objects. First, to see the dear one, if I could, once more—but only to see her—not to speak to her, or let her know that I was near. The other object, to elude pursuit, and to be lost. Do not blame the mother for her share. The assistance that she rendered me, she rendered on my strongest assurance that it was for the dear one's good. You remember her dead child. The men's consent I bought, but her help was freely given."

"'I came.' That was written," said my companion, "when she rested there. It bears out what I made of it. I was right."

The next was written at another time.

"I have wandered a long distance, and for many hours, and I know that I must soon die. These streets! I have no purpose but to die. When I left, I had a worse; but I am saved from adding that guilt to the rest. Cold, wet, and fatigue, are sufficient causes for my being found dead; but I shall die of others, though I suffer from these. It was right that all that had sustained me should give way at once, and that I should die of terror and my conscience."

"Take courage," said Mr. Bucket. "There's only a few words more."

These, too, were written at another time. To all appearance, almost in the dark.

"I have done all I could to be lost. I shall be soon forgotten so, and shall disgrace him least. I have nothing about me by which I can be recognised. This paper I part with now. The place where I shall lie down, if I can yet get so far, has been often in my mind. Farewell. Forgive."

Mr. Bucket, supporting me with his arm, lowered me gently into my chair. "Cheer up! Don't think me hard with you, my dear, but, as soon as ever you feel equal to it, get your shoes on and be ready."

I did as he required; but I was left there a long time, praying for my unhappy mother. They were all occupied with the poor girl, and I heard Mr. Woodcourt directing them, and speaking to her often. At length he came in with Mr. Bucket; and said that as it was important to address her gently, he thought it best that I should ask her for whatever information we desired to obtain. There was no doubt that she could now reply to questions, if she were soothed, and not alarmed. The questions, Mr. Bucket said, were, how she came by the letter, what passed between her and the person who gave her the letter, and where the person went. Holding my mind as steadily as I could to these points, I went into the next room with them. Mr. Woodcourt would have remained outside, but at my solicitation went in with us.

The poor girl was sitting on the floor where they had laid her down. They stood around her, though at a little distance, that she might have air. She was not pretty, and looked weak and poor; but she had a plaintive and a good face, though it was still a little wild. I kneeled on the ground beside her, and put her poor head on my shoulder; whereupon she drew her arm round my neck, and burst into tears.

"My poor girl," said I, laying my face against her forehead; for indeed I was crying too, and trembling; "it seems cruel to trouble you now, but more depends on our knowing something about this letter, than I could tell you in an hour."

She began piteously declaring that she didn't mean any harm, she didn't mean any harm, Mrs. Snagsby!

"We are all sure of that," said I. "But pray tell me how you got it."

"Yes, dear lady, I will, and tell you true. I'll tell true, indeed, Mrs. Snagsby."

"I am sure of that," said I. "And how was it?"

"I had been out on an errand, dear lady—long after it was dark—quite late; and when I came home, I found a common-looking person, all wet and muddy, looking up at our house. When she saw me coming in at the door, she called me back, and said did I live here? and I said yes, and she said she knew only one or two places about here, but had lost her way, and couldn't find them. Oh what shall I do, what shall I do? They won't believe me! She didn't say any harm to me, and I didn't say any harm to her, indeed, Mrs. Snagsby!"

It was necessary for her mistress to comfort her: which she did, I must say, with a good deal of contrition: before she could be got beyond this.

"She could not find those places," said I.

"No!" cried the girl, shaking her head. "No! Couldn't find them. And she was so faint, and lame, and miserable, oh so wretched! that if you had seen her, Mr. Snagsby, you'd have given her half-a-crown, I know!"

"Well, Guster, my girl," said he, at first not knowing what to say, "I hope I should."

"And yet she was so well spoken," said the girl, looking at me with wide open eyes, "that it made a person's heart bleed. And so she said to me, did I know the way to the burying-ground? And I asked her which burying-ground? And she said, the poor burying-ground. And so I told her I had been a poor child myself, and it was according to parishes. But she said she meant a poor burying-ground not very far from here, where there was an archway, and a step, and an iron gate."

As I watched her face, and soothed her to go on, I saw that Mr. Bucket received this with a look which I could not separate from one of alarm.

"Oh dear, dear!" cried the girl, pressing her hair back with her hands, "what shall I do, what shall I do! She meant the burying-ground where the man was buried that took the sleeping-stuff—that you came home and told us of, Mr. Snagsby—that frightened me so, Mrs. Snagsby. Oh I am frightened again. Hold me!"

THE MORNING.

"You are so much better now," said I. "Pray, pray tell me more."

"Yes I will, yes I will! But don't be angry with me, that's a dear lady, because I have been so ill."

Angry with her, poor soul!

"There! Now I will, now I will. So she said, could I tell her how to find it, and I said yes, and I told her; and she looked at me with eyes like almost as if she was blind, and herself all waving back. And so she took out the letter, and showed it me, and said if she was to put that in the post-office, it would be rubbed out and not minded and never sent; and would I take it from her, and send it, and the messenger would be paid at the house? And so I said yes, if it was no harm, and she said no—no harm. And so I took it from her, and she said she had nothing to give me, and I said I was poor myself and consequently wanted nothing. And so she said God bless you! and went."

"And did she go——?"

"Yes," cried the girl, anticipating the inquiry, "yes! she went the way I had shown her. Then I came in, and Mrs. Snagsby came behind me from somewhere, and laid hold of me, and I was frightened."

Mr. Woodcourt took her kindly from me. Mr. Bucket wrapped me up, and immediately we were in the street. Mr. Woodcourt hesitated, but I said, "Don't leave me now!" and Mr. Bucket added, "You'll be better with us, we may want you; don't lose time!"

I have the most confused impressions of that walk. I recollect that it was neither night nor day; that morning was dawning, but the street-lamps were not yet put out; that the sleet was still falling, and that all the ways were deep with it. I recollect a few chilled people passing in the streets. I recollect the wet housetops, the clogged and bursting gutters and water-spouts, the mounds of blackened ice and snow over which we passed, the narrowness of the courts by which we went. At the same time I remember, that the poor girl seemed to be yet telling her story audibly and plainly in my hearing; that I could feel her resting on my arm; that the stained house fronts put on human shapes and looked at me; that great water-gates seemed to be opening and closing in my head, or in the air; and that the unreal things were more substantial than the real.

At last we stood under a dark and miserable covered way, where one lamp was burning over an iron gate, and where the morning faintly struggled in. The gate was closed. Beyond it, was a burial-ground—a dreadful spot in which the night was very slowly stirring; but where I could dimly see heaps of dishonoured graves and stones, hemmed in by filthy houses, with a few dull lights in their windows, and on whose walls a thick humidity broke out like a disease. On the step at the gate, drenched in the fearful wet of such a place, which oozed and splashed down everywhere, I saw, with a cry of pity and horror, a woman lying —Jenny, the mother of the dead child.

I ran forward, but they stopped me, and Mr. Woodcourt entreated me, with the greatest earnestness, even with tears, before I went up to the figure, to listen for an instant to what Mr. Bucket said. I did so, as I thought. I did so, as I am sure.

"Miss Summerson, you'll understand me, if you think a moment. They changed clothes at the cottage."

They changed clothes at the cottage. I could repeat the words in my mind, and I knew what they meant of themselves; but I attached no meaning to them in any other connection.

"And one returned," said Mr. Bucket, "and one went on. And the one that went on, only went on a certain way agreed upon to deceive, and then turned across country, and went home. Think a moment!"

I could repeat this in my mind too, but I had not the least idea what it meant. I saw before me, lying on the step, the mother of the dead child. She lay there, with one arm creeping round a bar of the iron gate, and seemed to embrace it. She lay there, who had so lately spoken to my mother. She lay there, a distressed, unsheltered, sense-less creature. She who had brought my mother's letter, who could give me the only clue to where my mother was; she who was to guide us to rescue and save her whom we had sought so far, who had come to this condition by some means connected with my mother that I could not follow, and might be passing beyond our reach and help at that moment; she lay there, and they stopped me! I saw, but did not comprehend, the solemn and compassionate look in Mr. Woodcourt's face. I saw, but did not comprehend, his touching the other on the breast to keep him back. I saw him stand uncovered in the bitter air, with a reverence for something. But my understanding for all this was gone.

I even heard it said between them:

"Shall she go?"

"She had better go. Her hands should be the first to touch her. They have a higher right than ours."

I passed on to the gate, and stooped down. I lifted the heavy head, put the long dank hair aside, and turned the face. And it was my mother, cold and dead.

CHAPTER LX

PERSPECTIVE

I PROCEED to other passages of my narrative. From the goodness of all about me, I derived such consolation as I can never think of unmoved. I have already said so much of myself, and so much still remains, that I will not dwell upon my sorrow. I had an illness, but it was not a long one; and I would avoid even this mention of it, if I could quite keep down the recollection of their sympathy.

I proceed to other passages of my narrative.

During the time of my illness, we were still in London, where Mrs.

Woodcourt had come, on my guardian's invitation, to stay with us. When my guardian thought me well and cheerful enough to talk with him in our old way—though I could have done that sooner, if he would have believed me—I resumed my work, and my chair beside his. He had appointed the time himself, and we were alone.

"Dame Trot," said he, receiving me with a kiss, "welcome to the Growlery again, my dear. I have a scheme to develop, little woman. I purpose to remain here, perhaps for six months, perhaps for a longer time—as it may be. Quite to settle here for awhile, in short."

"And in the meanwhile leave Bleak House?" said I.

"Ay, my dear? Bleak House," he returned, "must learn to take care of itself."

I thought his tone sounded sorrowful; but, looking at him, I saw his kind face lighted up by its pleasantest smile.

"Bleak House," he repeated; and his tone did *not* sound sorrowful, I found, "must learn to take care of itself. It is a long way from Ada, my dear, and Ada stands much in need of you."

"It is like you, Guardian," said I, "to have been taking that into consideration, for a happy surprise to both of us."

"Not so disinterested either, my dear, if you mean to extol me for that virtue; since, if you were generally on the road, you could be seldom with me. And besides, I wish to hear as much and as often of Ada as I can, in this condition of estrangement from poor Rick. Not of her alone, but of him too, poor fellow."

"Have you seen Mr. Woodcourt this morning, Guardian?"

"I see Mr. Woodcourt every morning, Dame Durden."

"Does he still say the same of Richard?"

"Just the same. He knows of no direct bodily illness that he has; on the contrary he believes that he has none. Yet he is not easy about him; who *can* be?"

My dear girl had been to see us lately, every day; sometimes twice in a day. But we had foreseen, all along, that this would only last until I was quite myself. We knew full well that her fervent heart was as full of affection and gratitude towards her cousin John as it had ever been, and we acquitted Richard of laying any injunctions upon her to stay away; but we knew on the other hand that she felt it a part of her duty to him, to be sparing of her visits at our house. My guardian's delicacy had soon perceived this, and had tried to convey to her that he thought she was right.

"Dear, unfortunate, mistaken Richard," said I. "When will he awake from his delusion?"

"He is not in the way to do so now, my dear," replied my guardian. "The more he suffers, the more averse he will be to me: having made me the principal representative of the great occasion of his suffering."

I could not help adding, "So unreasonably!"

"Ah, Dame Trot, Dame Trot!" returned my guardian, "what shall we find reasonable in Jarndyce and Jarndyce! Unreason and injustice at the top, unreason and injustice at the heart and at the bottom, unreason and injustice from beginning to end—if it ever has an end—how should poor Rick, always hovering near it, pluck reason out of it? He no more gathers grapes from thorns, or figs from thistles, than older men did, in old times."

His gentleness and consideration for Richard, whenever we spoke of him, touched me so, that I was always silent on this subject very soon.

"I suppose the Lord Chancellor, and the Vice Chancellors, and the whole Chancery battery of great guns, would be infinitely astonished by such unreason and injustice in one of their suitors," pursued my guardian. "When those learned gentlemen begin to raise moss-roses from the powder they sow in their wigs, I shall begin to be astonished too!"

He checked himself in glancing towards the window to look where the wind was, and leaned on the back of my chair instead.

"Well, well, little woman! To go on, my dear. This rock we must leave to time, chance, aud hopeful circumstance. We must not shipwreck Ada upon it. She cannot afford, and he cannot afford, the remotest chance of another separation from a friend. Therefore, I have particularly begged of Woodcourt, and I now particularly beg of you, my dear, not to move this subject with Rick. Let it rest. Next week, next month, next year, sooner or later, he will see me with clearer eyes. I can wait."

But I had already discussed it with him, I confessed; and so, I thought, had Mr. Woodcourt.

"So he tells me," returned my guardian. "Very good. He has made his protest, and Dame Durden has made hers, and there is nothing more to be said about it. Now, I come to Mrs. Woodcourt. How do you like her, my dear?"

In answer to this question, which was oddly abrupt, I said I liked her very much, and thought she was more agreeable than she used to be.

"I think so too," said my guardian. "Less pedigree? Not so much of Morgan-ap—what's his name?"

That was what I meant, I acknowledged; though he was a very harmless person, even when we had had more of him.

"Still, upon the whole, he is as well in his native mountains," said my guardian. "I agree with you. Then, little woman, can I do better for a time than retain Mrs. Woodcourt here?"

No. And yet——

My guardian looked at me, waiting for what I had to say.

I had nothing to say. At least I had nothing in my mind that I could say. I had an undefined impression that it might have been better if we had had some other inmate, but I could hardly have explained why, even to myself. Or, if to myself, certainly not to anybody else.

"You see," said my guardian, "our neighbourhood is in Woodcourt's way, and he can come here to see her as often as he likes, which is agreeable to them both; and she is familiar to us, and fond of you."

Yes. That was undeniable. I had nothing to say against it. I could not have suggested a better arrangement; but I was not quite easy in my mind. Esther, Esther, why not? Esther, think!

"It is a very good plan indeed, dear Guardian, and we could not do better."

"Sure, little woman?"

Quite sure. I had had a moment's time to think, since I had urged that duty on myself, and I was quite sure.

"Good," said my guardian. "It shall be done. Carried unanimously."

"Carried unanimously," I repeated, going on with my work.

It was a cover for his book-table that I happened to be ornamenting. It had been laid by on the night preceding my sad journey, and never resumed. I showed it to him now, and he admired it highly. After I had explained the pattern to him, and all the great effects that were to come out by-and-by, I thought I would go back to our last theme.

"You said, dear Guardian, when we spoke of Mr. Woodcourt before Ada left us, that you thought he would give a long trial to another country. Have you been advising him since?"

"Yes, little woman; pretty often."

"Has he decided to do so?"

"I rather think not."

"Some other prospect has opened to him, perhaps?" said I.

"Why—yes—perhaps," returned my guardian, beginning his answer in a very deliberate manner. "About half a year hence or so, there is a medical attendant for the poor to be appointed at a certain place in Yorkshire. It is a thriving place, pleasantly situated; streams and streets, town and country, mill and moor; and seems to present an opening for such a man. I mean a man whose hopes and aims may sometimes lie (as most men's sometimes do, I dare say) above the ordinary level, but to whom the ordinary level will be high enough after all, if it should prove to be a way of usefulness and good service leading to no other. All generous spirits are ambitious, I suppose; but the ambition that calmly trusts itself to such a road, instead of spasmodically trying to fly over it, is of the kind I care for. It is Woodcourt's kind."

"And will he get this appointment?" I asked.

"Why, little woman," returned my guardian, smiling, "not being an oracle, I cannot confidently say; but I think so. His reputation stands very high; there were people from that part of the country in the shipwreck; and, strange to say, I believe the best man has the best chance. You must not suppose it to be a fine endowment. It is a very, very commonplace affair, my dear; an appointment to a great amount of work and a small amount of pay; but better things will gather about it, it may be fairly hoped."

"The poor of that place will have reason to bless the choice, if it falls on Mr. Woodcourt, Guardian."

"You are right, little woman; that I am sure they will."

We said no more about it, nor did he say a word about the future of Bleak House. But it was the first time I had taken my seat at his side in my mourning dress, and that accounted for it I considered.

I now began to visit my dear girl every day, in the dull dark corner where she lived. The morning was my usual time; but whenever I found I had an hour or so to spare, I put on my bonnet and bustled off to Chancery Lane. They were both so glad to see me at all hours, and used to brighten up so when they heard me opening the door and coming in (being quite at home, I never knocked), that I had no fear of becoming troublesome just yet.

On these occasions I frequently found Richard absent. At other times he would be writing, or reading papers in the Cause, at that table of his, so covered with papers, which were never disturbed. Sometimes I would come upon him, lingering at the door of Mr. Vholes's office. Sometimes I would meet him in the neighbourhood, lounging about, and biting his nails. I often met him wandering in Lincoln's Inn, near the place where I had first seen him, oh how different, how different!

That the money Ada brought him was melting away with the candles I used to see burning after dark in Mr. Vholes's office, I knew very well. It was not a large amount in the beginning; he had married in debt; and I could not fail to understand, by this time, what was meant by Mr. Vholes's shoulder being at the wheel—as I still heard it was. My dear made the best of housekeepers, and tried hard to save; but I knew that they were getting poorer and poorer every day.

She shone in the miserable corner like a beautiful star. She adorned and graced it so, that it became another place. Paler than she had been at home, and a little quieter than I had thought natural when she was yet so cheerful and hopeful, her face was so unshadowed, that I half believed she was blinded by her love for Richard to his ruinous career.

I went one day to dine with them, while I was under this impression. As I turned into Symond's Inn, I met little Miss Flite coming out. She had been to make a stately call upon the wards in Jarndyce, as she still called them, and had derived the highest gratification from that ceremony. Ada had already told me that she called every Monday at five o'clock, with one little extra white bow in her bonnet, which never appeared there at any other time, and with her largest reticule of documents on her arm.

"My dear!" she began. "So delighted! How do you do! So glad to see you. And you are going to visit our interesting Jarndyce wards? To be sure! Our beauty is at home, my dear, and will be charmed to see you."

"Then Richard is not come in yet?" said I. "I am glad of that, for I was afraid of being a little late."

"No, he is not come in," returned Miss Flite. "He has had a long day in court. I left him there, with Vholes. You don't like Vholes, I hope? Don't like Vholes. Dan-gerous man!"

"I am afraid you see Richard oftener than ever now?" said I.

"My dearest," returned Miss Flite, "daily and hourly. You know what I told you of the attraction on the Chancellor's table? My dear, next to myself he is the most constant suitor in court. He begins quite to amuse our little party. Ve-ry friendly little party, are we not?"

It was miserable to hear this from her poor mad lips, though it was no surprise.

"In short, my valued friend," pursued Miss Flite, advancing her lips to my ear, with an air of equal patronage and mystery, "I must tell you a secret. I have made him my executor. Nominated, constituted, and appointed him. In my will. Ye-es."

"Indeed?" said I.

"Ye-es," repeated Miss Flite, in her most genteel accents, "my executor, administrator, and assign. (Our Chancery phrases, my love.) I have reflected that if I should wear out, he will be able to watch that judgment. Being so very regular in his attendance."

It made me sigh to think of him.

"I did at one time mean," said Miss Flite, echoing the sigh, "to nominate, constitute, and appoint poor Gridley. Also very regular, my charming girl. I assure you, most exemplary! But he wore out, poor man, so I have appointed his successor. Don't mention it. This is in confidence."

She carefully opened her reticule a little way, and showed me a folded piece of paper inside, as the appointment of which she spoke.

"Another secret, my dear. I have added to my collection of birds."

"Really, Miss Flite?" said I, knowing how it pleased her to have her confidence received with an appearance of interest.

She nodded several times, and her face became overcast and gloomy. "Two more. I call them the Wards in Jarndyce. They are caged up with all the others. With Hope, Joy, Youth, Peace, Rest, Life, Dust, Ashes, Waste, Want, Ruin, Despair, Madness, Death, Cunning, Folly, Words, Wigs, Rags, Sheepskin, Plunder, Precedent, Jargon, Gammon, and Spinach!"

The poor soul kissed me, with the most troubled look I had ever seen in her; and went her way. Her manner of running over the names of her birds, as if she were afraid of hearing them even from her own lips, quite chilled me.

This was not a cheering preparation for my visit, and I could have dispensed with the company of Mr. Vholes, when Richard (who arrived within a minute or two after me) brought him to share our dinner. Although it was a very plain one, Ada and Richard were for some minutes both out of the room together, helping to get ready what we were to eat and drink. Mr. Vholes took that opportunity of holding a little conversation in a low voice with me. He came to the window where I was sitting, and began upon Symond's Inn.

"A dull place, Miss Summerson, for a life that is not an official one,"

2 R

said Mr. Vholes, smearing the glass with his black glove to make it clearer for me.

"There is not much to see here," said I.

"Nor to hear, miss," returned Mr. Vholes. "A little music does occasionally stray in; but we are not musical in the law, and soon eject it. I hope Mr. Jarndyce is as well as his friends could wish him?"

I thanked Mr. Vholes, and said he was quite well.

"I have not the pleasure to be admitted among the number of his friends myself," said Mr. Vholes, "and I am aware that the gentlemen of our profession are sometimes regarded in such quarters with an unfavourable eye. Our plain course, however, under good report and evil report, and all kinds of prejudice (we are the victims of prejudice), is to have everything openly carried on. How do you find Mr. C. looking, Miss Summerson?"

"He looks very ill. Dreadfully anxious."

"Just so," said Mr. Vholes.

He stood behind me, with his long black figure reaching nearly to the ceiling of those low rooms; feeling the pimples on his face as if they were ornaments, and speaking inwardly and evenly as though there were not a human passion or emotion in his nature.

"Mr. Woodcourt is in attendance upon Mr. C., I believe?" he resumed.

"Mr. Woodcourt is his disinterested friend," I answered.

"But I mean in professional attendance, medical attendance."

"That can do little for an unhappy mind," said I.

"Just so," said Mr. Vholes.

So slow, so eager, so bloodless and gaunt, I felt as if Richard were wasting away beneath the eyes of this adviser, and there were something of the Vampire in him.

"Miss Summerson," said Mr. Vholes, very slowly rubbing his gloved hands, as if, to his cold sense of touch, they were much the same in black kid or out of it, "this was an ill-advised marriage of Mr. C.'s."

I begged he would excuse me for discussing it. They had been engaged when they were both very young, I told him (a little indignantly), and when the prospect before them was much fairer and brighter. When Richard had not yielded himself to the unhappy influence which now darkened his life.

"Just so," assented Mr. Vholes again. "Still, with a view to everything being openly carried on, I will, with your permission, Miss Summerson, observe to you that I consider this a very ill-advised marriage, indeed. I owe the opinion, not only to Mr. C.'s connections, against whom I should naturally wish to protect myself, but also to my own reputation—dear to myself, as a professional man aiming to keep respectable; dear to my three girls at home, for whom I am striving to realise some little independence; dear, I will even say, to my aged father, whom it is my privilege to support."

"It would become a very different marriage, a much happier and better marriage, another marriage altogether, Mr. Vholes," said I, "if

Richard were persuaded to turn his back on the fatal pursuit in which you are engaged with him."

Mr. Vholes, with a noiseless cough—or rather gasp—into one of his black gloves, inclined his head as if he did not wholly dispute even that.

"Miss Summerson," he said, "it may be so; and I freely admit that the young lady who has taken Mr. C.'s name upon herself in so ill-advised a manner—you will I am sure not quarrel with me for throwing out that remark again, as a duty I owe to Mr. C.'s connections—is a highly genteel young lady. Business has prevented me from mixing much with general society, in any but a professional character; still I trust I am competent to perceive that she is a highly genteel young lady. As to beauty, I am not a judge of that myself, and I never did give much attention to it from a boy; but I dare say the young lady is equally eligible, in that point of view. She is considered so (I have heard) among the clerks in the Inn, and it is a point more in their way than in mine. In reference to Mr. C.'s pursuit of his interests——"

"Oh! His interests, Mr. Vholes!"

"Pardon me," returned Mr. Vholes, going on in exactly the same inward and dispassionate manner. "Mr. C. takes certain interests under certain wills disputed in the suit. It is a term we use. In reference to Mr. C.'s pursuit of his interests, I mentioned to you, Miss Summerson, the first time I had the pleasure of seeing you, in my desire that everything should be openly carried on—I used those words, for I happened afterwards to note them in my diary, which is producible at any time—I mentioned to you that Mr. C. had laid down the principle of watching his own interests; and that when a client of mine laid down a principle which was not of an immoral (that is to say, unlawful) nature, it devolved upon me to carry it out. I *have* carried it out; I *do* carry it out. But I will not smooth things over, to any connection of Mr. C.'s, on any account. As open as I was to Mr. Jarndyce, I am to you. I regard it in the light of a professional duty to be so, though it can be charged to no one. I openly say, unpalatable as it may be, that I consider Mr. C.'s affairs in a very bad way, that I consider Mr. C. himself in a very bad way, and that I regard this as an exceedingly ill-advised marriage.—Am I here, sir? Yes, I thank you; I am here, Mr. C., and enjoying the pleasure of some agreeable conversation with Miss Summerson, for which I have to thank you very much, sir!"

He broke off thus, in answer to Richard, who addressed him as he came into the room. By this time, I too well understood Mr. Vholes's scrupulous way of saving himself and his respectability, not to feel that our worst fears did but keep pace with his client's progress.

We sat down to dinner, and I had an opportunity of observing Richard, anxiously. I was not disturbed by Mr. Vholes (who took off his gloves to dine), though he sat opposite to me at the small table; for I doubt if, looking up at all, he once removed his eyes from his host's face. I found Richard thin and languid, slovenly in his dress, abstracted in his manner, forcing his spirits now and then, and at other intervals relapsing into a dull thoughtfulness. About his large bright eyes that used to be so merry, there was a wanness and a restlessness that changed them altogether. I cannot use the expression that he looked old. There is a ruin of youth which is not like age ; and into such a ruin Richard's youth and youthful beauty had all fallen away.

He ate little, and seemed indifferent what it was ; showed himself to be much more impatient than he used to be ; and was quick, even with Ada. I thought, at first, that his old light-hearted manner was all gone; but it shone out of him sometimes, as I had occasionally known little momentary glimpses of my own old face to look out upon me from the glass. His laugh had not quite left him either ; but it was like the echo of a joyful sound, and that is always sorrowful.

Yet he was as glad as ever, in his old affectionate way, to have me there ; and we talked of the old times pleasantly. These did not appear to be interesting to Mr. Vholes, though he occasionally made a gasp which I believe was his smile. He rose shortly after dinner, and said that with the permission of the ladies he would retire to his office.

"Always devoted to business, Vholes !" cried Richard.

"Yes, Mr. C.," he returned, "the interests of clients are never to be neglected, sir. They are paramount in the thoughts of a professional man like myself, who wishes to preserve a good name among his fellow-practitioners and society at large. My denying myself the pleasure of the present agreeable conversation, may not be wholly irrespective of your own interests, Mr. C."

Richard expressed himself quite sure of that, and lighted Mr. Vholes out. On his return he told us, more than once, that Vholes was a good fellow, a safe fellow, a man who did what he pretended to do, a very good fellow, indeed ! He was so defiant about it, that it struck me he had begun to doubt Mr. Vholes.

Then he threw himself on the sofa, tired out ; and Ada and I put things to rights, for they had no other servant than the woman who attended to the chambers. My dear girl had a cottage piano there, and quietly sat down to sing some of Richard's favourites ; the lamp being first removed into the next room, as he complained of its hurting his eyes.

I sat between them, at my dear girl's side, and felt very melancholy listening to her sweet voice. I think Richard did too ; I think he darkened the room for that reason. She had been singing some time, rising between-whiles to bend over him and speak to him ; when Mr. Woodcourt came in. Then he sat down by Richard ; and half playfully, half earnestly, quite naturally and easily, found out how he felt, and where he had been all day. Presently he proposed to accompany him in a short walk on one of the bridges, as it was a moonlight airy night ; and Richard readily consenting, they went out together.

They left my dear girl still sitting at the piano, and me still sitting beside her. When they were gone out, I drew my arm round her waist. She put her left hand in mine (I was sitting on that side), but kept her right upon the keys—going over and over them, without striking any note.

"Esther, my dearest," she said, breaking silence, "Richard is never so well, and I am never so easy about him, as when he is with Allan Woodcourt. We have to thank you for that."

I pointed out to my darling how this could scarcely be, because Mr. Woodcourt had come to her cousin John's house, and had known us all there; and because he had always liked Richard, and Richard had always liked him, and—and so forth.

"All true," said Ada; "but that he is such a devoted friend to us, we owe to you."

I thought it best to let my dear girl have her way, and to say no more about it. So I said as much. I said it lightly, because I felt her trembling.

"Esther, my dearest, I want to be a good wife, a very, very good wife indeed. You shall teach me."

I teach! I said no more; for I noticed the hand that was fluttering over the keys, and I knew that it was not I who ought to speak; that it was she who had something to say to me.

"When I married Richard, I was not insensible to what was before him. I had been perfectly happy for a long time with you, and I had never known any trouble or anxiety, so loved and cared for; but I understood the danger he was in, dear Esther."

"I know, I know, my darling."

"When we were married, I had some little hope that I might be able to convince him of his mistake; that he might come to regard it in a new way as my husband, and not pursue it all the more desperately for my sake—as he does. But if I had not had that hope, I would have married him just the same, Esther. Just the same!"

In the momentary firmness of the hand that was never still—a firmness inspired by the utterance of these last words, and dying away with them—I saw the confirmation of her earnest tones.

"You are not to think, my dearest Esther, that I fail to see what you see, and fear what you fear. No one can understand him better than I do. The greatest wisdom that ever lived in the world could scarcely know Richard better than my love does."

She spoke so modestly and softly, and her trembling hand expressed such agitation, as it moved to and fro upon the silent notes! My dear, dear girl!

"I see him at his worst, every day. I watch him in his sleep. I know every change of his face. But when I married Richard, I was quite determined, Esther, if Heaven would help me, never to show him that I grieved for what he did, and so to make him more unhappy. I want him, when he comes home, to find no trouble in my face. I want him, when he looks at me, to see what he loved in me. I married him to do this, and this supports me."

I felt her trembling more. I waited for what was yet to come, and I now thought I began to know what it was.

"And something else supports me, Esther."

She stopped a minute. Stopped speaking only; her hand was still in motion.

"I look forward a little while, and I don't know what great aid may come to me. When Richard turns his eyes upon me then, there may be something lying on my breast more eloquent than I have been, with greater power than mine to show him his true course, and win him back."

Her hand stopped now. She clasped me in her arms, and I clasped her in mine.

"If that little creature should fail too, Esther, I still look forward. I look forward a long while, through years and years, and think that then, when I am growing old, or when I am dead perhaps, a beautiful woman, his daughter, happily married, may be proud of him and a blessing to him. Or that a generous brave man, as handsome as he used to be, as hopeful, and far more happy, may walk in the sunshine with him, honouring his grey head, and saying to himself, 'I thank God this is my father! ruined by a fatal inheritance, and restored through me!'"

Oh, my sweet girl, what a heart was that which beat so fast against me!

"These hopes uphold me, my dear Esther, and I know they will. Though sometimes even they depart from me, before a dread that arises when I look at Richard."

I tried to cheer my darling, and asked her what it was? Sobbing and weeping, she replied:

"That he may not live to see his child."

CHAPTER LXI

A DISCOVERY

THE days when I frequented that miserable corner which my dear girl brightened, can never fade in my remembrance. I never see it, and I never wish to see it, now; I have been there only once since; but in my memory there is a mournful glory shining on the place, which will shine for ever.

Not a day passed without my going there, of course. At first I found Mr. Skimpole there, on two or three occasions, idly playing the piano, and talking in his usual vivacious strain. Now, besides my very much mistrusting the probability of his being there without making Richard poorer, I felt as if there were something in his careless gaiety too inconsistent with what I knew of the depths of Ada's life. I clearly perceived, too, that Ada shared my feelings. I therefore resolved, after much thinking of it, to make a private visit to Mr. Skimpole, and try delicately to explain myself. My dear girl was the great consideration that made me bold.

I set off one morning, accompanied by Charley, for Somers Town. As I approached the house, I was strongly inclined to turn back, for I felt what a desperate attempt it was to make an impression on Mr. Skimpole, and how extremely likely it was that he would signally defeat me. However, I thought that being there, I would go through with it. I knocked with a trembling hand at Mr. Skimpole's door—literally with a hand, for the knocker was gone—and after a long parley gained admission from an Irishwoman, who was in the area when I knocked, breaking up the lid of a water-butt with a poker, to light the fire with.

Mr. Skimpole, lying on the sofa in his room, playing the flute a little, was enchanted to see me. Now, who should receive me, he asked? Who would I prefer for mistress of the ceremonies? Would I have his Comedy daughter, his Beauty daughter, or his Sentiment daughter? Or would I have all the daughters at once, in a perfect nosegay?

I replied, half defeated already, that I wished to speak to himself only, if he would give me leave.

"My dear Miss Summerson, most joyfully! Of course," he said, bringing his chair nearer mine, and breaking into his fascinating smile, "of course it's not business. Then it's pleasure!"

I said it certainly was not business that I came upon, but it was not quite a pleasant matter.

"Then, my dear Miss Summerson," said he, with the frankest gaiety, "don't allude to it. Why should you allude to anything that is *not* a pleasant matter? *I* never do. And you are a much pleasanter creature, in every point of view, than I. You are perfectly pleasant; I am imperfectly pleasant; then, if I never allude to an unpleasant matter, how much less should you! So that's disposed of, and we will talk of something else."

Although I was embarrassed, I took courage to intimate that I still wished to pursue the subject.

"I should think it a mistake," said Mr. Skimpole, with his airy laugh, "if I thought Miss Summerson capable of making one. But I don't!"

"Mr. Skimpole," said I, raising my eyes to his, "I have so often heard you say that you are unacquainted with the common affairs of life——"

"Meaning our three banking-house friends, L, S, and who's the junior partner? D?" said Mr. Skimpole brightly. "Not an idea of them!"

"—That, perhaps," I went on, "you will excuse my boldness on that account. I think you ought most seriously to know that Richard is poorer than he was."

"Dear me!" said Mr. Skimpole. "So am I, they tell me."

"And in very embarrassed circumstances."

"Parallel case, exactly!" said Mr. Skimpole, with a delighted countenance.

"This at present naturally causes Ada much secret anxiety; and as I think she is less anxious when no claims are made upon her by visitors, and as Richard has one uneasiness always heavy on his mind, it has occurred to me to take the liberty of saying that—if you would—not——"

I was coming to the point with great difficulty, when he took me by both hands, and, with a radiant face and in the liveliest way, anticipated it.

"Not go there? Certainly not, my dear Miss Summerson, most assuredly not. Why *should* I go there? When I go anywhere, I go for pleasure. I don't go anywhere for pain, because I was made for pleasure. Pain comes to *me* when it wants me. Now, I have had very little pleasure at our dear Richard's, lately, and your practical sagacity demonstrates why. Our young friends, losing the youthful poetry which was once so captivating in them, begin to think, 'this is a man who wants pounds.' So I am; I always want pounds; not for myself, but because tradespeople always want them of me. Next, our young friends begin to think, becoming mercenary, 'this is the man who *had* pounds, —who borrowed them'; which I did. I always borrow pounds. So our young friends, reduced to prose (which is much to be regretted), degenerate in their power of imparting pleasure to me. Why should I go to see them, therefore? Absurd!"

Through the beaming smile with which he regarded me, as he reasoned thus, there now broke forth a look of disinterested benevolence quite astonishing.

"Besides," he said, pursuing his argument, in his tone of light-hearted conviction, "if I don't go anywhere for pain—which would be a perversion of the intention of my being, and a monstrous thing to do—why should I go anywhere to be the cause of pain? If I went to see our young friends in their present ill-regulated state of mind, I should give them pain. The associations with me would be disagreeable. They might say, 'this is the man who had pounds, and who can't pay pounds,' which I can't, of course; nothing could be more out of the question! Then, kindness requires that I shouldn't go near them—and I won't."

He finished by genially kissing my hand, and thanking me. Nothing but Miss Summerson's fine tact, he said, would have found this out for him.

I was much disconcerted; but I reflected that if the main point were gained, it mattered little how strangely he perverted everything leading to it. I had determined to mention something else, however, and I thought I was not to be put off in that.

"Mr. Skimpole," said I, "I must take the liberty of saying, before I conclude my visit, that I was much surprised to learn, on the best authority, some little time ago, that you knew with whom that poor boy left Bleak House, and that you accepted a present on that occasion. I have not mentioned it to my guardian, for I fear it would hurt him unnecessarily; but I may say to you that I was much surprised."

"No? Really surprised, my dear Miss Summerson?" he returned, inquiringly, raising his pleasant eyebrows.

"Greatly surprised."

He thought about it for a little while, with a highly agreeable and whimsical expression of face; then quite gave it up, and said, in his most engaging manner:

"You know what a child I am. Why surprised?"

I was reluctant to enter minutely into that question; but as he begged

I would, for he was really curious to know, I gave him to understand, in the gentlest words I could use, that his conduct seemed to involve a disregard of several moral obligations. He was much amused and interested when he heard this, and said, "No, really?" with ingenuous simplicity.

"You know I don't pretend to be responsible. I never could do it. Responsibility is a thing that has always been above me—or below me," said Mr. Skimpole, "I don't even know which; but, as I understand the way in which my dear Miss Summerson (always remarkable for her practical good sense and clearness) puts this case, I should imagine it was chiefly a question of money, do you know?"

I incautiously gave a qualified assent to this.

"Ah! Then you see," said Mr. Skimpole, shaking his head, "I am hopeless of understanding it."

I suggested, as I rose to go, that it was not right to betray my guardian's confidence for a bribe.

"My dear Miss Summerson," he returned, with a candid hilarity that was all his own, "I can't be bribed."

"Not by Mr. Bucket?" said I.

"No," said he. "Not by anybody. I don't attach any value to money. I don't care about it, I don't know about it, I don't want it, I don't keep it—it goes away from me directly. How can *I* be bribed?"

I showed that I was of a different opinion, though I had not the capacity for arguing the question.

"On the contrary," said Mr. Skimpole, "I am exactly the man to be placed in a superior position, in such a case as that. I am above the rest of mankind, in such a case as that. I can act with philosophy, in such a case as that. I am not warped by prejudices, as an Italian baby is by bandages. I am as free as the air. I feel myself as far above suspicion as Cæsar's wife."

Anything to equal the lightness of his manner, and the playful impartiality with which he seemed to convince himself, as he tossed the matter about like a ball of feathers, was surely never seen in anybody else!

"Observe the case, my dear Miss Summerson. Here is a boy received into the house and put to bed, in a state that I strongly object to. The boy being in bed, a man arrives—like the house that Jack built. Here is the man who demands the boy who is received into the house and put to bed in a state that I strongly object to. Here is a bank-note produced by the man who demands the boy who is received into the house and put to bed in a state that I strongly object to. Here is the Skimpole who accepts the bank-note produced by the man who demands the boy who is received into the house and put to bed in a state that I strongly object to. Those are the facts. Very well. Should the Skimpole have refused the note? *Why* should the Skimpole have refused the note? Skimpole protests to Bucket; 'What's this for? I don't understand it, it is of no use to me, take it away.' Bucket still entreats Skimpole to accept it. Are there reasons why Skimpole, not being warped by prejudices, should accept it? Yes. Skimpole perceives them. What are they? Skimpole reasons with himself, this is a tamed lynx, an active police-officer, an intelligent man, a person of a peculiarly directed energy and great subtlety both of conception and execution, who discovers our friends and enemies for us when they run away, recovers our property for us when we are robbed, avenges us comfortably when we are murdered. This active police-officer and intelligent man has acquired, in the exercise of his art, a strong faith in money; he finds it very useful to him, and he makes it very useful to society. Shall I shake that faith in Bucket, because I want it myself; shall I deliberately blunt one of Bucket's weapons: shall I possibly paralyse Bucket in his next detective operation? And again. If it is blamable in Skimpole to take the note, it is blamable in Bucket to offer the note—much more blamable in Bucket, because he is the knowing man. Now, Skimpole wishes to think well of Bucket; Skimpole deems it essential, in its little place, to the general cohesion of things, that he *should* think well of Bucket. The State expressly asks him to trust to Bucket. And he does. And that's all he does!"

I had nothing to offer in reply to this exposition, and therefore took my leave. Mr. Skimpole, however, who was in excellent spirits, would not hear of my returning home attended only by "Little Coavinses," and accompanied me himself. He entertained me, on the way, with a variety of delightful conversation; and assured me, at parting, that he should never forget the fine tact with which I had found that out for him about our young friends.

As it so happened that I never saw Mr. Skimpole again, I may at once finish what I know of his history. A coolness arose between him and my guardian, based chiefly on the foregoing grounds, and on his having heartlessly disregarded my guardian's entreaties (as we afterwards learned from Ada) in reference to Richard. His being heavily in my guardian's debt, had nothing to do with their separation. He died some five years afterwards, and left a diary behind him, with letters and other materials towards his Life; which was published, and which showed him to have been the victim of a combination on the part of mankind against an amiable child. It was considered very pleasant reading, but I never read more of it myself than the sentence on which I chanced to light on opening the book. It was this. "Jarndyce, in common with most other men I have known, is the Incarnation of Selfishness."

And now I come to a part of my story, touching myself very nearly indeed, and for which I was quite unprepared when the circumstance occurred. Whatever little lingerings may have now and then revived in my mind, associated with my poor old face, had only revived as belonging to a part of my life that was gone—gone like my infancy or my childhood. I have suppressed none of my many weaknesses on that subject, but have written them as faithfully as my memory has recalled them. And I hope to do, and mean to do, the same down to the last words of these pages; which I see now, not so very far before me.

The months were gliding away; and my dear girl, sustained by the hopes she had confided to me, was the same beautiful star in the miserable corner. Richard, more worn and haggard, haunted the court day after day; listlessly sat there the whole day long, when he knew there was no remote chance of the suit being mentioned; and became one of the stock sights of the place. I wonder whether any of the gentlemen remembered him as he was when he first went there.

So completely was he absorbed in his fixed idea, that he used to avow in his cheerful moments, that he should never have breathed the fresh air now "but for Woodcourt." It was only Mr. Woodcourt who could occasionally divert his attention, for a few hours at a time; and rouse him, even when he sunk into a lethargy of mind and body that alarmed us greatly, and the returns of which became more frequent as the months went on. My dear girl was right in saying that he only pursued his errors the more desperately for her sake. I have no doubt that his desire to retrieve what he had lost, was rendered the more intense by his grief for his young wife, and became like the madness of a gamester.

I was there, as I have mentioned, at all hours. When I was there at night, I generally went home with Charley in a coach; sometimes my guardian would meet me in the neighbourhood, and we would walk home together. One evening he had arranged to meet me at eight o'clock. I could not leave, as I usually did, quite punctually to the time, for I was working for my dear girl, and had a few stitches more to do, to finish what I was about; but it was within a few minutes of the hour, when I bundled up my little work-basket, gave my darling my last kiss for the night, and hurried downstairs. Mr. Woodcourt went with me, as it was dusk.

When we came to the usual place of meeting—it was close by, and Mr. Woodcourt had often accompanied me before—my guardian was not there. We waited half-an-hour, walking up and down; but there were no signs of him. We agreed that he was either prevented from coming, or that he had come, and gone away; and Mr. Woodcourt proposed to walk home with me.

It was the first walk we had ever taken together, except that very short one to the usual place of meeting. We spoke of Richard and Ada the whole way. I did not thank him, in words, for what he had done —my appreciation of it had risen above all words then—but I hoped he might not be without some understanding of what I felt so strongly.

Arriving at home and going upstairs, we found that my guardian was out, and that Mrs. Woodcourt was out too. We were in the very same room into which I had brought my blushing girl, when her youthful lover, now her so altered husband, was the choice of her young heart; the very same room, from which my guardian and I had watched them going away through the sunlight, in the fresh bloom of their hope and promise.

We were standing by the opened window, looking down into the street, when Mr. Woodcourt spoke to me. I learned in a moment that he loved me. I learned in a moment that my scarred face was all unchanged to him. I learned in a moment that what I had thought was pity and compassion, was devoted, generous, faithful love. Oh, too late to know it now, too late, too late. That was the first ungrateful thought I had. Too late.

"When I returned," he told me, "when I came back, no richer than I went away, and found you newly risen from a sick bed, yet so inspired by sweet consideration for others, and so free from a selfish thought——"

"Oh, Mr. Woodcourt, forbear, forbear!" I entreated him. "I do not deserve your high praise. I had many selfish thoughts at that time, many!"

"Heaven knows, beloved of my life," said he, "that my praise is not a lover's praise, but the truth. You do not know what all around you see in Esther Summerson, how many hearts she touches and awakens, what sacred admiration and what love she wins."

"Oh, Mr. Woodcourt," cried I, "it is a great thing to win love, it is a great thing to win love! I am proud of it, and honoured by it; and the hearing of it causes me to shed these tears of mingled joy and sorrow —joy that I have won it, sorrow that I have not deserved it better; but I am not free to think of yours."

I said it with a stronger heart; for when he praised me thus, and when I heard his voice thrill with his belief that what he said was true, I aspired to be more worthy of it. It was not too late for that. Although I closed this unforeseen page in my life to-night, I could be worthier of it all through my life. And it was a comfort to me, and an impulse to me, and I felt a dignity rise up within me that was derived from him, when I thought so.

He broke the silence.

"I should poorly show the trust that I have in the dear one who will evermore be as dear to me as now," and the deep earnestness with which he said it, at once strengthened me and made me weep, "if, after her assurance that she is not free to think of my love, I urged it. Dear Esther, let me only tell you that the fond idea of you which I took abroad, was exalted to the Heavens when I came home. I have always hoped, in the first hour when I seemed to stand in any ray of good fortune, to tell you this. I have always feared that I should tell it you in vain. My hopes and fears are both fulfilled to-night. I distress you. I have said enough."

Something seemed to pass into my place that was like the Angel he thought me, and I felt so sorrowful for the loss he had sustained! I wished to help him in his trouble, as I had wished to do when he showed that first commiseration for me.

"Dear Mr. Woodcourt," said I, "before we part to-night, something is left for me to say. I never could say it as I wish—I never shall—but——"

I had to think again of being more deserving of his love, and his affliction, before I could go on.

"—I am deeply sensible of your generosity, and I shall treasure its remembrance to my dying hour. I know full well how changed I am, I know you are not unacquainted with my history, and I know what a noble love that is which is so faithful. What you have said to me, could have affected me so much from no other lips; for there are none that could give it such a value to me. It shall not be lost. It shall make me better."

He covered his eyes with his hand, and turned away his head. How could I ever be worthy of those tears?

"If, in the unchanged intercourse we shall have together—in tending Richard and Ada; and I hope in many happier scenes of life—you ever find anything in me which you can honestly think is better than it used to be, believe that it will have sprung up from to-night, and that I shall owe it to you. And never believe, dear, dear Mr. Woodcourt, never believe, that I forget this night; or that while my heart beats, it can be insensible to the pride and joy of having been beloved by you."

He took my hand and kissed it. He was like himself again, and I felt still more encouraged.

"I am induced, by what you said just now," said I, "to hope that you have succeeded in your endeavour?"

"I have," he answered. "With such help from Mr. Jarndyce, as you who know him so well can imagine him to have rendered me, I have succeeded."

"Heaven bless him for it," said I, giving him my hand; "and Heaven bless you in all you do!"

"I shall do it better for the wish," he answered; "it will make me enter on these new duties, as on another sacred trust from you."

"Ah! Richard!" I exclaimed involuntarily, "what will he do when you are gone?"

"I am not required to go yet; I would not desert him, dear Miss Summerson, even if I were."

One other thing I felt it needful to touch upon, before he left me. I knew that I should not be worthier of the love I could not take, if I reserved it.

"Mr. Woodcourt," said I, "you will be glad to know from my lips before I say Good night, that in the future, which is clear and bright before me, I am most happy, most fortunate, have nothing to regret or to desire."

It was indeed a glad hearing to him, he replied.

"From my childhood I have been," said I, "the object of the untiring goodness of the best of human beings; to whom I am so bound by every tie of attachment, gratitude, and love, that nothing I could do in the compass of a life could express the feelings of a single day."

"I share those feelings," he returned. "You speak of Mr. Jarndyce."

"You know his virtues well," said I, "but few can know the greatness of his character as I know it. All its highest and best qualities have been revealed to me in nothing more brightly than in the shaping out of that future in which I am so happy. And if your highest homage and respect had not been his already,—which I know they are—they would have been his, I think, on this assurance, and in the feeling it would have awakened in you towards him for my sake."

He fervently replied, that indeed indeed they would have been. I gave him my hand again.

" Good night," I said ; " Good-bye."

" The first, until we meet to-morrow ; the second, as a farewell to this theme between us for ever ? "

" Yes."

" Good night ; good-bye ! "

He left me, and I stood at the dark window watching the street. His love, in all its constancy and generosity, had come so suddenly upon me, that he had not left me a minute when my fortitude gave way again, and the street was blotted out by my rushing tears.

But they were not tears of regret and sorrow. No. He had called me the beloved of his life, and had said I would be evermore as dear to him as I was then ; and I felt as if my heart would not hold the triumph of having heard those words. My first wild thought had died away. It was not too late to hear them, for it was not too late to be animated by them to be good, true, grateful, and contented. How easy my path ; how much easier than his !

CHAPTER LXII

ANOTHER DISCOVERY

I HAD not the courage to see any one that night. I had not even the courage to see myself, for I was afraid that my tears might a little reproach me. I went up to my room in the dark, and prayed in the dark, and lay down in the dark to sleep. I had no need of any light to read my guardian's letter by, for I knew it by heart. I took it from the place where I kept it, and repeated its contents by its own clear light of integrity and love, and went to sleep with it on my pillow.

I was up very early in the morning, and called Charley to come for a walk. We bought flowers for the breakfast-table, and came back and arranged them, and were as busy as possible. We were so early, that I had good time still for Charley's lesson, before breakfast ; Charley (who was not in the least improved in the old defective article of grammar) came through it with great applause ; and we were altogether very notable. When my guardian appeared, he said, " Why, little woman, you look fresher than your flowers ! " And Mrs. Woodcourt repeated and translated a passage from the Mewlinnwillinwodd, expressive of my being like a mountain with the sun upon it.

This was all so pleasant, that I hope it made me still more like the mountain than I had been before. After breakfast, I waited my opportunity, and peeped about a little, until I saw my guardian in his own room—the room of last night—by himself. Then I made an excuse to go in with my housekeeping keys, shutting the door after me.

"Well, Dame Durden?" said my guardian; the post had brought him several letters, and he was writing. "You want money?"

"No, indeed, I have plenty in hand."

"There never was such a Dame Durden," said my guardian, "for making money last."

He had laid down his pen, and leaned back in his chair looking at me. I have often spoken of his bright face, but I thought I had never seen it look so bright and good. There was a high happiness upon it, which made me think, "He has been doing some great kindness this morning."

"There never was," said my guardian, musing as he smiled upon me, "such a Dame Durden for making money last."

He had never yet altered his old manner. I loved it, and him, so much, that when I now went up to him and took my usual chair, which was always put at his side—for sometimes I read to him, and sometimes I talked to him, and sometimes I silently worked by him—I hardly liked to disturb it by laying my hand on his breast. But I found I did not disturb it at all.

"Dear Guardian," said I, "I want to speak to you. Have I been remiss in anything?"

"Remiss in anything, my dear!"

"Have I not been what I have meant to be, since—I brought the answer to your letter, Guardian?"

"You have been everything I could desire, my love."

"I am very glad indeed to hear that," I returned. "You know, you said to me, was this the mistress of Bleak House? And I said, yes."

"Yes," said my guardian, nodding his head. He had put his arm about me, as if there were something to protect me from; and looked in my face, smiling.

"Since then," said I, "we have never spoken on the subject except once."

"And then I said, Bleak House was thinning fast; and so it was, my dear."

"And I said," I timidly reminded him, "but its mistress remained."

He still held me, in the same protecting manner, and with the same bright goodness in his face.

"Dear Guardian," said I, "I know how you have felt all that has happened, and how considerate you have been. As so much time has passed, and as you spoke only this morning of my being so well again, perhaps you expect me to renew the subject. Perhaps I ought to do so. I will be the mistress of Bleak House when you please."

"See," he returned gaily; "what a sympathy there must be between us! I have had nothing else, poor Rick excepted—it's a large exception —in my mind. When you came in, I was full of it. When shall we give Bleak House its mistress, little woman?"

"When you please."

"Next month?"

"Next month, dear Guardian."

"The day on which I take the happiest and best step of my life—the day on which I shall be a man more exulting and more enviable than any other man in the world—the day on which I give Bleak House its little mistress—shall be next month, then," said my guardian.

I put my arms round his neck and kissed him, just as I had done on the day when I brought my answer.

A servant came to the door to announce Mr. Bucket, which was quite unnecessary, for Mr. Bucket was already looking in over the servant's shoulder. "Mr. Jarndyce and Miss Summerson," said he, rather out of breath, "with all apologies for intruding, *will* you allow me to order up a person that's on the stairs, and that objects to being left there in case of becoming the subject of observations in his absence? Thank you. Be so good as chair that there Member in this direction, will you?" said Mr. Bucket, beckoning over the banisters.

This singular request produced an old man in a black skull-cap, unable to walk, who was carried up by a couple of bearers, and deposited in the room near the door. Mr. Bucket immediately got rid of the bearers, mysteriously shut the door, and bolted it.

"Now you see, Mr. Jarndyce," he then began, putting down his hat, and opening his subject with a flourish of his well-remembered finger, "you know me, and Miss Summerson knows me. This gentleman likewise knows me, and his name is Smallweed. The discounting line is his line principally, and he's what you may call a dealer in bills. That's about what *you* are, you know, ain't you?" said Mr. Bucket, stopping a little to address the gentleman in question, who was exceedingly suspicious of him.

He seemed about to dispute this designation of himself, when he was seized with a violent fit of coughing.

"Now, Moral, you know!" said Mr. Bucket, improving the accident. "Don't you contradict when there ain't no occasion, and you won't be took in that way. Now, Mr. Jarndyce, I address myself to you. I've been negotiating with this gentleman on behalf of Sir Leicester Dedlock, Baronet; and one way and another I've been in and out and about his premises a deal. His premises are the premises formerly occupied by Krook, Marine Store Dealer—a relation of this gentleman's, that you saw in his lifetime, if I don't mistake?"

My guardian replied "Yes."

"Well! You are to understand," said Mr. Bucket, "that this gentleman he come into Krook's property, and a good deal of Magpie property there was. Vast lots of waste paper among the rest. Lord bless you, of no use to nobody!"

The cunning of Mr. Bucket's eye, and the masterly manner in which he contrived, without a look or a word against which his watchful auditor could protest, to let us know that he stated the case according to previous agreement, and could say much more of Mr. Smallweed if he thought it advisable, deprived us of any merit in quite understanding him. His difficulty was increased by Mr. Smallweed's being deaf as well as suspicious, and watching his face with the closest attention.

"Among them odd heaps of old papers, this gentleman, when he comes into the property, naturally begins to rummage, don't you see?" said Mr. Bucket.

"To which? Say that again," cried Mr. Smallweed, in a shrill, sharp voice.

"To rummage," repeated Mr. Bucket. "Being a prudent man, and accustomed to take care of your own affairs, you begin to rummage among the papers as you have come into; don't you?"

"Of course I do," cried Mr. Smallweed.

"Of course you do," said Mr. Bucket conversationally, "and much to blame you would be if you didn't. And so you chance to find, you know," Mr. Bucket went on, stooping over him with an air of cheerful raillery which Mr. Smallweed by no means reciprocated, "and so you chance to find, you know, a paper, with the signature of Jarndyce to it. Don't you?"

Mr. Smallweed glanced with a troubled eye at us, and grudgingly nodded assent.

"And coming to look at that paper, at your full leisure and convenience—all in good time, for you're not curious to read it, and why should you be?—what do you find it to be but a Will, you see. That's the drollery of it," said Mr. Bucket, with the same lively air of recalling a joke for the enjoyment of Mr. Smallweed, who still had the same crestfallen appearance of not enjoying it at all; "what do you find it to be but a Will?"

"I don't know that it's good as a Will, or as anything else," snarled Mr. Smallweed.

Mr. Bucket eyed the old man for a moment—he had slipped and shrunk down in his chair into a mere bundle—as if he were much disposed to pounce upon him; nevertheless, he continued to bend over him with the same agreeable air, keeping the corner of one of his eyes upon us.

"Notwithstanding which," said Mr. Bucket, "you get a little doubtful and uncomfortable in your mind about it, having a very tender mind of your own."

"Eh? What do you say I have got of my own?" asked Mr. Smallweed, with his hand to his ear.

"A very tender mind."

"Ho! Well, go on," said Mr. Smallweed.

"And as you've heard a good deal mentioned regarding a celebrated Chancery Will case, of the same name; and as you know what a card Krook was for buying all manner of old pieces of furniter, and books, and papers, and what not, and never liking to part with 'em, and always agoing to teach himself to read; you begin to think—and you never was more correct in your born days—'Ecod, if I don't look about me, I may get into trouble regarding this Will.'"

"Now, mind how you put it, Bucket," cried the old man anxiously, with his hand at his ear. "Speak up; none of your brimstone tricks. Pick me up; I want to hear better. O Lord, I am shaken to bits!"

Mr. Bucket had certainly picked him up at a dart. However, as soon as he could be heard through Mr. Smallweed's coughing, and his vicious ejaculations of "O my bones! O dear! I've no breath in my body! I'm worse than the chattering, clattering, brimstone pig at home!" Mr. Bucket proceeded in the same convivial manner as before.

"So, as I happen to be in the habit of coming about your premises, you take me into your confidence, don't you?"

I think it would be impossible to make an admission with more ill-will, and a worse grace, than Mr. Smallweed displayed when he admitted this; rendering it perfectly evident that Mr. Bucket was the very last person he would have thought of taking into his confidence, if he could by any possibility have kept him out of it.

"And I go into the business with you—very pleasant we are over it; and I confirm you in your well-founded fears, that you will-get-yourself-in-to-a-most precious line if you don't come out with that there Will," said Mr. Bucket emphatically; "and accordingly you arrange with me that it shall be delivered up to this present Mr. Jarndyce, on no conditions. If it should prove to be valuable, you trusting yourself to him for your reward; that's about where it is, ain't it?"

"That's what was agreed," Mr. Smallweed assented, with the same bad grace.

"In consequence of which," said Mr. Bucket, dismissing his agreeable manner all at once, and becoming strictly business-like, "you've got that Will upon your person at the present time; and the only thing that remains for you to do is, just to Out with it!"

Having given us one glance out of the watching corner of his eye, and having given his nose one triumphant rub with his forefinger, Mr. Bucket stood with his eyes fastened on his confidential friend, and his hand stretched forth ready to take the paper and present it to my guardian. It was not produced without much reluctance, and many declarations on the part of Mr. Smallweed that he was a poor industrious man, and that he left it to Mr. Jarndyce's honour not to let him lose by his honesty. Little by little, he very slowly took from a breast-pocket a stained, discoloured paper, which was much singed upon the outside, and a little burnt at the edges, as if it had long ago been thrown upon a fire, and hastily snatched off again. Mr. Bucket lost no time in transferring this paper, with the dexterity of a conjurer, from Mr. Smallweed to Mr. Jarndyce. As he gave it to my guardian, he whispered behind his fingers:

"Hadn't settled how to make their market of it. Quarrelled and hinted about it. I laid out twenty pounds upon it. First, the avaricious grandchildren split upon him, on account of their objections to his living so unreasonably long, and then they split on one another. Lord! there ain't one of the family that wouldn't sell the other for a pound or two, except the old lady—and she's only out of it because she's too weak in her mind to drive a bargain."

"Mr. Bucket," said my guardian aloud, "whatever the worth of this paper may be to any one, my obligations are great to you; and if it be of any worth, I hold myself bound to see Mr. Smallweed remunerated accordingly."

"Not according to your merits, you know," said Mr. Bucket, in friendly explanation to Mr. Smallweed. "Don't you be afraid of that. According to its value."

"That is what I mean," said my guardian. "You may observe, Mr. Bucket, that I abstain from examining this paper myself. The plain truth is, I have forsworn and abjured the whole business these many years, and my soul is sick of it. But Miss Summerson and I will immediately place the paper in the hands of my solicitor in the cause, and its existence shall be made known without delay to all other parties interested."

"Mr. Jarndyce can't say fairer than that, you understand," observed Mr. Bucket, to his fellow-visitor. "And it being now made clear to you that nobody's agoing to be wronged—which must be a great relief to *your* mind—we may proceed with the ceremony of chairing you home again."

He unbolted the door, called in the bearers, wished us good morning, and with a look full of meaning, and a crook of his finger at parting, went his way.

We went our way too, which was to Lincoln's Inn, as quickly as possible. Mr. Kenge was disengaged; and we found him at his table in his dusty room, with the inexpressive-looking books, and the piles of papers. Chairs having been placed for us by Mr. Guppy, Mr. Kenge expressed the surprise and gratification he felt at the unusual sight of Mr. Jarndyce in his office. He turned over his double eye-glass as he spoke, and was more Conversation Kenge than ever.

"I hope," said Mr. Kenge, "that the genial influence of Miss Summerson," he bowed to me, "may have induced Mr. Jarndyce," he bowed to him, "to forego some little of his animosity towards a Cause and towards a Court which are—shall I say, which take their place in the stately vista of the pillars of our profession?"

"I am inclined to think," returned my guardian, "that Miss Summerson has seen too much of the effects of the Court and the Cause to exert any influence in their favour. Nevertheless, they are a part of the occasion of my being here. Mr. Kenge, before I lay this paper on your desk, and have done with it, let me tell you how it has come into my hands."

He did so shortly and distinctly.

"It could not, sir," said Mr. Kenge, "have been stated more plainly and to the purpose, if it had been a case at law."

"Did you ever know English law, or equity either, plain and to the purpose?" said my guardian.

"Oh fie!" said Mr. Kenge.

At first he had not seemed to attach much importance to the paper, but when he saw it he appeared more interested, and when he had opened and read a little of it through his eyeglass, he became amazed. "Mr. Jarndyce," he said, looking off it, "you have perused this?"

"Not I!" returned my guardian.

"But, my dear sir," said Mr. Kenge, "it is a Will of later date than any in the suit. It appears to be all in the Testator's handwriting. It is duly executed and attested. And even if intended to be cancelled, as might possibly be supposed to be denoted by these marks of fire, it is *not* cancelled. Here it is, a perfect instrument!"

"Well!" said my guardian. "What is that to me?"

"Mr. Guppy!" cried Mr. Kenge, raising his voice.—"I beg your pardon, Mr. Jarndyce."

"Sir."

"Mr. Vholes of Symond's Inn. My compliments. Jarndyce and Jarndyce. Glad to speak with him."

Mr. Guppy disappeared.

"You ask me what is this to you, Mr. Jarndyce. If you had perused this document, you would have seen that it reduces your interest considerably, though still leaving it a very handsome one, still leaving it a very handsome one," said Mr. Kenge, waving his hand persuasively and blandly. "You would further have seen, that the interests of Mr. Richard Carstone, and of Miss Ada Clare, now Mrs. Richard Carstone, are very materially advanced by it."

"Kenge," said my guardian, "if all the flourishing wealth that the suit brought into this vile court of Chancery could fall to my two young cousins, I should be well contented. But do you ask *me* to believe that any good is to come of Jarndyce and Jarndyce?"

"Oh really, Mr. Jarndyce! Prejudice, prejudice. My dear sir, this is a very great country, a very great country. Its system of equity is a very great system, a very great system. Really, really!"

My guardian said no more, and Mr. Vholes arrived. He was modestly impressed by Mr. Kenge's professional eminence.

"How do you do, Mr. Vholes? Will you be so good as to take a chair here by me, and look over this paper?"

Mr. Vholes did as he was asked, and seemed to read it every word. He was not excited by it; but he was not excited by anything. When he had well examined it, he retired with Mr. Kenge into a window, and shading his mouth with his black glove, spoke to him at some length. I was not surprised to observe Mr. Kenge inclined to dispute what he said before he had said much, for I knew that no two people ever did agree about anything in Jarndyce and Jarndyce. But he seemed to get the better of Mr. Kenge too, in a conversation that sounded as if it were almost composed of the words, "Receiver-General," "Accountant-General," "Report," "Estate," and "Costs." When they had finished, they came back to Mr. Kenge's table, and spoke aloud.

"Well! But this is a very remarkable document, Mr. Vholes?" said Mr. Kenge.

Mr. Vholes said, "Very much so."

"And a very important document, Mr. Vholes?" said Mr. Kenge.

Again Mr. Vholes said, "Very much so."

"And as you say, Mr. Vholes, when the Cause is in the paper next Term, this document will be an unexpected and interesting feature in it," said Mr. Kenge, looking loftily at my guardian.

Mr. Vholes was gratified, as a smaller practitioner striving to keep respectable, to be confirmed in any opinion of his own by such an authority.

"And when," asked my guardian, rising after a pause, during which Mr. Kenge had rattled his money, and Mr. Vholes had picked his pimples, "when is next Term?"

"Next Term, Mr. Jarndyce, will be next month," said Mr. Kenge. "Of course we shall at once proceed to do what is necessary with this document, and to collect the necessary evidence concerning it; and of course you will receive our usual notification of the Cause being in the paper."

"To which I shall pay, of course, my usual attention."

"Still bent, my dear sir," said Mr. Kenge, showing us through the outer office to the door, "still bent, even with your enlarged mind, on echoing a popular prejudice? We are a prosperous community, Mr. Jarndyce, a very prosperous community. We are a great country, Mr. Jarndyce, we are a very great country. This is a great system, Mr. Jarndyce, and would you wish a great country to have a little system? Now, really, really!"

He said this at the stair-head, gently moving his right hand as if it were a silver trowel, with which to spread the cement of his words on the structure of the system, and consolidate it for a thousand ages.

CHAPTER LXIII

STEEL AND IRON

GEORGE'S shooting-gallery is to let, and the stock is sold off, and George himself is at Chesney Wold, attending on Sir Leicester in his rides, and riding very near his bridle-rein, because of the uncertain hand with which he guides his horse. But not to-day is George so occupied. He is journeying to-day into the iron country farther north, to look about him.

As he comes into the iron country farther north, such fresh green woods as those of Chesney Wold are left behind; and coalpits and ashes, high chimneys and red bricks, blighted verdure, scorching fires, and a heavy never-lightening cloud of smoke, become the features of the scenery. Among such objects rides the trooper, looking about him, and always looking for something he has come to find.

At last, on the black canal bridge of a busy town, with a clang of iron in it, and more fires and more smoke than he has seen yet, the trooper, swart with the dust of the coal roads, checks his horse, and asks a workman does he know the name of Rouncewell thereabouts?

"Why, master," quoth the workman, "do I know my own name?"

"'Tis so well known here, is it, comrade?" asked the trooper.

"Rouncewells? Ah! you're right."

"And where might he be now?" asks the trooper, with a glance before him.

"The bank, the factory, or the house?" the workman wants to know.

"Hum! Rouncewells is so great apparently," mutters the trooper, stroking his chin, "that I have as good as half a mind to go back again. Why, I don't know which I want. Should I find Mr. Rouncewell at the factory, do you think?"

"'Tain't easy to say where you'd find him—at this time of the day you might find either him or his son there, if he's in town; but his contracts take him away."

And which is the factory? Why, he sees those chimneys—the tallest ones! Yes, he sees *them*. Well! let him keep his eye on those chimneys, going on as straight as ever he can, and presently he'll see 'em down a turning on the left, shut in by a great brick wall which forms one side of the street. That's Rouncewells.

The trooper thanks his informant, and rides slowly on, looking about him. He does not turn back, but puts up his horse (and is much disposed to groom him too) at a public-house where some of Rouncewell's hands are dining, as the hostler tells him. Some of Rouncewell's hands have just knocked off for dinner time, and seem to be invading the whole town. They are very sinewy and strong, are Rouncewell's hands—a little sooty too.

He comes to a gateway in the brick wall, looks in, and sees a great perplexity of iron lying about, in every stage, and in a vast variety of shapes; in bars, in wedges, in sheets; in tanks, in boilers, in axles, in wheels, in cogs, in cranks, in rails; twisted and wrenched into eccentric and perverse forms, as separate parts of machinery; mountains of it broken up, and rusty in its age; distant furnaces of it glowing and bubbling in its youth; bright fireworks of it showering about, under the blows of the steam hammer; red-hot iron, white-hot iron, cold-black iron; an iron taste, an iron smell, and a Babel of iron sounds.

"This is a place to make a man's head ache, too!" says the trooper, looking about him for a counting-house. "Who comes here? This is very like me before I was set up. This ought to be my nephew, if likenesses run in families. Your servant, sir."

"Yours, sir. Are you looking for any one?"

"Excuse me. Young Mr. Rouncewell, I believe?"

"Yes."

"I was looking for your father, sir. I wished to have a word with him."

The young man, telling him he is fortunate in his choice of a time, for his father is there, leads the way to the office where he is to be found. "Very like me before I was set up—devilish like me !" thinks the trooper, as he follows. They come to a building in the yard; with an office on an upper floor. At sight of the gentleman in the office, Mr. George turns very red.

"What name shall I say to my father?" asks the young man.

George, full of the idea of iron, in desperation answers "Steel," and is so presented. He is left alone with the gentleman in the office, who sits at a table with account-books before him, and some sheets of paper, blotted with hosts of figures and drawings of cunning shapes. It is a bare office, with bare windows, looking on the iron view below. Tumbled together on the table are some pieces of iron, purposely broken to be tested, at various periods of their service, in various capacities. There is iron-dust on everything; and the smoke is seen, through the windows, rolling heavily out of the tall chimneys, to mingle with the smoke from a vaporous Babylon of other chimneys.

"I am at your service, Mr. Steel," says the gentleman, when his visitor has taken a rusty chair.

"Well, Mr. Rouncewell," George replies, leaning forward, with his left arm on his knee, and his hat in his hand ; and very chary of meeting his brother's eye; "I am not without my expectations, that in the present visit I may prove to be more free than welcome. I have served as a Dragoon in my day ; and a comrade of mine that I was once rather partial to, was, if I don't deceive myself, a brother of yours. I believe you had a brother who gave his family some trouble, and ran away, and never did any good but in keeping away?"

"Are you quite sure," returns the ironmaster, in an altered voice, "that your name is Steel?"

The trooper falters, and looks at him. His brother starts up, calls him by his name, and grasps him by both hands.

"You are too quick for me !" cries the trooper, with the tears springing out of his eyes. "How do you do, my dear old fellow? I never could have thought you would have been half so glad to see me as all this. How do you do, my dear old fellow, how do you do !"

They shake hands and embrace each other, over and over again ; the trooper still coupling his "How do you do, my dear old fellow !" with his protestation that he never thought his brother would have been half so glad to see him as all this !

"So far from it," he declares, at the end of a full account of what has preceded his arrival there, "I had very little idea of making myself known. I thought, if you took by any means forgivingly to my name, I might gradually get myself up to the point of writing a letter. But I should not have been surprised, brother, if you had considered it anything but welcome news to hear of me."

"We will show you at home what kind of news we think it, George," returns his brother. "This is a great day at home, and you could not have arrived, you bronzed old soldier, on a better. I make an agreement with my son Watt to-day, that on this day twelvemonth he shall marry as pretty and as good a girl as you have seen in all your travels. She goes to Germany to-morrow, with one of your nieces, for a little polishing up in her education. We make a feast of the event, and you will be made the hero of it."

Mr. George is so entirely overcome at first by this prospect, that he resists the proposed honour with great earnestness. Being overborne, however, by his brother and his nephew—concerning whom he renews his protestations that he never could have thought they would have been half so glad to see him—he is taken home to an elegant house, in all the arrangements of which there is to be observed a pleasant mixture of the originally simple habits of the father and mother, with such as are suited to their altered station and the higher fortunes of their children. Here, Mr. George is much dismayed by the graces and accomplishments of his nieces that are; and by the beauty of Rosa, his niece that is to be; and by the affectionate salutations of these young ladies, which he receives in a sort of dream. He is sorely taken aback, too, by the dutiful behaviour of his nephew; and has a woeful consciousness upon him of being a scapegrace. However, there is great rejoicing, and a very hearty company, and infinite enjoyment; and Mr. George comes bluff and martial through it all; and his pledge to be present at the marriage and give away the bride, is received with universal favour. A whirling head has Mr. George that night, when he lies down in the state-bed of his brother's house, to think of all these things, and to see the images of his nieces (awful all the evening in their floating muslins), waltzing, after the German manner, over his counterpane.

The brothers are closeted next morning in the ironmaster's room; where the elder is proceeding, in his clear sensible way, to show how he thinks he may best dispose of George in his business, when George squeezes his hand and stops him.

"Brother, I thank you a million times for your more than brotherly welcome, and a million times more to that for your more than brotherly intentions. But my plans are made. Before I say a word as to them, I wish to consult you upon one family point. How," says the trooper, folding his arms, and looking with indomitable firmness at his brother, "how is my mother to be got to scratch me?"

"I am not sure that I understand you, George," replies the ironmaster.

"I say, brother, how is my mother to be got to scratch me? She must be got to do it, somehow."

"Scratch you out of her will, I think you mean?"

"Of course I do. In short," says the trooper, folding his arms more resolutely yet, "I mean—*to*—scratch me!"

"My dear George," returns his brother, "is it so indispensable that you should undergo that process?"

"Quite! Absolutely! I couldn't be guilty of the meanness of coming back without it. I should never be safe not to be off again. I have not sneaked home to rob your children, if not yourself, brother, of your rights. I, who forfeited mine, long ago! If I am to remain, and hold up my head, I must be scratched. Come. You are a man of celebrated penetration and intelligence, and you can tell me how it's to be brought about."

"I can tell you, George," replies the ironmaster deliberately, "how it is not to be brought about, which I hope may answer the purpose as well. Look at our mother, think of her, recall her emotion when she recovered you. Do you believe there is a consideration in the world that would induce her to take such a step against her favourite son? Do you believe there is any chance of her consent, to balance against the outrage it would be to her (loving dear old lady!) to propose it. If you do, you are wrong. No, George! You must make up your mind to remain *un*scratched. I think," there is an amused smile on the ironmaster's face, as he watches his brother, who is pondering, deeply disappointed; "I think you may manage almost as well as if the thing were done, though."

"How, brother?"

"Being bent upon it, you can dispose by will of anything you have the misfortune to inherit, in any way you like, you know."

"That's true!" says the trooper, pondering again. Then he wistfully asks, with his hand on his brother's, "Would you mind mentioning that, brother, to your wife and family?"

"Not at all."

"Thank you. You wouldn't object to say, perhaps, that although an undoubted vagabond, I am a vagabond of the harum-scarum order, and not of the mean sort?"

The ironmaster, repressing his amused smile, assents.

"Thank you. Thank you. It's a weight off my mind," says the trooper, with a heave of his chest as he unfolds his arms, and puts a hand on each leg; "though I had set my heart on being scratched, too!"

The brothers are very like each other, sitting face to face; but a certain massive simplicity, and absence of usage in the ways of the world, is all on the trooper's side.

"Well," he proceeds, throwing off his disappointment, "next and last, those plans of mine. You have been so brotherly as to propose to me to fall in here, and take my place among the products of your perseverance and sense. I thank you heartily. It's more than brotherly, as I said before; and I thank you heartily for it," shaking him a long time by the hand. "But the truth is, brother, I am a—I am a kind of a Weed, and it's too late to plant me in a regular garden."

"My dear George," returns the elder, concentrating his strong steady brow upon him, and smiling confidently; "leave that to me, and let me try."

George shakes his head. "You could do it, I have not a doubt, if anybody could; but it's not to be done. Not to be done, sir! Whereas it so falls out, on the other hand, that I am able to be of some trifle of use to Sir Leicester Dedlock since his illness—brought on by family sorrows;

and that he would rather have that help from our mother's son than from anybody else."

"Well, my dear George," returns the other, with a very slight shade upon his open face, "if you prefer to serve in Sir Leicester Dedlock's household brigade——"

"There it is, brother!" cries the trooper, checking him, with his hand upon his knee again : "there it is! You don't take kindly to that idea ; I don't mind it. You are not used to being officered; I am. Everything about you is in perfect order and discipline ; everything about me requires to be kept so. We are not accustomed to carry things with the same hand, or to look at 'em from the same point. I don't say much about my garrison manners, because I found myself pretty well at my ease last night, and they wouldn't be noticed here, I dare say, once and away. But I shall get on best at Chesney Wold—where there's more room for a Weed than there is here ; and the dear old lady will be made happy besides. Therefore I accept of Sir Leicester Dedlock's proposals. When I come over next year to give away the bride, or whenever I come, I shall have the sense to keep the household brigade in ambuscade, and not to manœuvre it on your ground. I thank you heartily again, and am proud to think of the Rouncewells as they'll be founded by you."

"You know yourself, George," says the elder brother, returning the grip of his hand, "and perhaps you know me better than I know myself. Take your way. So that we don't quite lose one another again, take your way."

"No fear of that!" returns the trooper. "Now, before I turn my horse's head home'ards, brother, I will ask you—if you'll be so good— to look over a letter for me. I brought it with me to send from these parts, as Chesney Wold might be a painful name just now to the person it's written to. I am not much accustomed to correspondence myself, and I am particular respecting this present letter, because I want it to be both straightforward and delicate."

Herewith he hands a letter, closely written in somewhat pale ink but in a neat round hand, to the ironmaster, who reads as follows :

"MISS ESTHER SUMMERSON,—A communication having been made to me by Inspector Bucket of a letter to myself being found among the papers of a certain person, I take the liberty to make known to you that it was but a few lines of instruction from abroad, when where, and how to deliver an enclosed letter to a young and beautiful lady, then unmarried in England. I duly observed the same.

"I further take the liberty to make known to you, that it was got from me as a proof of handwriting only, and that otherwise I would not have given it up as appearing to be the most harmless in my possession, without being previously shot through the heart.

"I further take the liberty to mention, that if I could have supposed a certain unfortunate gentleman to have been in existence, I never could and never would have rested until I had discovered his retreat, and shared my last farthing with him, as my duty and my inclination would have equally been. But he was (officially) reported drowned, and assuredly went over the side of a transport-ship at night in an Irish harbour, within a few hours of her arrival from the West Indies, as I have myself heard both from officers and men on board, and know to have been (officially) confirmed.

"I further take the liberty to state that in my humble quality as one of the rank and file, I am, and shall ever continue to be, your thoroughly devoted and admiring servant, and that I esteem the qualities you possess above all others, far beyond the limits of the present despatch. I have the honour to be,   GEORGE."

"A little formal," observes the elder brother, refolding it with a puzzled face.

"But nothing that might not be sent to a pattern young lady?" asks the younger.

"Nothing at all."

Therefore it is sealed, and deposited for posting among the iron correspondence of the day. This done, Mr. George takes a hearty farewell of the family party, and prepares to saddle and mount. His brother, however, unwilling to part with him so soon, proposes to ride with him in a light, open carriage to the place where he will bait for the night, and there remain with him until morning: a servant riding, for so much of the journey, on the thorough-bred old grey from Chesney Wold. The offer being gladly accepted, is followed by a pleasant ride, a pleasant dinner, and a pleasant breakfast, all in brotherly communion. Then they once more shake hands long and heartily, and part; the ironmaster turning his face to the smoke and fires, and the trooper to the green country. Early in the afternoon, the subdued sound of his heavy military trot is heard on the turf in the avenue, as he rides on with imaginary clank and jingle of accoutrements under the old elm trees.

CHAPTER LXIV

ESTHER'S NARRATIVE

SOON after I had had that conversation with my guardian, he put a sealed paper in my hand one morning, and said, "This is for next month, my dear." I found in it two hundred pounds.

I now began very quietly to make such preparations as I thought were necessary. Regulating my purchases by my guardian's taste, which I knew very well of course, I arranged my wardrobe to please him, and hoped I should be highly successful. I did it all so quietly, because I was not quite free from my old apprehension that Ada would be rather sorry, and because my guardian was so quiet himself. I had no doubt that under all the circumstances we should be married in the most private and simple manner. Perhaps I should only have to say to Ada, " Would you like to come and see me married to-morrow, my pet?" Perhaps our wedding might even be as unpretending as her own, and I might not find it necessary to say anything about it until it was over. I thought that if I were to choose, I would like this best.

The only exception I made was Mrs. Woodcourt. I told her that I was going to be married to my guardian, and that we had been engaged some time. She highly approved. She could never do enough for me; and was remarkably softened now, in comparison with what she had been when we first knew her. There was no trouble she would not have taken to have been of use to me; but I need hardly say that I only allowed her to take as little as gratified her kindness without tasking it.

Of course this was not a time to neglect my guardian; and, of course, it was not a time for neglecting my darling. So I had plenty of occupation—which I was glad of; and as to Charley, she was absolutely not to be seen for needlework. To surround herself with great heaps of it —baskets full and tables full—and do a little, and spend a great deal of time in staring with her round eyes at what there was to do, and persuade herself that she was going to do it, were Charley's great dignities and delights.

Meanwhile, I must say, I could not agree with my guardian on the subject of the Will, and I had some sanguine hopes of Jarndyce and Jarndyce. Which of us was right will soon appear, but I certainly did encourage expectations. In Richard, the discovery gave occasion for a burst of business and agitation that buoyed him up for a little time; but he had lost the elasticity even of hope now, and seemed to me to retain only its feverish anxieties. From something my guardian said one day, when we were talking about this, I understood that my marriage would not take place until after the Term-time we had been told to look forward to; and I thought the more, for that, how rejoiced I should be if I could be married when Richard and Ada were a little more prosperous.

The Term was very near indeed, when my guardian was called out of town, and went down into Yorkshire on Mr. Woodcourt's business. He had told me beforehand that his presence there would be necessary. I had just come in one night from my dear girl's, and was sitting in the midst of all my new clothes, looking at them all around me, and thinking, when a letter from my guardian was brought to me. It asked me to join him in the country; and mentioned by what stage-coach my place was taken, and at what time in the morning I should have to leave town. It added in a postscript that I would not be many hours away from Ada.

I expected few things less than a journey at that time, but I was ready for it in half-an-hour, and set off as appointed early next morning. I travelled all day, wondering all day what I could be wanted for at such a distance; now I thought it might be for this purpose, and now I thought it might be for that purpose; but I was never, never, never near the truth.

It was night when I came to my journey's end, and found my guardian waiting for me. This was a great relief, for towards evening I had begun to fear (the more so as his letter was a very short one) that he might be ill. However, there he was, as well as it was possible to be; and when I saw his genial face again at its brightest and best, I said to myself he has been doing some other great kindness. Not that it required much penetration to say that, because I knew that his being there at all was an act of kindness.

Supper was ready at the hotel, and when we were alone at table he said:

"Full of curiosity, no doubt, little woman, to know why I have brought you here?"

"Well, guardian," said I, "without thinking myself a Fatima, or you a Blue Beard, I am a little curious about it."

"Then to ensure your night's rest, my love," he returned gaily, "I won't wait until to-morrow to tell you. I have very much wished to express to Woodcourt, somehow, my sense of his humanity to poor unfortunate Jo, his inestimable services to my young cousins, and his value to us all. When it was decided that he should settle here, it came into my head that I might ask his acceptance of some unpretending and suitable little place, to lay his own head in. I, therefore, caused such a place to be looked out for, and such a place was found on very easy terms, and I have been touching it up for him and making it habitable. However, when I walked over it the day before yesterday, and it was reported ready, I found that I was not housekeeper enough to know whether things were all as they ought to be. So I sent off for the best little housekeeper that could possibly be got, to come and give me her advice and opinion. And here she is," said my guardian, "laughing and crying both together!"

Because he was so dear, so good, so admirable. I tried to tell him what I thought of him, but I could not articulate a word.

"Tut, tut!" said my guardian. "You make too much of it, little woman. Why how you sob, Dame Durden, how you sob!"

"It is with exquisite pleasure, Guardian—with a heart full of thanks."

"Well, well," said he, "I am delighted that you approve. I thought you would. I meant it as a pleasant surprise for the little mistress of Bleak House."

I kissed him, and dried my eyes. "I know now!" said I. "I have seen this in your face a long while."

"No; have you really, my dear?" said he. "What a Dame Durden it is to read a face!"

He was so quaintly cheerful that I could not long be otherwise, and was almost ashamed of having been otherwise at all. When I went to bed, I cried. I am bound to confess that I cried; but I hope it was with pleasure, though I am not quite sure it was with pleasure. I repeated every word of the letter twice over.

A most beautiful summer morning succeeded; and after breakfast we went out, arm-in-arm, to see the house of which I was to give my mighty housekeeping opinion. We entered a flower-garden by a gate in a side wall, of which he had the key; and the first thing I saw, was, that the beds and flowers were all laid out according to the manner of my beds and flowers at home.

"You see, my dear," observed my guardian, standing still, with a delighted face, to watch my looks; "knowing there could be no better plan, I borrowed yours."

We went on by a pretty little orchard, where the cherries were nestling among the green leaves, and the shadows of the apple-trees were sporting on the grass, to the house itself—a cottage, quite a rustic cottage of doll's rooms; but such a lovely place, so tranquil and so beautiful, with such a rich and smiling country spread around it; with water sparkling away into the distance, here all overhung with summer-growth, there turning a humming-mill; at its nearest point glancing through a meadow by the cheerful town, where cricket-players were assembling in bright groups, and a flag was flying from a white tent that rippled in the sweet west wind. And still, as we went through the pretty rooms, out at the little rustic verandah doors, and underneath the tiny wooden colonnades, garlanded with woodbine, jasmine, and honeysuckle, I saw, in the papering on the walls, in the colours of the furniture, in the arrangement of all the pretty objects, *my* little tastes and fancies, *my* little methods and inventions, which they used to laugh at while they praised them, my odd ways everywhere.

I could not say enough in admiration of what was all so beautiful, but one secret doubt arose in my mind, when I saw this. I thought, oh would he be the happier for it! Would it not have been better for his peace that I should not have been so brought before him? Because, although I was not what he thought me, still he loved me very dearly, and it might remind him mournfully of what he believed he had lost. I did not wish him to forget me—perhaps he might not have done so, without these aids to his memory—but my way was easier than his, and I could have reconciled myself even to that, so that he had been the happier for it.

"And now, little woman," said my guardian, whom I had never seen so proud and joyful as in showing me these things, and watching my appreciation of them, "now, last of all, for the name of this house."

"What is it called, dear Guardian?"

"My child," said he, "come and see."

He took me to the porch; which he had hitherto avoided, and said, pausing before we went out:

"My dear child, don't you guess the name?"

"No!" said I.

We went out of the porch; and he showed me written over it, BLEAK HOUSE.

He led me to a seat among the leaves close by, and sitting down beside me, and taking my hand in his, spoke to me thus:

"My darling girl, in what there has been between us, I have, I hope, been really solicitous for your happiness. When I wrote you the letter to which you brought the answer," smiling as he referred to it, "I had my own too much in view ; but I had yours too. Whether, under different circumstances, I might ever have renewed the old dream I sometimes dreamed when you were very young, of making you my wife one day, I need not ask myself. I did renew it, and I wrote my letter, and you brought your answer. You are following what I say, my child ?"

I was cold, and I trembled violently ; but not a word he uttered was lost. As I sat looking fixedly at him, and the sun's rays descended, softly shining through the leaves, upon his bare head, I felt as if the brightness on him must be like the brightness of the Angels.

"Hear me, my love, but do not speak. It is for me to speak now. When it was that I began to doubt whether what I had done would really make you happy, is no matter. Woodcourt came home, and I soon had no doubt at all."

I clasped him round the neck, and hung my head upon his breast, and wept. "Lie lightly, confidently, here, my child," said he, pressing me gently to him. "I am your guardian and your father now. Rest confidently here."

Soothingly, like the gentle rustling of the leaves ; and genially, like the ripening weather ; and radiantly and beneficently, like the sunshine ; he went on.

"Understand me, my dear girl. I had no doubt of your being contented and happy with me, being so dutiful and so devoted ; but I saw with whom you would be happier. That I penetrated his secret when Dame Durden was blind to it, is no wonder ; for I knew the good that could never change in her, better far than she did. Well ! I have long been in Allan Woodcourt's confidence, although he was not, until yesterday, a few hours before you came here, in mine. But I would not have my Esther's bright example lost ; I would not have a jot of my dear girl's virtues unobserved and unhonoured ; I would not have her admitted on sufferance into the line of Morgan ap-Kerrig, no not for the weight in gold of all the mountains in Wales !"

He stopped to kiss me on the forehead, and I sobbed and wept afresh. For I felt as if I could not bear the painful delight of his praise.

"Hush, little woman ! Don't cry ; this is to be a day of joy. I have looked forward to it," he said exultingly, "for months on months ! A few words more, Dame Trot, and I have said my say. Determined not to throw away one atom of my Esther's worth, I took Mrs. Woodcourt into a separate confidence. 'Now, madam,' said I, 'I clearly perceive—and indeed, I know, to boot—that your son loves my ward. I am further very sure that my ward loves your son, but will sacrifice her love to a sense of duty and affection, and will sacrifice it so completely, so entirely, so religiously, that you should never suspect it, though you watched her night and day.' Then I told her all our story—ours—yours and mine. 'Now, madam,' said I, 'come you, knowing this, and live with us. Come you, and see my child from hour to hour ; set what you see, against her pedigree, which is this, and this'—for I scorned to mince it—'and tell me what is the true legitimacy, when you shall have quite made up your mind on that subject.' Why, honour to her old Welsh blood, my dear!" cried my guardian, with enthusiasm, "I believe the heart it animates beats no less warmly, no less admiringly, no less lovingly, towards Dame Durden, than my own!"

He tenderly raised my head, and as I clung to him, kissed me in his old fatherly way again and again. What a light, now, on the protecting manner I had thought about!

"One more last word. When Allan Woodcourt spoke to you, my dear, he spoke with my knowledge and consent—but I gave him no encouragement, not I, for these surprises were my great reward, and I was too miserly to part with a scrap of it. He was to come, and tell me all that passed; and he did. I have no more to say. My dearest, Allan Woodcourt stood beside your father when he lay dead—stood beside your mother. This is Bleak House. This day I give this house its little mistress; and before God, it is the brightest day in all my life!"

He rose, and raised me with him. We were no longer alone. My husband—I have called him by that name full seven happy years now —stood at my side.

"Allan," said my guardian, "take from me a willing gift, the best wife that ever a man had. What more can I say for you, than that I know you deserve her? Take with her the little home she brings you. You know what she will make it, Allan; you know what she has made its namesake. Let me share its felicity sometimes, and what do I sacrifice? Nothing, nothing."

He kissed me once again; and now the tears were in his eyes, as he said more softly:

"Esther, my dearest, after so many years, there is a kind of parting in this too. I know that my mistake has caused you some distress. Forgive your old guardian in restoring him to his old place in your affections; and blot it out of your memory. Allan, take my dear."

He moved away from under the green roof of leaves, and stopping in the sunlight outside, and turning cheerfully towards us, said:

"I shall be found about here somewhere. It's a West wind, little woman, due West! Let no one thank me any more; for I'm going to revert to my bachelor habits, and if anybody disregards this warning, I'll run away, and never come back!"

What happiness was ours that day, what joy, what rest, what hope, what gratitude, what bliss! We were to be married before the month was out; but when we were to come and take possession of our own house, was to depend on Richard and Ada.

We all three went home together next day. As soon as we arrived in town, Allan went straight to see Richard, and to carry our joyful news to him and my darling. Late as it was, I meant to go to her for a few minutes before lying down to sleep; but I went home with my guardian first, to make his tea for him, and to occupy the old chair by his side ; for I did not like to think of its being empty so soon.

When we came home, we found that a young man had called three times in the course of that one day, to see me ; and that, having been told, on the occasion of his third call, that I was not expected to return before ten o'clock at night, he had left word, "that he would call about then." He had left his card three times, MR. GUPPY.

As I naturally speculated on the object of these visits, and as I always associated something ludicrous with the visitor, it fell out that in laughing about Mr. Guppy I told my guardian of his old proposal, and his subsequent retractation. "After that," said my guardian, "we will certainly receive this hero." So, instructions were given that Mr. Guppy should be shown in, when he came again ; and they were scarcely given when he did come again.

He was embarrassed when he found my guardian with me, but recovered himself, and said, "How de do, sir ? "

"How do you do, sir ? " returned my guardian.

"Thank you, sir, I am tolerable," returned Mr. Guppy. "Will you allow me to introduce my mother, Mrs. Guppy of the Old Street Road, and my particular friend, Mr. Weevle. That is to say, my friend has gone by the name of Weevle, but his name is really and truly Jobling."

My guardian begged them to be seated, and they all sat down.

"Tony," said Mr. Guppy to his friend, after an awkward silence. "Will you open the case ? "

"Do it yourself," returned the friend, rather tartly.

"Well, Mr. Jarndyce, sir," Mr. Guppy, after a moment's consideration, began ; to the great diversion of his mother, which she displayed by nudging Mr. Jobling with her elbow, and winking at me in a most remarkable manner ; "I had an idea that I should see Miss Summerson by herself, and was not quite prepared for your esteemed presence. But Miss Summerson has mentioned to you, perhaps, that something has passed between us on former occasions ? "

"Miss Summerson," returned my guardian, smiling, "has made a communication to that effect to me."

"That," said Mr. Guppy, "makes matters easier. Sir, I have come out of my articles at Kenge and Carboy's, and I believe with satisfaction to all parties. I am now admitted (after undergoing an examination that's enough to badger a man blue, touching a pack of nonsense that he don't want to know) on the roll of attorneys, and have taken out my certificate, if it would be any satisfaction to you to see it."

"Thank you, Mr. Guppy," returned my guardian. "I am quite willing —I believe I use a legal phrase—to admit the certificate."

Mr. Guppy therefore desisted from taking something out of his pocket, and proceeded without it.

"I have no capital myself, but my mother has a little property which takes the form of an annuity ; " here Mr. Guppy's mother rolled her head as if she never could sufficiently enjoy the observation, and put her

2 T

handkerchief to her mouth, and again winked at me; "and a few pounds for expenses out of pocket in conducting business, will never be wanting, free of interest, which is an advantage, you know," said Mr. Guppy, feelingly.

"Certainly an advantage," returned my guardian.

"I *have* some connection," pursued Mr. Guppy, "and it lays in the direction of Walcot Square, Lambeth. I have therefore taken a ouse in that locality, which, in the opinion of my friends, is a hollow bargain (taxes ridiculous, and use of fixtures included in the rent), and intend setting up professionally for myself there, forthwith."

Here Mr. Guppy's mother fell into an extraordinary passion of rolling her head, and smiling waggishly at anybody who would look at her.

"It's a six-roomer, exclusive of kitchens," said Mr. Guppy, "and in the opinion of my friends, a commodious tenement. When I mention my friends, I refer principally to my friend Jobling, who, I believe, has known me," Mr. Guppy looked at him with a sentimental air, "from boyhood's hour?"

Mr. Jobling confirmed this with a sliding movement of his legs.

"My friend Jobling will render me his assistance in the capacity of clerk, and will live in the ouse," said Mr. Guppy. "My mother will likewise live in the ouse, when her present quarter in the Old Street Road shall have ceased and expired; and consequently there will be no want of society. My friend Jobling is naturally aristocratic by taste; and besides being acquainted with the movements of the upper circles, fully backs me in the intentions I am now developing."

Mr. Jobling said "certainly," and withdrew a little from the elbow of Mr. Guppy's mother.

"Now, I have no occasion to mention to you, sir, you being in the confidence of Miss Summerson," said Mr. Guppy, "(mother, I wish you'd be so good as to keep still), that Miss Summerson's image was formerly imprinted on my art, and that I made her a proposal of marriage."

"That I have heard," returned my guardian.

"Circumstances," pursued Mr. Guppy, "over which I had no control, but quite the contrary, weakened the impression of that image for a time. At which time Miss Summerson's conduct was highly genteel; I may even add, magnanimous."

My guardian patted me on the shoulder, and seemed much amused.

"Now, sir," said Mr. Guppy, "I have got into that state of mind myself, that I wish for a reciprocity of magnanimous behaviour. I wish to prove to Miss Summerson that I can rise to a heighth, of which perhaps she hardly thought me capable. I find that the image which I did suppose had been eradicated from my art, is *not* eradicated. Its influence over me is still tremenjous; and yielding to it I am willing to overlook the circumstances over which none of us have had any control, and to renew those proposals to Miss Summerson which I had the honour to make at a former period. I beg to lay the ouse in Walcot Square, the business, and myself, before Miss Summerson for her acceptance."

MAGNANIMOUS CONDUCT OF MR. GUPPY.

"Very magnanimous, indeed, sir," observed my guardian.

"Well, sir," replied Mr. Guppy, with candour, "my wish is to *be* magnanimous. I do not consider that in making this offer to Miss Summerson, I am by any means throwing myself away; neither is that the opinion of my friends. Still, there are circumstances which I submit may be taken into account as a set-off against any little drawbacks of mine, and so a fair and equitable balance arrived at."

"I take upon myself, sir," said my guardian, laughing as he rang the bell, "to reply to your proposals on behalf of Miss Summerson. She is very sensible of your handsome intentions, and wishes you good evening, and wishes you well."

"Oh!" said Mr. Guppy, with a blank look. "Is that tantamount, sir, to acceptance, or rejection, or consideration?"

"To decided rejection, if you please!" returned my guardian.

Mr. Guppy looked incredulously at his friend, and at his mother who suddenly turned very angry, and at the floor, and at the ceiling.

"Indeed?" said he. "Then, Jobling, if you was the friend you represent yourself, I should think you might hand my mother out of the gangway, instead of allowing her to remain where she ain't wanted."

But Mrs. Guppy positively refused to come out of the gangway. She wouldn't hear of it. "Why, get along with you," said she to my guardian, "what do you mean? Ain't my son good enough for you? You ought to be ashamed of yourself. Get out with you!"

"My good lady!" returned my guardian, "it is hardly reasonable to ask me to get out of my own room."

"I don't care for that," said Mrs. Guppy. "Get out with you. If we ain't good enough for you, go and procure somebody that is good enough. Go along and find 'em."

I was quite unprepared for the rapid manner in which Mrs. Guppy's power of jocularity merged into a power of taking the profoundest offence.

"Go along and find somebody that's good enough for you," repeated Mrs. Guppy. "Get out!" Nothing seemed to astonish Mr. Guppy's mother so much, and to make her so very indignant, as our not getting out. "Why don't you get out?" said Mrs. Guppy. "What are you stopping here for?"

"Mother," interposed her son, always getting before her, and pushing her back with one shoulder, as she sidled at my guardian, "*will* you hold your tongue?"

"No, William," she returned; "I won't! Not unless he gets out, I won't!"

However, Mr. Guppy and Mr. Jobling together closed on Mr. Guppy's mother (who began to be quite abusive), and took her, very much against her will, downstairs; her voice rising a stair higher every time her figure got a stair lower, and insisting that we should immediately go and find somebody who was good enough for us, and above all things that we should get out.

CHAPTER LXV

BEGINNING THE WORLD

THE term had commenced, and my guardian found an intimation from Mr. Kenge that the Cause would come on in two days. As I had sufficient hopes of the Will to be in a flutter about it, Allan and I agreed to go down to the court that morning. Richard was extremely agitated, and was so weak and low, though his illness was still of the mind, that my dear girl indeed had sore occasion to be supported. But she looked forward—a very little way ncw—to the help that was to come to her, and never drooped.

It was at Westminster that the Cause was to come on. It had come on there, I dare say, a hundred times before, but I could not divest myself of an idea that it *might* lead to some result now. We left home directly after breakfast, to be at Westminster Hall in good time; and walked down there through the lively streets—so happily and strangely it seemed!—together.

As we were going along, planning what we should do for Richard and Ada, I heard somebody calling "Esther! My dear Esther! Esther!" And there was Caddy Jellyby, with her head out of the window of a little carriage which she hired now to go about in to her pupils (she had so many), as if she wanted to embrace me at a hundred yards' distance. I had written her a note to tell her of all that my guardian had done, but had not had a moment to go and see her. Of course we turned back; and the affectionate girl was in that state of rapture, and was so overjoyed to talk about the night when she brought me the flowers, and was so determined to squeeze my face (bonnet and all) between her hands, and go on in a wild manner altogether, calling me all kinds of precious names, and telling Allan I had done I don't know what for her, that I was just obliged to get into the little carriage and calm her down, by letting her say and do exactly what she liked. Allan, standing at the window, was as pleased as Caddy; and I was as pleased as either of them; and I wonder that I got away as I did, rather than that I came off, laughing, and red, and anything but tidy, and looking after Caddy, who looked after us out of the coach-window as long as she could see us.

This made us some quarter of an hour late, and when we came to Westminster Hall we found that the day's business was begun. Worse than that, we found such an unusual crowd in the Court of Chancery that it was full to the door, and we could neither see nor hear what was passing within. It appeared to be something droll, for occasionally there was a laugh, and a cry of "Silence!" It appeared to be something interesting, for every one was pushing and striving to get nearer. It appeared to be something that made the professional gentlemen very merry, for there were several young counsellors in wigs and whiskers on the outside of the crowd, and when one of them told the others about it, they put their hands in their pockets, and quite doubled themselves up with laughter, and went stamping about the pavement of the Hall.

We asked a gentleman by us, if he knew what cause was on? He told us Jarndyce and Jarndyce. We asked him if he knew what was doing in it? He said, really no he did not, nobody ever did; but as well as he could make out, it was over. Over for the day? we asked him. No, he said; over for good.

Over for good!

When we heard this unaccountable answer, we looked at one another, quite lost in amazement. Could it be possible that the Will had set things right at last, and that Richard and Ada were going to be rich? It seemed too good to be true. Alas it was!

Our suspense was short; for a break up soon took place in the crowd, and the people came streaming out looking flushed and hot, and bringing a quantity of bad air with them. Still they were all exceedingly amused, and were more like people coming out from a Farce or a Juggler than from a court of Justice. We stood aside, watching for any countenance we knew; and presently great bundles of paper began to be carried out—bundles in bags, bundles too large to be got into any bags, immense masses of papers of all shapes and no shapes, which the bearers staggered under, and threw down for the time being, anyhow, on the Hall pavement, while they went back to bring out more. Even these clerks were laughing. We glanced at these papers, and seeing Jarndyce and Jarndyce everywhere, asked an official-looking person who was standing in the midst of them, whether the cause was over. "Yes," he said; "it was all up with it at last!" and burst out laughing too.

At this juncture, we perceived Mr. Kenge coming out of court with an affable dignity upon him, listening to Mr. Vholes, who was deferential, and carried his own bag. Mr. Vholes was the first to see us. "Here is Miss Summerson, sir," he said. "And Mr. Woodcourt."

"Oh indeed! Yes. Truly!" said Mr. Kenge, raising his hat to me with polished politeness. "How do you do? Glad to see you. Mr. Jarndyce is not here?"

No. He never came there, I reminded him.

"Really," returned Mr. Kenge, "it is as well that he is *not* here to-day, for his—shall I say, in my good friend's absence, his indomitable singularity of opinion?—might have been strengthened, perhaps; not reasonably, but might have been strengthened."

"Pray what has been done to-day?" asked Allan.

"I beg your pardon?" said Mr. Kenge, with excessive urbanity.

"What has been done to-day?"

"What has been done," repeated Mr. Kenge. "Quite so. Yes. Why, not much has been done; not much. We have been checked—brought up suddenly, I would say—upon the—shall I term it threshold?"

"Is this Will considered a genuine document, sir?" said Allan; "will you tell us that?"

"Most certainly, if I could," said Mr. Kenge; "but we have not gone into that, we have not gone into that."

"We have not gone into that," repeated Mr. Vholes, as if his low inward voice were an echo.

"You are to reflect, Mr. Woodcourt," observed Mr. Kenge, using his silver trowel, persuasively and smoothingly, "that this has been a great cause, that this has been a protracted cause, that this has been a complex cause. Jarndyce and Jarndyce has been termed, not inaptly, a Monument of Chancery practice."

"And Patience has sat upon it a long time," said Allan.

"Very well indeed, sir," returned Mr. Kenge, with a certain condescending laugh he had. "Very well! You are further to reflect, Mr. Woodcourt," becoming dignified almost to severity, "that on the numerous difficulties, contingencies, masterly fictions, and forms of procedure in this great cause, there has been expended study, ability, eloquence, knowledge, intellect, Mr. Woodcourt, high intellect. For many years, the—a—I would say the flower of the Bar, and the—a— I would presume to add, the matured autumnal fruits of the Woolsack— have been lavished upon Jarndyce and Jarndyce. If the public have the benefit, and if the country have the adornment, of this great Grasp, it must be paid for in money or money's worth, sir."

"Mr. Kenge," said Allan, appearing enlightened all in a moment. "Excuse me, our time presses. Do I understand that the whole estate is found to have been absorbed in costs?"

"Hem! I believe so," returned Mr. Kenge. "Mr. Vholes, what do you say?"

"I believe so," said Mr. Vholes.

"And that thus the suit lapses and melts away?"

"Probably," returned Mr. Kenge. "Mr. Vholes?"

"Probably," said Mr. Vholes.

"My dearest life," whispered Allan, "this will break Richard's heart!"

There was such a shock of apprehension in his face, and he knew Richard so perfectly, and I too had seen so much of his gradual decay, that what my dear girl had said to me in the fulness of her foreboding love, sounded like a knell in my ears.

"In case you should be wanting Mr. C., sir," said Mr. Vholes, coming after us, "you'll find him in court. I left him there resting himself a little. Good day, sir; good day, Miss Summerson." As he gave me that slowly devouring look of his, while twisting up the strings of his bag, before he hastened with it after Mr. Kenge, the benignant shadow of whose conversational presence he seemed afraid to leave, he gave one gasp as if he had swallowed the last morsel of his client, and his black buttoned-up unwholesome figure glided away to the low door at the end of the Hall.

"My dear love," said Allan, "leave to me, for a little while, the charge you gave me. Go home with this intelligence, and come to Ada's by-and-by ! "

I would not let him take me to a coach, but entreated him to go to Richard without a moment's delay, and leave me to do as he wished. Hurrying home, I found my guardian, and told him gradually with what news I had returned. "Little woman," said he, quite unmoved for himself, "to have done with the suit on any terms is a greater blessing than I had looked for. But my poor young cousins ! "

We talked about them all the morning, and discussed what it was possible to do. In the afternoon, my guardian walked with me to Symond's Inn, and left me at the door. I went upstairs. When my darling heard my footsteps, she came out into the small passage and threw her arms round my neck ; but she composed herself directly, and said that Richard had asked for me several times. Allan had found him sitting in a corner of the court, she told me, like a stone figure. On being roused, he had broken away, and made as if he would have spoken in a fierce voice to the Judge. He was stopped by his mouth being full of blood, and Allan had brought him home.

He was lying on the sofa with his eyes closed, when I went in. There were restoratives on the table ; the room was made as airy as possible, and was darkened, and was very orderly and quiet. Allan stood behind him, watching him gravely. His face appeared to me to be quite destitute of colour, and, now that I saw him without his seeing me, I fully saw, for the first time, how worn away he was. But he looked handsomer than I had seen him look for many a day.

I sat down by his side in silence. Opening his eyes by-and-by, he said, in a weak voice, but with his old smile, "Dame Durden, kiss me, my dear ! "

It was a great comfort and surprise to me, to find him in his low state cheerful and looking forward. He was happier, he said, in our intended marriage, than he could find words to tell me. My husband had been a guardian angel to him and Ada, and he blessed us both, and wished us all the joy that life could yield us. I almost felt as if my own heart would have broken, when I saw him take my husband's hand, and hold it to his breast.

We spoke of the future as much as possible, and he said several times that he must be present at our marriage if he could stand upon his feet. Ada would contrive to take him, somehow, he said. "Yes, surely, dearest Richard ! " But as my darling answered him thus hopefully, so serene and beautiful, with the help that was to come to her so near,—I knew—I knew !

It was not good for him to talk too much ; and when he was silent, we were silent too. Sitting beside him, I made a pretence of working for my dear, as he had always been used to joke about my being busy. Ada leaned upon his pillow, holding his head upon her arm. He dozed often; and whenever he awoke without seeing him, said, first of all, "Where is Woodcourt ? "

Evening had come on, when I lifted up my eyes, and saw my guardian standing in the little hall. " Who is that, Dame Durden ? " Richard asked me. The door was behind him, but he had observed in my face that some one was there.

I looked to Allan for advice, and as he nodded " Yes," bent over Richard and told him. My guardian saw what passed, came softly by me in a moment, and laid his hand on Richard's. " Oh sir," said Richard, " you are a good man, you are a good man ! " and burst into tears for the first time.

My guardian, the picture of a good man, sat down in my place, keeping his hand on Richard's.

" My dear Rick," said he, " the clouds have cleared away, and it is bright now. We can see now. We were all bewildered, Rick, more or less. What matters ! And how are you, my dear boy ? "

" I am very weak, sir, but I hope I shall be stronger. I have to begin the world."

" Ay, truly ; well said ! " cried my guardian.

" I will not begin it in the old way now," said Richard, with a sad smile. " I have learned a lesson now, sir. It was a hard one ; but you shall be assured, indeed, that I have learned it."

" Well, well," said my guardian, comforting him ; " well, well, well, dear boy ! "

" I was thinking, sir," resumed Richard, " that there is nothing on earth I should so much like to see as their house—Dame Durden's and Woodcourt's house. If I could be moved there when I begin to recover my strength, I feel as if I should get well there, sooner than anywhere."

" Why, so have I been thinking, too, Rick," said my guardian, " and our little woman likewise ; she and I have been talking of it, this very day. I dare say her husband won't object. What do you think ? "

Richard smiled ; and lifted up his arm to touch him, as he stood behind the head of his couch.

" I say nothing of Ada," said Richard, " but I think of her, and have thought of her very much. Look at her ! see her here, sir, bending over this pillow when she has so much need to rest upon it herself, my dear love, my poor girl ! "

He clasped her in his arms, and none of us spoke. He gradually released her ; and she looked upon us, and looked up to Heaven, and moved her lips.

" When I get down to Bleak House," said Richard, " I shall have much to tell you, sir, and you will have much to show me. You will go, won't you ? "

" Undoubtedly, dear Rick."

" Thank you ; like you, like you," said Richard. " But it's all like you. They have been telling me how you planned it, and how you remembered all Esther's familiar tastes and ways. It will be like coming to the old Bleak House again."

" And you will come there too, I hope, Rick. I am a solitary man now, you know, and it will be a charity to come to me. A charity to come to me, my love!" he repeated to Ada, as he gently passed his hand over her golden hair, and put a lock of it to his lips. (I think he vowed within himself to cherish her if she were left alone.)

"It was all a troubled dream?" said Richard, clasping both my guardian's hands eagerly.

"Nothing more, Rick; nothing more."

"And you, being a good man, can pass it as such, and forgive and pity the dreamer, and be lenient and encouraging when he wakes?"

"Indeed I can. What am I but another dreamer, Rick?"

"I will begin the world!" said Richard, with a light in his eyes.

My husband drew a little nearer towards Ada, and I saw him solemnly lift up his hand to warn my guardian.

"When shall I go from this place, to that pleasant country where the old times are, where I shall have strength to tell what Ada has been to me, where I shall be able to recall my many faults and blindnesses, where I shall prepare myself to be a guide to my unborn child?" said Richard. "When shall I go?"

"Dear Rick, when you are strong enough," returned my guardian.

"Ada, my darling!"

He sought to raise himself a little. Allan raised him so that she could hold him on her bosom; which was what he wanted.

"I have done you many wrongs, my own. I have fallen like a poor stray shadow on your way, I have married you to poverty and trouble, I have scattered your means to the winds. You will forgive me all this, my Ada, before I begin the world?"

A smile irradiated his face, as she bent to kiss him. He slowly laid his face down upon her bosom, drew his arms closer round her neck, and with one parting sob began the world. Not this world, oh not this! The world that sets this right.

When all was still, at a late hour, poor crazed Miss Flite came weeping to me, and told me that she had given her birds their liberty.

CHAPTER LXVI

DOWN IN LINCOLNSHIRE

THERE is a hush upon Chesney Wold in these altered days, as there is upon a portion of the family history. The story goes, that Sir Leicester paid some who could have spoken out, to hold their peace; but it is a lame story, feebly whispering and creeping about, and any brighter spark of life it shows soon dies away. It is known for certain that the handsome Lady Dedlock lies in the mausoleum in the park, where the trees arch darkly overhead, and the owl is heard at night making the woods ring; but whence she was brought home, to be laid among the echoes of that solitary place, or how she died, is all mystery. Some of her old friends, principally to be found among the peachy-cheeked charmers with the skeleton throats, did once occasionally say, as they toyed in a ghastly manner with large fans—like charmers reduced to flirting with grim Death, after losing all their other beaux—did once occasionally say, when the World assembled together, that they wondered the ashes of the Dedlocks, entombed in the mausoleum, never rose against the profanation of her company. But the dead-and-gone Dedlocks take it very calmly, and have never been known to object.

Up from among the fern in the hollow, and winding by the bridle-road among the trees, comes sometimes to this lonely spot the sound of horses' hoofs. Then may be seen Sir Leicester—invalided, bent, and almost blind, but of worthy presence yet—riding with a stalwart man beside him, constant to his bridle-rein. When they come to a certain spot before the mausoleum-door, Sir Leicester's accustomed horse stops of his own accord, and Sir Leicester, pulling off his hat, is still for a few moments before they ride away.

War rages yet with the audacious Boythorn, though at uncertain intervals, and now hotly, and now coolly; flickering like an unsteady fire. The truth is said to be, that when Sir Leicester came down to Lincolnshire for good, Mr. Boythorn showed a manifest desire to abandon his right of way, and do whatever Sir Leicester would: which Sir Leicester, conceiving to be a condescension to his illness or misfortune, took in such high dudgeon, and was so magnificently aggrieved by, that Mr. Boythorn found himself under the necessity of committing a flagrant trespass to restore his neighbour to himself. Similarly Mr. Boythorn continues to post tremendous placards on the disputed thoroughfare, and (with his bird upon his head) to hold forth vehemently against Sir Leicester in the sanctuary of his own home; similarly, also, he defies him as of old in the little church, by testifying a bland unconsciousness of his existence. But it is whispered that when he is most ferocious towards his old foe, he is really most considerate; and that Sir Leicester, in the dignity of being implacable, little supposes how much he is humoured. As little does he think how near together he and his antagonist have suffered, in the fortunes of two sisters; and his antagonist, who knows it now, is not the man to tell him. So the quarrel goes on to the satisfaction of both.

In one of the lodges of the park; that lodge within sight of the house where, once upon a time, when the waters were out down in Lincolnshire, my Lady used to see the Keeper's child; the stalwart man, the trooper formerly, is housed. Some relics of his old calling hang upon the walls, and these it is the chosen recreation of a little lame man about the stable-yard to keep gleaming bright. A busy little man he always is, in the polishing at harness-house doors, of stirrup-irons, bits, curb-chains, harness bosses, anything in the way of a stable-yard that will take a polish: leading a life of friction. A shaggy little damaged man, withal, not unlike an old dog of some mongrel breed, who has been considerably knocked about. He answers to the name of Phil.

A goodly sight it is to see the grand old housekeeper (harder of hearing now) going to church on the arm of her son, and to observe—which few do, for the house is scant of company in these times—the relations of both towards Sir Leicester, and his towards them. They have visitors in the high summer weather, when a grey cloak and umbrella, unknown to Chesney Wold at other periods, are seen among the leaves; when two young ladies are occasionally found gambolling, in sequestered saw-pits, and such nooks of the park; and when the smoke of two pipes wreathes away in the fragrant evening air, from the trooper's door. Then is a fife heard trolling within the lodge, on the inspiring topic of the British Grenadiers; and, as the evening closes in, a gruff inflexible voice is heard to say, while two men pace together up and down, "But I never own to it before the old girl. Discipline must be maintained."

The greater part of the house is shut up, and it is a show-house no longer; yet Sir Leicester holds his shrunken state in the long drawing-room for all that, and reposes in his old place before my Lady's picture. Closed in by night with broad screens, and illumined only in that part, the light of the drawing-room seems gradually contracting and dwindling until it shall be no more. A little more, in truth, and it will be all extinguished for Sir Leicester; and the damp door in the mausoleum which shuts so tight, and looks so obdurate, will have opened and received him.

Volumnia, growing with the flight of time pinker as to the red in her face, and yellower as to the white, reads to Sir Leicester in the long evenings, and is driven to various artifices to conceal her yawns: of which the chief and most efficacious is the insertion of the pearl necklace between her rosy lips. Long-winded treatises on the Buffy and Boodle question, showing how Buffy is immaculate and Boodle villainous, and how the country is lost by being all Boodle and no Buffy, or saved by being all Buffy and no Boodle (it must be one of the two, and cannot be anything else), are the staple of her reading. Sir Leicester is not particular what it is, and does not appear to follow it very closely; further than that he always comes broad awake the moment Volumnia ventures to leave off, and, sonorously repeating her last word, begs with some displeasure to know if she finds herself fatigued? However, Volumnia, in the course of her bird-like hopping about and pecking at papers, has lighted on a memorandum concerning herself, in the event of "anything happening" to her kinsman, which is handsome compensation for an extensive course of reading, and holds even the dragon Boredom at bay.

The cousins generally are rather shy of Chesney Wold in its dulness, but take to it a little in the shooting season, when guns are heard in the plantations, and a few scattered beaters and keepers wait at the old places of appointment, for low spirited twos and threes of cousins. The debilitated cousin, more debilitated by the dreariness of the place, gets into a fearful state of depression, groaning under penitential sofa-pillows in his gunless hours, and protesting that such fernal old jail's—nough t'sew fler up—frever.

The only great occasions for Volumnia, in this changed aspect of the place in Lincolnshire, are those occasions, rare and widely-separated, when something is to be done for the county, or the country, in the way of gracing a public ball. Then, indeed, does the tuckered sylph come out in fairy form, and proceed with joy under cousinly escort to the exhausted old assembly-room, fourteen heavy miles off: which, during three hundred and sixty-four days and nights of every ordinary year, is a kind of Antipodean lumber-room, full of old chairs and tables, upside down. Then, indeed, does she captivate all hearts by her condescension, by her girlish vivacity, and by her skipping about as in the days when the hideous old general with the mouth too full of teeth, had not cut one of them at two guineas each. Then does she twirl and twine, a pastoral nymph of good family, through the mazes of the dance. Then do the swains appear with tea, with lemonade, with sandwiches, with homage. Then is she kind and cruel, stately and unassuming, various, beautifully wilful. Then is there a singular kind of parallel between her and the little glass chandeliers of another age, embellishing that assembly-room; which, with their meagre stems, their spare little drops, their disappointing knobs where no drops are, their bare little stalks from which knobs and drops have both departed, and their little feeble prismatic twinkling, all seem Volumnias.

For the rest, Lincolnshire life to Volumnia is a vast blank of overgrown house looking out upon trees, sighing, wringing their hands, bowing their heads, and casting their tears upon the window-panes in monotonous depression. A labyrinth of grandeur, less the property of an old family of human beings and their ghostly likenesses, than of an old family of echoings and thunderings which start out of their hundred graves at every sound, and go resounding through the building. A waste of unused passages and staircases, in which to drop a comb upon a bedroom floor at night is to send a stealthy footfall on an errand through the house. A place where few people care to go about alone; where a maid screams if an ash drops from the fire, takes to crying at all times and seasons, becomes the victim of a low disorder of the spirits, and gives warning and departs.

Thus Chesney Wold. With so much of itself abandoned to darkness and vacancy; with so little change under the summer shining or the wintry lowering; so sombre and motionless always—no flag flying now by day, no rows of lights sparkling by night; with no family to come and go, no visitors to be the souls of pale cold shapes of rooms, no stir of life about it;—passion and pride, even to the stranger's eye, have died away from the place in Lincolnshire, and yielded it to dull repose.

CHAPTER LXVII

FULL seven happy years I have been the mistress of Bleak House. The few words that I have to add to what I have written, are soon penned; then I, and the unknown friend to whom I write, will part for ever. Not without much dear remembrance on my side. Not without some, I hope, on his or hers.

They gave my darling into my arms, and through many weeks I never left her. The little child who was to have done so much, was born before the turf was planted on its father's grave. It was a boy; and I, my husband, and my guardian, gave him his father's name.

The help that my dear counted on, did come to her; though it came, in the Eternal wisdom, for another purpose. Though to bless and restore his mother, not his father, was the errand of this baby, its power was mighty to do it. When I saw the strength of the weak little hand, and how its touch could heal my darling's heart, and raise up hope within her, I felt a new sense of the goodness and the tenderness of God.

They throve; and by degrees I saw my dear girl pass into my country garden, and walk there with her infant in her arms. I was married then. I was the happiest of the happy.

It was at this time that my guardian joined us, and asked Ada when she would come home?

"Both houses are your home, my dear," said he, "but the older Bleak House claims priority. When you and my boy are strong enough to do it, come and take possession of your home."

Ada called him "her dearest cousin, John." But he said, No, it must be guardian now. He was her guardian henceforth, and the boy's; and he had an old association with the name. So she called him guardian, and has called him guardian ever since. The children know him by no other name.—I say the children; I have two little daughters.

It is difficult to believe that Charley (round-eyed still, and not at all grammatical) is married to a miller in our neighbourhood; yet so it is; and even now, looking up from my desk as I write, early in the morning at my summer window, I see the very mill beginning to go round. I hope the miller will not spoil Charley; but he is very fond of her, and Charley is rather vain of such a match—for he is well to do, and was in great request. So far as my small maid is concerned, I might suppose Time to have stood for seven years as still as the mill did half-an-hour ago; since little Emma, Charley's sister, is exactly what Charley used to be. As to Tom, Charley's brother, I am really afraid to say what he did at school in ciphering, but I think it was Decimals. He is apprenticed to the miller, whatever it was; and is a good bashful fellow, always falling in love with somebody, and being ashamed of it.

Caddy Jellyby passed her very last holidays with us, and was a dearer creature than ever; perpetually dancing in and out of the house with the children, as if she had never given a dancing-lesson in her life. Caddy keeps her own little carriage now, instead of hiring one, and lives full two miles further westward from Newman Street. She works very hard, her husband (an excellent one) being lame, and able to do very little. Still, she is more than contented, and does all she has to do with all her heart. Mr. Jellyby spends his evenings at her new house with his head against the wall, as he used to do in her old one. I have heard that Mrs. Jellyby was understood to suffer great mortification, from her daughter's ignoble marriage and pursuits; but I hope she got over it in time. She has been disappointed in Borrioboola-Gha, which turned out a failure in consequence of the King of Borrioboola wanting to sell everybody—who survived the climate—for Rum; but she has taken up with the rights of women to sit in Parliament, and Caddy tells me it is a mission involving more correspondence than the old one. I had almost forgotten Caddy's poor little girl. She is not such a mite now; but she is deaf and dumb. I believe there never was a better mother than Caddy, who learns, in her scanty intervals of leisure, innumerable deaf and dumb arts, to soften the affliction of her child.

As if I were never to have done with Caddy, I am reminded here of Peepy and old Mr. Turveydrop. Peepy is in the Custom House, and doing extremely well. Old Mr. Turveydrop, very apoplectic, still exhibits his Deportment about town; still enjoys himself in the old manner; is still believed in, in the old way. He is constant in his patronage of Peepy, and is understood to have bequeathed him a favourite French clock in his dressing-room—which is not his property.

With the first money we saved at home, we added to our pretty house by throwing out a little Growlery expressly for my guardian; which we inaugurated with great splendour the next time he came down to see us. I try to write all this lightly, because my heart is full in drawing to an end; but when I write of him, my tears will have their way.

I never look at him, but I hear our poor dear Richard calling him a good man. To Ada and her pretty boy, he is the fondest father; to me, he is what he has ever been, and what name can I give to that? He is my husband's best and dearest friend, he is our children's darling, he is the object of our deepest love and veneration. Yet while I feel towards him as if he were a superior being, I am so familiar with him, and so easy with him, that I almost wonder at myself. I have never lost my old names, nor has he lost his; nor do I ever, when he is with us, sit in any other place than in my old chair at his side. Dame Trot, Dame Durden, Little Woman!—all just the same as ever; and I answer, Yes, dear Guardian! just the same.

I have never known the wind to be in the East for a single moment, since the day when he took me to the porch to read the name. I remarked to him once, that the wind seemed never in the East now: and he said, No, truly; it had finally departed from that quarter on that very day.

I think my darling girl is more beautiful than ever. The sorrow that has been in her face—for it is not there now—seems to have purified even its innocent expression, and to have given it a diviner quality. Sometimes, when I raise my eyes and see her, in the black dress that she still wears, teaching my Richard, I feel—it is difficult to express—as if it were so good to know that she remembers her dear Esther in her prayers.

I call him my Richard! But he says that he has two mammas, and I am one.

We are not rich in the bank, but we have always prospered, and we have quite enough. I never walk out with my husband, but I hear the people bless him. I never go into a house of any degree, but I hear his praises, or see them in grateful eyes. I never lie down at night, but I know that in the course of that day he has alleviated pain, and soothed some fellow-creature, in the time of need. I know that from the beds of those who were past recovery, thanks have often, often gone up, in the last hour, for his patient ministration. Is not this to be rich?

The people even praise Me as the doctor's wife. The people even like Me as I go about, and make so much of me that I am quite abashed. I owe it all to him, my love, my pride! They like me for his sake, as I do everything I do in life for his sake.

A night or two ago, after bustling about preparing for my darling and my guardian and little Richard, who are coming to-morrow, I was sitting out in the porch of all places, that dearly memorable porch, when Allan came home. So he said, "My precious little woman, what are you doing here?" And I said, "The moon is shining so brightly, Allan, and the night is so delicious, that I have been sitting here, thinking."

"What have you been thinking about, my dear?" said Allan then.

"How curious you are!" said I. "I am almost ashamed to tell you, but I will. I have been thinking about my old looks—such as they were."

"And what have you been thinking about *them*, my busy bee?" said Allan.

"I have been thinking, that I thought it was impossible that you *could* have loved me any better, even if I had retained them."

"—Such as they were?" said Allan, laughing.

"Such as they were, of course."

"My dear Dame Durden," said Allan, drawing my arm through his, "do you ever look in the glass?"

"You know I do; you see me do it."

"And don't you know that you are prettier than you ever were?"

I did not know that; I am not certain that I know it now. But I know that my dearest little pets are very pretty, and that my darling is very beautiful, and that my husband is very handsome, and that my guardian has the brightest and most benevolent face that ever was seen; and that they can very well do without much beauty in me—even supposing——.

THE END

Printed by BALLANTYNE, HANSON & Co.
Edinburgh & London